S0-BYU-600

Test Bank

to accompany

# Educational Psychology
## Developing Learners

**Fourth Edition**

**Jeanne Ellis Ormrod**

*With contributions by Ann U. Shump, Theresa J. Kirby, and Nancy J. Thrailkill*

Upper Saddle River, New Jersey
Columbus, Ohio

**Copyright © 2003 by Pearson Education, Inc., Upper Saddle River, New Jersey 07458.** All rights reserved. Printed in the United States of America. This publication is protected by Copyright and permission should be obtained from the publisher prior to any prohibited reproduction, storage in a retrieval system, or transmission in any form or by any means, electronic, mechanical, photocopying, recording, or likewise. For information regarding permission(s), write to: Rights and Permissions Department.

Instructors of classes using Ormrod, *Educational Psychology: Developing Learners, Fourth Edition,* may reproduce material from the test bank for classroom use.

10 9 8 7 6 5 4 3 2 1

Merrill
Prentice Hall

ISBN: 0-13-088716-1

# PREFACE

My guiding principle as I wrote *Educational Psychology: Developing Learners* was to focus on those aspects of the field that teachers are most likely to find useful in the classroom. I used the same principle as I developed this test bank: I tried to emphasize the most applicable concepts and principles, and I placed many of my questions within the context of actual classroom situations.

The test items come from several sources. Many of them are "tried and true" questions that I have used over the past twenty-eight years in my own classes. Others are taken from the test bank for my *Human Learning* book; in some cases, I have modified these items to be more suitable for the audience that is likely to read *Educational Psychology*. Still others have been written by Ann Shump, Theresa Kirby, Nancy Thrailkill, and myself to match the specific content in the fourth edition of the book. Regardless of source, you will, I hope, find that the test questions emphasize meaningful learning and, in many cases, higher-level thinking skills, rather than knowledge acquired at a rote level. As I indicate in Chapter 15 of the textbook, students are more likely to engage in meaningful learning when they expect to be *assessed* for meaningful learning.

Accompanying the test bank is the Prentice Hall Test Manager, which allows use of the test items on either a Macintosh or Windows-based computer. Microsoft Word documents containing the test items are also available for either Macintosh or PC. You can obtain any of these by contacting your local Prentice Hall sales representative or by calling the Faculty Support Services Department at 1–800–526–0485. Technical support is available to users of Prentice Hall Test Manager at 1–800–550–1701, or via e-mail at support@esatest.com.

J.E.O.

This Test Item File is just one part of Prentice Hall's comprehensive testing support service, which also includes Prentice Hall Test Manager for Windows 95/98/NT and Macintosh, and Prentice Hall Telephone Testing Service.

## Prentice Hall Test Manager

To run the Prentice Hall Test Manager you must have a Pentium 133 or greater, with a minimum of 32 MB of RAM, and Windows 95, 98, or NT installed. This powerful program makes organization a snap by using five basic databases: User, Course, Question, Test, and Grade. "Screen Wizards" are incorporated into all five databases. Each one will walk you through the important tasks from start to finish.

The User database stores information about your students that allows you to issue on-line tests and assign grades. The Course database stores information about the classes you teach. The Question database stores the content for each question in your question bank. The test-generation process, contained in the Test database, is fast, simple, and error-free. Once you create a test, you can make it available to students on-line using the On-Line Testing Facility.* After each student completes an on-line test, the results appear in the Grade database.

Finally, Test Manager also produces full sets of various class and individual statistics. These allow you to analyze the performance of test questions, students, an individual class or section, a course with multiple sections, or assignment types such as homework and on-line tests.

The Prentice Hall Test Manager is free. To order a specific Prentice Hall Test Manager title, you may contact your local rep or call our Faculty Support Services Department at 1-800-526-0485. Please identify the main text author and title.

Toll-free **technical support** is offered to users of Prentice Hall Test Manager at 1-800-550-1701, or via e-mail at support@esatest.com.

## Prentice Hall Telephone Testing Service

This service is offered to those instructors without access to a computer. It's simple, fast, and efficient. Simply pick the questions you'd like on your test from this test item file, and call the Prentice Hall Testing Service at 1-800-550-1701; outside the US and Canada call 612-550-1705. Identify the main text and test questions you'd like, as well as any special instructions. We will create the test (or multiple versions if you wish) and send you a master copy for duplication within 48 hours. This service is free to adopters for the duration of text use.

*Prentice Hall Test Manager provides on-line testing via these networks: Windows 95, Windows NT server, Novell Netware Network, and Windows NT Workstation.

# CONTENTS


| | | |
|---|---|---|
| | Overview of Test Items | 1 |
| Chapter 1 | Educational Psychology and Teacher Decision Making | 3 |
| | Answer Key | 11 |
| Chapter 2 | Cognitive and Linguistic Development | 12 |
| | Answer Key | 33 |
| Chapter 3 | Personal, Social, and Moral Development | 37 |
| | Answer Key | 56 |
| Chapter 4 | Individual and Group Differences | 59 |
| | Answer Key | 73 |
| Chapter 5 | Students with Special Educational Needs | 76 |
| | Answer Key | 97 |
| Chapter 6 | Learning and Cognitive Processes | 101 |
| | Answer Key | 121 |
| Chapter 7 | Knowledge Construction | 123 |
| | Answer Key | 138 |
| Chapter 8 | Higher-Level Thinking Skills | 141 |
| | Answer Key | 159 |
| Chapter 9 | Behaviorist Views of Learning | 162 |
| | Answer Key | 183 |
| Chapter 10 | Social Cognitive Views of Learning | 187 |
| | Answer Key | 202 |
| Chapter 11 | Motivation and Affect | 205 |
| | Answer Key | 215 |
| Chapter 12 | Cognitive Factors in Motivation | 217 |
| | Answer Key | 236 |
| Chapter 13 | Instructional Strategies | 240 |
| | Answer Key | 259 |
| Chapter 14 | Creating and Maintaining a Productive Classroom Environment | 262 |
| | Answer Key | 272 |
| Chapter 15 | Basic Concepts and Issues in Assessment | 274 |
| | Answer Key | 297 |
| Chapter 16 | Classroom Assessment Strategies | 300 |
| | Answer Key | 318 |
| Chapters 1-16 | Integrative Questions | 321 |
| | Answer Key | 331 |
| Appendix A | Describing Relationships with Correlation Coefficients | 341 |
| | Answer Key | 343 |

• • •

| | | |
|---|---|---|
| Study Guide | Readings #1- #7 | 344 |
| | Answer Key | 348 |
| | Reading #8: Learning in the Content Areas | 350 |
| | Answer Key | 362 |

# OVERVIEW OF TEST ITEMS

This test bank provides multiple-choice and essay questions for the Chapters 1–16 and Appendix A of the textbook, as well as for the supplementary readings in the *Study Guide and Reader*. It also includes a set of "integrative" questions—items that encompass two or more textbook chapters simultaneously (I myself often use such questions). The items have been developed with a variety of possible instructional objectives in mind. I urge you to consider the objectives that you have for your own students and to select items that best match those objectives.

The test items are at two difficulty levels. **Level 1 items**, which are designated by a single dot (•) in the left margin, are lower-level questions that assess *knowledge* or *comprehension* of material presented in the text. **Level 2 items**, which are designated by double dots (••) in the left margin, are higher-level questions that assess *application* or *analysis* of material presented in the text.

## Providing Directions for the Test Items

Although most of your students are apt to be familiar with both multiple-choice and essay formats, a few of them may not know exactly what you expect them to do. Accordingly, it is usually a good idea to provide specific directions for how to respond to your questions. Here are examples of test directions I myself have successfully used:

> Read each question and all alternatives carefully. Choose the best answer in each case. Indicate your choice directly on the exam by circling the letter to the left of your choice.
>
> Read each question and all alternatives carefully. Choose the best answer in each case. Indicate your choice by blackening the corresponding circle on the answer sheet. If you have questions about any item, please seek clarification.
>
> For each item, circle the letter corresponding to the single best answer. Whenever you wish to do so, you may explain your choice in the margin beside the item. Such explanations are optional and will be evaluated only in cases where answers are otherwise "incorrect."
>
> For each question, choose the single best answer. Mark all answers on the answer sheet. Please do not mark the test booklet. You may provide a written justification for any question you wish on the back of the answer sheet.
>
> Answer each of the following short answer and essay questions clearly and concretely. Be sure to answer all parts of each question. There are __ points possible, including __ points on the closed book portion and __ points on the open book portion.
>
> Answer each question as clearly and completely as you can. Please speak with me if: (1) you don't understand what a question is asking you to do, or (2) you're not sure if one of your responses communicates what you want it to. Although I

> cannot tell you if you are right or wrong while you are still taking the exam, I can tell you if you are answering the questions I have asked and communicating your ideas clearly.

In addition, it is helpful for students to know the specific point values you plan to assign to each part of an essay question; you may want to insert these directly into the essay questions you ask.

## Guidelines for Scoring Tests

Scoring criteria are provided for each item. Scoring responses to the multiple-choice questions should be relatively simple. If you allow students to defend their choices in the margins (as I usually do), you will have some subjective judgments to make about the appropriateness of their reasoning behind what are otherwise incorrect choices. Scoring responses to the essay questions will naturally be more difficult and time-consuming, but I have provided scoring criteria for each question that should help you score them consistently and reliably. In some cases, I have identified the essential elements of a correct response. In other cases, and particularly for open-ended and relatively unstructured items, students' responses will vary considerably; for these, I have provided general scoring criteria and sections of the textbook to which you can refer.

Chapter 1

# EDUCATIONAL PSYCHOLOGY AND TEACHER DECISION MAKING

| CHAPTER OUTLINE | RELEVANT TEST BANK ITEMS |
|---|---|
| OOPS—A PRETEST | Multiple-Choice 1–3 |
| DRAWING CONCLUSIONS FROM PSYCHOLOGICAL AND EDUCATIONAL RESEARCH<br>Descriptive Studies<br>Correlational Studies<br>Experimental Studies<br>An Example: Research on Visual-Spatial Thinking<br>A Cautionary Note | Multiple-Choice 4–18<br>Essay 31–32 |
| USING PRINCIPLES AND THEORIES IN CLASSROOM DECISION MAKING | Multiple-Choice 19–22 |
| IMPORTANCE OF ONGOING ASSESSMENT IN CLASSROOM DECISION MAKING | Multiple-Choice 23–24 |
| DEVELOPING AS A TEACHER | Multiple-Choice 25–27 |
| LOOKING AHEAD TO THE FOLLOWING CHAPTERS | Multiple-Choice 28–29 |
| STUDYING EDUCATIONAL PSYCHOLOGY MORE EFFECTIVELY | Multiple-Choice 30 |

## Multiple-Choice Questions

• 1. Considering the research findings described in the textbook, which one of the following is a true statement?
   a. Repeating something over and over is usually the most effective way to learn it.
   b. Girls have a definite advantage over boys on verbal tasks.
   c. For optimal performance, students should never feel the least bit anxious in the classroom.
   d. Students often study differently for different kinds of classroom assessments.

• 2. Considering the research findings described in the textbook, which one of the following is a true statement?
   a. Most experts discourage teachers from having children tutor one another.
   b. By the time children are eight or nine years old, most of them have developed effective ways of learning classroom material.
   c. Students who see a classmate rewarded for doing something may engage in the same behavior themselves.
   d. Students are usually the best judges of what they do and do not know.

•• 3. Which one of the following is an example of <u>elaboration</u>?
   a. Sharon automatically knows how she can best study for an upcoming history test.
   b. Melissa makes up stories to help her remember the various species she studies in biology.
   c. Darren repeats the detailed excuses his friend Logan suggests he use to explain his tardiness.
   d. Rosie repeats the spelling of each word several times the night before her spelling test.

• 4. A study that tells us whether two variables are related, but does <u>not</u> tell us if one variable causes or influences the other, is a(n):
   a. Correlational study
   b. Descriptive study
   c. Experimental study without a control group
   d. Experimental study with one or more control groups

• 5. Which one of the following statements about educational research is <u>true</u>?
   a. Experimental research can only be conducted in the laboratory under somewhat artificial conditions.
   b. Descriptive research gives us the most information for making decisions about teaching practice.
   c. Experimental research allows us to draw cause-and-effect conclusions.
   d. Correlational research is more difficult and time-consuming than experimental research.

• 6. Experimental research requires which one of the following?
   a. Manipulating an aspect of the environment.
   b. Being able to predict two or more variables.
   c. Describing each variable in considerable detail.
   d. Studying behavior in an actual classroom environment.

• 7. In general, experimental studies have which one of the following advantages over descriptive and correlational studies?

a. Only experimental studies allow us to be specific about our teaching objectives.
b. Only experimental studies allow us to identify the possible factors influencing behavior.
c. Only experimental studies allow us to analyze data statistically and therefore arrive at precise results.
d. Only experimental studies enable us to draw accurate conclusions.

•• 8. A research study finds that students who weigh more do better in school. Which one of the following is an appropriate deduction from this information?

a. Parents should feed their children as much as possible.
b. The school cafeteria should decrease the fat content of the food it serves.
c. On the average, students who eat more do better in school.
d. There is a correlation between weight and classroom performance.

•• 9. A researcher is interested in the effect of teacher-student ratios. She finds 10 fifth-grade classrooms with 30-40 students per class and 10 others with 15-25 students per class. She discovers that there is a correlation between class size and student achievement. Which one of the following conclusions can we draw from this study?

a. Class size can help us predict school achievement.
b. Classes should be as large as reasonably possible.
c. Classes should be as small as reasonably possible.
d. The researcher has conducted a descriptive study.

•• 10. Which one of the following conclusions can be drawn only from an experimental study?

a. Boys are more likely to show aggressive behavior than girls.
b. Drugs administered during childbirth affect a child's early development.
c. Children grow taller as they get older.
d. Children's muscular coordination improves as they grow older.

•• 11. Mr. Jacobs wants to find out whether a new program for teaching physical education promotes students' physical development. So he gives his students a number of tests before they begin the program (pretests) and the same tests again after they have been in the program for eight months (posttests). He finds that the students' posttest scores are higher than their pretest scores and so concludes that the program is effective. What is definitely wrong with Mr. Jacobs' conclusion?

a. Eight months is too short a time for such a program to have a long-term effect.
b. There are other possible explanations for his results.
c. Tests are not a good measure of physical development.
d. The posttests should always be different from the pretests.

•• 12. Dr. Kenney conducts a study in which she gives some students (chosen randomly) logically organized learning material; she gives other students the same material presented in a haphazard, unpredictable sequence. She finds that students with the organized material remember more. This study can best be described as a(n):

a. Descriptive study
b. Theoretical study
c. Experimental study
d. Correlational study

•• 13. Which one of the following conclusions could be drawn from a <u>descriptive</u> study?

a. Approximately 80% of the students at Southside High School are planning to go on to college.
b. Students are more likely to appreciate classical music if they are exposed to it on a regular basis.
c. Concrete experiences help students understand abstract ideas better.
d. Children from two-parent families are more likely to do well in school than children from single-parent homes.

•• 14. A French teacher reads an article about how visual imagery (i.e., "picturing" things in one's mind) can be used to help students learn French vocabulary words. To find out if visual imagery is more effective than verbal repetition in learning vocabulary words, she develops two different study guides for her students—one that tells students how to use visual imagery to learn French words, and one that tells them just to repeat the words over and over again—and randomly distributes the two study guides to her students. Over the next few weeks, the teacher finds that students using visual imagery study guides achieve higher average quiz scores. She concludes that the study guides describing the visual imagery technique help her students learn their French vocabulary words. Is the teacher's conclusion valid?

a. No, because she used random assignment.
b. No, because her experiment wasn't conducted in a laboratory.
c. Yes, because her students probably all had similar IQ scores.
d. Yes, because she was able to manipulate a variable in the environment.

•• 15. Mr. Jones, a physical education teacher, notices that some of his students are better basketball players than others. He wonders if having a basketball net at home fosters the development of basketball skills. He gives his students a short survey that asks them if they have a basketball net at home. Sure enough, Mr. Jones finds that the better basketball players are more likely to have a net at home. He concludes that having a basketball net at home facilitates the development of basketball skills. Is his conclusion appropriate?

a. No, because he didn't conduct an experimental study.
b. No, because his study wasn't conducted in a scientific laboratory.
c. Yes, provided that his students responded truthfully to the survey.
d. Yes, because he used random assignment.

•• 16. Professor Moriarty conducts an experiment to test whether or not the Holmes Approach to Studying Psychology (HASP) is superior to the Watson Approach to Studying Psychology (WASP). He convinces Dr. Ormrod to use HASP in her 9:00 class and WASP in her 10:00 class. Students exposed to the HASP method do better on the final exam than students exposed to the WASP method. Prof. Moriarty concludes that HASP is better than WASP. What is <u>definitely</u> wrong with Moriarty's experiment?

a. The final exam is not a good measure of what students have learned.
b. Students in the 9:00 class are probably more motivated.
c. Students in the 9:00 class are probably smarter.
d. There are several possible explanations for his results.

•• 17. Dr. Lesgold finds that students in private schools perform better on achievement tests than do students in public schools. He can conclude that:

a. The difference is probably due to differences in family income.
b. The difference is probably due to the fact that private schools have smaller classes.
c. The difference is probably due to the fact that private schools are more likely to "teach to the test."
d. Students' achievement test scores can be predicted to some extent by the kind of school they attend.

•• 18. Judging from the textbook's discussion of educational research, which one of the following would be the best course of action for teachers to take?

a. Teachers shouldn't take research findings very seriously, because there are too many "holes" in what we know from research.
b. Teachers should focus on research that relates to a single theoretical perspective (such as Piaget's theory or information processing theory).
c. Teachers can use findings from educational research to guide their classroom decision making.
d. Teachers should always go with their common sense and "gut" feelings about how to teach, regardless of any research findings to the contrary.

• 19. A <u>principle</u> can best be characterized as:

a. A description of the results of a particular research study.
b. A statement that describes how a particular variable affects learning or development.
c. An objective measure of how a student behaves in a particular situation.
d. An explanation of how and why learning or development occurs.

• 20. A <u>theory</u> can best be characterized as:

a. A description of the results of a particular research study.
b. A statement that describes how a particular variable affects learning or development.
c. An objective measure of how a student behaves in a particular situation.
d. An explanation of how and why learning or development occurs.

• 21. We can best derive principles about human behavior from:

a. A single, well-designed correlational research study
b. Detailed observations of a single student in a controlled setting
c. Multiple research studies that yield similar results
d. Theoretical explanations about learning and development

• 22. Which one of the following statements is most accurate regarding psychological theories?
  a. They have been proven to be true.
  b. They will eventually be replaced by physiological (brain-based) explanations of behavior.
  c. They are continually modified as new data emerge.
  d. Any single theory can be used to explain virtually every aspect of human behavior.

•• 23. As the textbook points out, assessment in the classroom can take a variety of forms. Three of the following are examples of assessment in the classroom. Which one definitely does not, in and of itself, illustrate assessment?
  a. A teacher decides to use a new approach to teach reading this year.
  b. A teacher observes that Lani rarely interacts with her classmates during recess.
  c. A teacher asks students to write an essay describing the pros and cons of a free enterprise system.
  d. A teacher sees her students growing increasingly restless during a lengthy lecture.

• 24. Judging from the textbook's discussion of assessment, we can best think of classroom assessment practices as mechanisms and procedures that:
  a. Allow us to draw conclusions about how students' motivations and personality traits affect their classroom performance
  b. Enable us to form tentative hypotheses about what students know and can do
  c. Give us hard, indisputable facts that we can use to assign grades
  d. Are most likely to be accurate when they take the form of paper-and-pencil tests

• 25. As a beginning teacher, you may sometimes find yourself overwhelmed by the many decisions you will have to make on a daily basis. The situation will improve over time, however, because:
  a. Fellow teachers are usually more helpful and supportive later in the school year, after they've gotten to know you better.
  b. Most students know that they should behave when they have an older and more experienced teacher.
  c. As you gain experience, you will be able to make some classroom decisions more quickly and easily.
  d. Children are typically more sedate and cooperative during the winter months than they are in the fall.

•• 26. Which one of the following is the best example of a teacher's pedagogical content knowledge?
  a. Knowing what researchers have discovered about the effectiveness of discovery learning approaches to instruction
  b. Knowing an effective way to teach students about negative numbers
  c. Making a reasonable guess as to why a particular student misbehaves just before lunch time every day
  d. Understanding why water expands when it freezes

•• 27. Which one of the following is the best example of action research?
   a. A teacher gives her students a questionnaire that asks them to describe how often they study and what kinds of strategies they use when they study. She will use the results to develop several lessons on effective study skills.
   b. A graduate student quietly observes adolescents' behaviors in the school cafeteria. He plans to describe his observations in his masters thesis.
   c. A college professor recruits sixth graders to come to his lab, where she assesses their responses and reaction times in a variety of challenging problem-solving tasks. Her results will help her refine the theory of problem solving she has been developing.
   d. All of the school districts in a particular state are instructed to give the same mathematics achievement test to their high school juniors. The average test scores for each district will be presented in a report that will be released to the general public.

• 28. Students with special needs are students who:
   a. Have cognitive and emotional deficits that impair their classroom performance.
   b. Have physical disabilities such as cerebral palsy, multiple sclerosis, spinal cord injury, epilepsy, or AIDS.
   c. Have inherited conditions (e.g., Down's syndrome, dyslexia) that adversely affect their ability to achieve at appropriate levels in the classroom.
   d. Are different enough from their classmates that they require specially adapted instruction or materials.

• 29. The practice of inclusion involves which of the following?
   a. Keeping students with special needs together in one class so they can take part in all of their classroom's activities.
   b. Selecting high achieving students to help with the instruction of special needs students.
   c. Educating all students, including those with special needs, in the general education classroom.
   d. Incorporating instruction in social skills into the regular classroom curriculum.

• 30. The textbook offers several suggestions for studying a textbook effectively. Which one of the following is not necessarily recommended?
   a. Take detailed notes on the book's content.
   b. Occasionally stop and check to make sure you understand.
   c. Draw inferences from the things you read.
   d. Relate new ideas to things you already know.

## Essay Questions

•• 31. A psychologist conducts a research study and finds that abused children have more difficulty in school than nonabused children.

a. Is this a descriptive, correlational, or experimental study? Justify your choice.

b. Based on the study, the psychologist draws the conclusion that an abusive home life leads to poorer school performance in school. Is this conclusion justified? Why or why not?

•• 32. Dr. Carey gives a variety of achievement and aptitude tests to 1000 ten-year-old children from Southside Elementary School and 1000 ten-year-old children from Northside Elementary School. He finds that, on the average, the Southside students perform better on the tests than the Northside students. He concludes that the teachers at Southside are superior to those at Northside. Is this conclusion warranted? Why or why not?

## ANSWER KEY

### Multiple-Choice Questions

| | | | | |
|---|---|---|---|---|
| 1. d | 7. b | 13. a | 19. b | 25. c |
| 2. c | 8. d | 14. d | 20. d | 26. b |
| 3. b | 9. a | 15. a | 21. c | 27. a |
| 4. a | 10. b | 16. d | 22. c | 28. d |
| 5. c | 11. b | 17. d | 23. a | 29. c |
| 6. a | 12. c | 18. c | 24. b | 30. a |

### Essay Questions

31. Responses to the two parts of the question are as follows:
    a. It is a correlational study because it investigates the relationship between two variables, abuse and school performance.
    b. The conclusion is not justified. Conclusions about cause-effect relationships cannot be drawn from correlational studies.

32. Dr. Carey's conclusion is not warranted because he has failed to control for other possible explanations for the differences in test scores (class size, educational level of the parents, etc.).

## Chapter 2

# COGNITIVE AND LINGUISTIC DEVELOPMENT

| CHAPTER OUTLINE | RELEVANT TEST BANK ITEMS |
|---|---|
| BASIC PRINCIPLES OF HUMAN DEVELOPMENT | Multiple-Choice 1–5 |
| ROLE OF THE BRAIN IN COGNITIVE DEVELOPMENT | Multiple-Choice 6–7 |
| PIAGET'S THEORY OF COGNITIVE DEVELOPMENT<br>Piaget's Basic Assumptions<br>Piaget's Stages of Cognitive Development<br>Current Perspectives on Piaget's Theory | Multiple-Choice 8–46<br>Essay 94–98 |
| VYGOTSKY'S THEORY OF COGNITIVE DEVELOPMENT<br>Vygotsky's Basic Assumptions<br>Current Perspectives on Vygotsky's Theory | Multiple-Choice 47–60<br>Essay 99 |
| AN INFORMATION PROCESSING VIEW OF COGNITIVE DEVELOPMENT<br>Attention<br>Learning Strategies<br>Knowledge<br>Metacognition | Multiple-Choice 61–70<br>Essay 100 |
| LINGUISTIC DEVELOPMENT<br>Theoretical Perspectives on Language Development<br>Trends in Language Development<br>Learning a Second Language | Multiple-Choice 71–87<br>Essay 101 |
| CONSIDERING DIVERSITY IN COGNITIVE AND LINGUISTIC DEVELOPMENT<br>Accommodating Students with Special Needs | Multiple-Choice 88–91 |

| THE BIG PICTURE<br>Developmental Principles in the Classroom<br>Cognitive Development<br>Linguistic Development<br>General Themes in Cognitive and Linguistic Development | Multiple-Choice 92–93<br>Essay 102 |
|---|---|
| The items in the "Integrative Questions" chapter of this Test Bank integrate the content of two or more textbook chapters. Within that chapter, the items listed to the right are relevant to Chapter 2. | Multiple-Choice 1–10<br>Essay 19–21, 39 |

## Multiple-Choice Questions

• 1. Most developmental theorists agree that:
   a. Development occurs in stages, with each stage occurring at the same age for all children.
   b. Developmental milestones appear in a consistent sequence for most children.
   c. Physical development occurs in a predictable sequence, but cognitive development does not.
   d. Cognitive development occurs in a predictable sequence, but physical development does not.

• 2. Which one of the following statements reflects what developmentalists mean by the term maturation?
   a. Developmental changes that are controlled in large part by heredity.
   b. Changes related specifically to children's physical development.
   c. Changes related specifically to children's emotional development.
   d. Changes that reflect increasingly appropriate social behavior.

•• 3. Which one of the following statements best illustrates a universal in development as developmentalists define the term?
   a. Piaget proposed that formal operational thought is characterized by an ability to think abstractly about a wide variety of topics.
   b. Contemporary theorists have derived the concept cognitive apprenticeship from Vygotsky's theory of development.
   c. Young children show similar patterns in their language development regardless of the specific language that they learn.
   d. Piaget neglected to consider the influence of prior knowledge and experience on children's ability to think logically.

•• 4. Which one of the following pairs of children best illustrates a difference in temperament?
   a. Ann enjoys dancing; Alice prefers singing.
   b. Bob likes to spend his time reading; Bill would rather watch a good movie.
   c. Carol is very sociable and outgoing; Christ is more quiet and reserved around peers.
   d. Dan likes to think about abstract ideas; David learns more effectively when he can manipulate concrete objects.

• 5. A sensitive period in development can best be described as:
   a. A stage of development in which children display unpredictable (and often inappropriate) emotional responses
   b. A period during children's cognitive development in which they are highly distractible and so are frequently off task in the classroom
   c. An approach to teaching or parenting that takes a child's developmental level into account
   d. An age range during which environmental conditions are most likely to have an effect on a particular aspect of a child's development

• 6. During the elementary and secondary school years, much of the brain's development occurs in the region of the brain that is largely responsible for
   a. Regulation of emotions
   b. Muscular strength and coordination
   c. Inhibition of inappropriate behaviors
   d. Thinking and reasoning

• 7. According to the textbook, which one of the following conclusions is most warranted from research on brain development?
   a. It is essential that children begin studying basic mathematics and science before the age of seven.
   b. Classroom experiences can affect students' cognitive development throughout the elementary and secondary school years.
   c. The ability to think abstractly depends on the development of many synaptic connections during the first five years of life.
   d. Children probably won't acquire the skills essential to success in the adult world unless they begin developing those skills in the early elementary grades.

• 8. According to Piaget, three of the following are essential for cognitive development. Which one is not?
   a. High self-esteem
   b. Interaction with the physical environment
   c. Neurological maturation
   d. Social interaction

• 9. From Piaget's perspective, children are:
   a. Most likely to learn when parents and teachers entice them to do so
   b. Most likely to learn things that bring about desirable consequences
   c. More likely to develop cognitively in a formal school setting than at home
   d. Eager to interact with and make sense of their world

•• 10. Five-year-old Becky is playing with blocks, stacking them one on top of another until her towers eventually tumble, and then stacking them again. Which one of the following best reflects Piaget's view of how Becky is probably learning in this situation?

a. Because she is probably still in the sensorimotor stage, she will remember what she learns about the blocks only while the blocks are still in front of her.
b. She is absorbing information about how the environment behaves (e.g., "objects fall") without consciously thinking about it.
c. She is actively thinking about and interpreting the results of her actions.
d. Because she builds one tower after another, she is obviously reinforced by watching her towers tumble down.

• 11. Which one of the following statements best describes Piaget's view of how children develop knowledge about the world?

a. Children are naturally disposed to think about their environment in particular ways; in a sense, some basic knowledge about the world is "pre-wired."
b. Children actively construct their own view of the world from their experiences with the environment.
c. Initially, children unconsciously develop a rather complex and confused view of the world, but this view becomes simpler and more straightforward as time goes on.
d. Children repeatedly parrot their parents' and teachers' beliefs, eventually adopting these beliefs as their own "knowledge."

• 12. In Piaget's theory, a <u>scheme</u> can best be described as:

a. An organized group of similar thoughts or actions
b. A set of motor skills that preschoolers develop
c. A lifestyle or family pattern
d. A mental picture of oneself

•• 13. Which one of the following clearly illustrates Piaget's concept of <u>assimilation</u>?

a. A kindergarten child drawing on the chalkboard with a large white crayon instead of with chalk
b. A third grader developing the necessary eye-hand coordination for writing letters
c. A sixth grader moving to a different school and changing styles to fit the fashions
d. An eighth grader being discouraged from using the word "awesome" to describe everything he sees

•• 14. Louis receives a new soccer ball and begins to dribble it in the same way he dribbles his basketball. His dribbling of the new ball reflects Piaget's concept of:

a. Concrete operations
b. Accommodation
c. Cognitive structure
d. Assimilation

•• 15. Which one of the following best illustrates Piaget's concept of accommodation?
   a. Anne is given 10 more addition problems when she does the first 10 carelessly.
   b. Betsy writes down her definition of a mollusk—something she learned word for word from her textbook.
   c. Carol copies down what her teacher writes on the blackboard.
   d. Donna revises her understanding of what clouds are like when she studies them in science.

• 16. The processes of assimilation and accommodation both involve:
   a. Concrete operational thought
   b. Relating new information to prior knowledge
   c. Abstract thought processes such as inductive reasoning
   d. Oral communication skills

•• 17. Which one of the following teachers is definitely keeping in mind Piaget's idea that assimilation and accommodation are both necessary for learning and cognitive development to occur?
   a. Mr. Ames presents brand new topics every day, expecting the continual novelty to keep students interested and motivated.
   b. Ms. Baretta makes sure that students have learned one topic very, very well before moving on to another.
   c. Mr. Chang shows students how a new topic is similar to the things they already know, but also different in certain ways.
   d. Ms. Doherty uses a lot of drill and practice exercises, encouraging students to work faster every time.

• 18. Which one of the following best describes Piaget's notion of equilibration?
   a. A child assimilates without accommodating.
   b. A child cannot explain new ideas using his or her existing schemes.
   c. A child doesn't encounter any new or challenging ideas.
   d. A child revises existing schemes to incorporate new information.

• 19. Piaget's view of cognitive development can best be described as:
   a. A gradual and steady progression of intellectual capabilities
   b. Discrete stages in which distinctly different forms of logical thought emerge
   c. Changes in the brain that result in increasingly rapid learning
   d. An increasing number of stimulus-response connections over time

•• 20. Mr. Johnson teaches a class of twenty 8-year-old third graders. His goal for the upcoming school year is to help at least 50% of his students reach formal operations. Judging from Piaget's theory, we would expect that Mr. Johnson's goal is:
   a. An easy one to attain.
   b. Almost impossible to attain.
   c. Attainable only if he emphasizes abstract reasoning throughout the school year.
   d. Attainable only if his students have had enriched educational experiences most of their lives.

• 21. Piaget's sensorimotor stage is characterized by:
   a. Schemes based primarily on perceptions and behaviors
   b. Inaccurate mental representations of the world around them
   c. The beginnings of deductive logic
   d. Rudimentary schemes for dealing with abstract ideas

• 22. Piaget proposed that true thought emerges when children begin to develop:
   a. Symbolic thinking
   b. Conservation
   c. Egocentric language
   d. Abstract thinking abilities

• 23. From the perspective of Piaget's theory, why is language critical for children's cognitive development?
   a. It allows them to get what they want.
   b. It gives them a means for thinking about things symbolically.
   c. It takes up most of their mental energy, thereby keeping them from being easily distracted.
   d. It gives them a better self-image, because they are now aware that they can communicate effectively with other human beings.

•• 24. Piaget spoke of egocentrism in both the thought and speech of the preoperational child. Three of the following are examples of egocentrism as Piaget defined it. Which one is not?
   a. Justin is constantly grabbing objects and pulling them toward himself.
   b. Lois tells a story as if her listeners already know many details they can't possibly know.
   c. Kate cannot relate to the question, "How do you think Molly feels?"
   d. Isabel cannot understand why she must share classroom equipment with others.

•• 25. Which one of the following children shows signs that he or she is in Piaget's preoperational stage of cognitive development?
   a. Jimmy is able to reason logically about what it would be like to grow old, yet he cannot envision what it would be like to turn into a fish.
   b. Jenny learns hundreds of new words and phrases in only a few months.
   c. Joslyn thinks that when a stuffed dog disappears under a box, it no longer exists.
   d. Jason is able to understand how another boy feels when his bicycle is stolen.

•• 26. Roger is shown two piles of sand and says that each pile has the same amount. However, when one pile is flattened with a shovel, he now claims emphatically that the flattened pile has less sand. Based on this information, Roger is probably in Piaget's _______ stage of development.
   a. concrete operations
   b. sensorimotor
   c. formal operations
   d. preoperational

•• 27. Marcy is given her choice of two Hershey bars, one of which has been broken into four pieces. Marcy chooses the broken candy bar, believing that it has more candy. Marcy is showing a lack of _______, indicating that she has not yet completed the transition to the _________ stage of development.

a. combinatorial thought; concrete operations
b. combinatorial thought; formal operations
c. conservation; concrete operations
d. conservation; formal operations

•• 28. Which one of the following statements shows <u>transductive reasoning</u>?

a. "The two glasses of water must still have the same amount because you haven't added any water or taken any away."
b. "It snows in the wintertime because it's Christmas."
c. "Six and one are seven because you just take six and count one more."
d. "If you have four people, you can make six possible pairs of them."

•• 29. Linda's teacher shows her a small ball of clay. He then squashes the ball so it looks like a pancake and asks Linda which has more clay, the ball or the pancake. Linda replies that they both have the same amount. "How do you know?" asks her teacher. "Look," says Linda, "I can roll the pancake back into the same ball it was before." Linda's response shows:

a. Formal operational logic
b. A distinction between physical and psychological events
c. Reversibility
d. Transductive reasoning

• 30. Imagine that you are a third-grade teacher. Considering Piaget's theory of cognitive development, you should expect most or all of your students to exhibit ______ thinking.

a. preoperational
b. formal operational
c. sensorimotor
d. concrete operational

•• 31. Which one of the following reflects <u>multiple classification</u> as Piaget described it?

a. Identifying a shape as a square one day but as a triangle the next.
b. Realizing that things that are cars can also be vehicles.
c. Getting cows and horses confused.
d. Understanding that some behaviors that are perfectly acceptable at home are unacceptable at school.

• 32. Which one of the following is associated with Piaget's <u>concrete operations</u> stage?

a. An inability to classify objects as belonging to more than one category
b. Separation and control of variables
c. Reasoning about hypothetical ideas
d. Deductive reasoning

•• 33. The following four junior high school science teachers are teaching the concept molecule to their students. In each classroom, some of the students are at Piaget's formal operations stage and others are at the concrete operations stage. In which classroom are the concrete operational students most likely to have difficulty understanding?

a. Mr. Armani lets students touch and manipulate concrete models of various molecules.
b. Mr. Bendetti lets students look at the same concrete models that Mr. Armani has used.
c. Mr. Carmen verbally describes how different elements are made up of different numbers of neutrons, protons, and electrons.
d. Mr. Davidson has students role-play being neutrons, protons, and electrons. The "neutron" and "proton" students huddle together in the middle of the room, and the "electrons" move around them.

• 34. One thing that children in Piaget's formal operations stage can do, but children in the concrete operations stage cannot, is:

a. Distinguish between their own feelings and those of others
b. Consider someone else's perspective on an issue
c. Understand that some actions, when done, can also be undone, or reversed
d. Reason logically about strictly hypothetical situations

•• 35. Considering Piaget's theory of cognitive development, we would expect a student in the concrete operational stage to have the greatest difficulty with which one of the following questions?

a. An apple pie is cut into 4 pieces. A blueberry pie of the same size is cut into 12 pieces. How many pieces of blueberry pie do you need to have the same amount as 3 pieces of the apple pie?
b. How are an apple and a blueberry alike?
c. If we have one row of blueberries arranged like so: o o o o o o<br>and another row of blueberries arranged like so: o  o  o  o  o  o<br>then does one row have more blueberries than the other?
d. If you have 8 Macintosh apples and 2 Jonathan apples, then do you have more Macintoshes or more apples?

•• 36. Mary agrees with this logic:

> If all violins are musical instruments,
> And if all musical instruments make noise,
> Then all violins must make noise.

However, we then present this situation:

> If all Cheetos are rutabagas,
> And if all rutabagas are oysters,
> Then all Cheetos are oysters.

Mary vehemently denies that Cheetos can possibly be oysters. Based on this information, we would conclude that Mary is in the ______ stage of development.

a. sensorimotor
b. preoperational
c. concrete operational
d. formal operational

•• 37. Which one of the following would Piaget be <u>least</u> likely to advocate for elementary school children?
   a. Discussions with classmates
   b. Laboratory-type experiences with concrete objects
   c. Field trips to hands-on science museums
   d. Lectures that describe interesting scientific facts

• 38. Piaget claimed that an adolescent's overly optimistic idealism about the world is due to ____ during the formal operations stage.
   a. egocentrism
   b. irreversibility
   c. an incompletely developed ability to think abstractly
   d. centration

•• 39. James is talking about how much better the world would be if everyone got along with everyone else. James is probably in the ________ stage of development.
   a. concrete operations
   b. sensorimotor
   c. formal operations
   d. preoperational

•• 40. From Piaget's perspective, why might it be wise to postpone the teaching of complex fractions until middle school or high school?
   a. Younger students don't know their math facts well enough.
   b. Younger students cannot learn complex equations.
   c. Younger students haven't attained conservation.
   d. Younger students haven't attained proportional reasoning.

•• 41. At which one of Piaget's stages will you first see the following behavior: Carl can correctly answer a question such as, "If all flegs are blats, and if all blats are dulms, are all flegs also dulms?"
   a. Preoperational
   b. Formal operational
   c. Sensorimotor
   d. Concrete operational

•• 42. Olivia understands why 3/5 and 9/15 are equivalent fractions. Based on this information, Olivia is probably in Piaget's _______ stage of development.
   a. concrete operations
   b. preoperations
   c. formal operations
   d. sensorimotor

•• 43. Which one of the following statements reflects a concern about the <u>separation and control of variables</u>?
   a. "How do you think I should make amends with Martha? If I tell her I'm sorry, she might think I'm lying."
   b. "I'm catching more tadpoles today, but I don't know if it's because I'm using a larger container to catch them or because I'm working in a different part of the frog pond."
   c. "I have two tests to study for tonight—science and Spanish. I'll study one subject before dinner and the other one after dinner so I don't get them confused."
   d. "I'm trying to learn how to do a lay-up shot. Can you show me all the things I should do, going one step at a time?"

•• 44. Three of the following teaching practices are consistent with Piaget's theory of cognitive development. Which one is <u>not</u>?
   a. When Sue leaves out important details as she tries to explain something, her teacher says, "I don't understand what you mean when you say. . . ."
   b. A second-grade teacher encourages students to speculate about possible explanations as to why kites can fly, and then to test each explanation systematically.
   c. When a high school student claims that people should "Make love, not war," his teacher urges him to consider whether such an approach would have been advisable when the Fascist movement was gaining ground in Europe in the late 1930s and early 1940s.
   d. When Martin says that two nickels are worth more than one dime because there are two of them and they're bigger, his teacher asks, "How can that be? Two nickels are worth ten cents; one dime is also worth ten cents."

• 45. Choose the statement below that most accurately reflects recent research findings concerning Piaget's theory of cognitive development.
   a. The order in which various logical thinking capabilities emerge is consistent with the sequence that Piaget proposed.
   b. Preoperational egocentrism continues to be common even in the upper elementary grades.
   c. Concrete operational thinking abilities, such as deductive reasoning and multiple classification, develop later than Piaget believed.
   d. Formal operational thinking abilities, such as the ability to think and reason about abstract and hypothetical ideas, begin to emerge in the preschool years.

• 46. Which one of the following conclusions can be derived from recent research regarding Piaget's theory of cognitive development?
   a. Middle school and secondary school students typically have an easier time thinking logically in the social sciences than they do in the physical and life sciences.
   b. Students will think more logically about a topic when they have acquired relevant knowledge and experiences related to the topic.
   c. Many students continue to show signs of preoperational thinking until well into the high school years.
   d. Students have an easier time understanding fractions and proportions later on if such concepts are first introduced at the same time that division is introduced (e.g., in third grade).

• 47. Which one of the following statements best describes Vygotsky's concept of internalization?
   a. As children grow older, they develop an increasing ability to think about events in abstract rather than concrete terms.
   b. With age, children become more sophisticated problem solving skills, largely because their parents and teachers give them increasingly challenging problems to solve.
   c. Over time, children acquire more self-confidence about their ability to deal with the world.
   d. Through their social interactions with other people, children develop ways of mentally approaching and thinking about a task.

•• 48. Students in a fourth-grade reading group are reading a passage about snakes. Their teacher asks, "Who can think of a good title that summarizes what this passage is about?" After hearing several good suggestions, the teacher says, "The author says that snakes are helpful to farmers. What evidence does she give to support her statement?" If we consider Vygotsky's concept of internalization, we might predict that such a discussion will:
   a. Be more beneficial for students who are working outside their zones of proximal development than for students working inside their ZPDs.
   b. Help students develop a greater interest in learning for its own sake.
   c. Help students develop effective reading comprehension strategies (e.g., summarizing, looking for supporting statements).
   d. Be confusing and counterproductive for students who are not yet capable of abstract thought.

• 49. From Vygotsky's perspective, what important role does inner speech play?
   a. By giving ourselves directions about what to do next, we guide ourselves through complex tasks.
   b. By practicing linguistic structures mentally, we develop more complex language capabilities.
   c. By using words mentally as well as orally, we develop a more abstract representation of the world.
   d. By talking to ourselves about what we should have done or said in a particular situation, we remember that situation more vividly.

•• 50. Kiley is having trouble learning the steps involved in using a microscope correctly. If we consider Vygotsky's description of how children help themselves through difficult tasks, we should suggest that Kiley:
   a. Practice each step separately many times over
   b. Go through the procedure in slow motion a few times
   c. Talk herself through the steps
   d. Learn the reasons why each step is important

• 51. If you were interested in how a child's culture influences cognitive development, you would be most likely to consider ________ approach to cognitive development.
   a. Vygotsky's
   b. a neurological
   c. information processing theory's
   d. Piaget's

• 52. Vygotsky's notion of the <u>zone of proximal development</u> refers to:
   a. The degree of maturation necessary to accomplish complex physical tasks
   b. Children's ability to know how much they know
   c. The range of tasks children can perform by themselves
   d. The range of tasks children can accomplish only with help

•• 53. Which one of the following students is definitely working in his or her <u>zone of proximal development</u>?
   a. Arnold uses correct grammar and punctuation when he writes short stories.
   b. Berta is beginning to learn basic woodworking techniques. She has trouble hammering a nail straight into a piece of wood unless her teacher stands beside her, helping her and reminding her of what to do.
   c. Calvin is playing the clarinet in the band. He finds that it helps to keep the tempo if he taps the beat with his foot.
   d. Doreen finds it virtually impossible to solve mathematical word problems, even when her teacher gives her helpful hints.

• 54. Which one of the following statements most accurately describes Lev Vygotsky's theory of cognitive development?
   a. Children's cognitive growth should be judged on the basis of their actual developmental level, not on the basis of their level of potential development.
   b. Cognitive development progresses through four distinct stages; each stage is characterized by increasingly more complex thought and language.
   c. Children develop by working on challenging tasks with the assistance of more competent individuals.
   d. Language and thought, although closely intertwined in the first few years of life, become increasingly distinct entities over time.

•• 55. Several parents who are making costumes for an elementary school play ask the young cast members to assist them with such tasks as cutting fabric, pinning pieces together, and sewing simple hems. Using the language of Vygotskian theorists, we can say that the parents are
   a. Engaging the students in guided participation
   b. Presenting tasks that exceed the students' zone of proximal development
   c. Encouraging the separation of thought and language
   d. Creating a cognitive apprenticeship

• 56. From a Vygotskian perspective, <u>scaffolding</u> serves what purpose in instruction?
   a. It gives them an idea of what they need to do to get good grades.
   b. It keeps school tasks within their actual developmental level.
   c. It lets them learn by watching one another.
   d. It supports them as they perform difficult tasks.

•• 57. Three of the following teachers are using <u>scaffolding</u> to help their students learn. Which one is <u>not</u> necessarily providing scaffolding?

a. Ms. Applegate gives her students a structure to follow when they write their first essay.

b. Mr. Bernardo teaches a backhand tennis swing by gently guiding each student through the correct movement a few times.

c. Ms. Chen gives her class some hints about how to solve an especially difficult word problem.

d. Mr. Donaldson takes his students on a field trip to the art museum.

• 58. Which one of the following examples illustrates a <u>cognitive apprenticeship</u>?

a. Mr. Ferguson gives students numerous word problems involving addition until they can solve such problems easily.

b. Mr. Johnson and a student work together to solve a challenging word problem, with Mr. Johnson modeling effective ways of thinking about the problem.

c. Ms. Lupinsky asks students to do easy word problems, as a way of boosting their self-confidence for the more difficult problems that will soon follow.

d. Ms. Pang individualizes the word problems she gives each student.

•• 59. Which one of the following examples most clearly illustrates a <u>cognitive apprenticeship</u>?

a. A junior high school English class is reading Robert Frost's "Stopping by Woods on a Snowy Evening." At the end of each verse, the teacher describes the visual images and feelings that the poem elicits for him, and he encourages his students to do likewise.

b. An elementary school teacher gives his students lots of practice doing addition, subtraction, multiplication, and division problems so that they will be able to solve word problems more effectively later in the school year.

c. In a high school chemistry lab, a teacher clearly describes the steps that she expects her students to take as they conduct the day's laboratory experiment. She also lists the things that students should do when they clean up after the experiment.

d. A middle school physical education teacher puts her students in pairs as they practice their forward and backward rolls. She asks the students in each pair to observe each other and give each other feedback about how to improve.

•• 60. Ms. Killian and her fourth graders have been growing sunflowers under various conditions—they have grown sunflowers in different kinds of soil, with different amounts of water, and in varying degrees of sunlight. Below are four statements that Ms. Killian makes related to the sunflowers. Which one is most consistent with the idea of a <u>cognitive apprenticeship</u>?

a. "Who can tell me what <u>photosynthesis</u> is?"

b. "How many of you have grown sunflowers at home? How many of you have moms or dads who are gardeners?"

c. "This sunflower is taller than that sunflower over there. Let's consider what the growing conditions for the two flowers have been and try to figure out what might have led to the difference we see."

d. "Elaine, please give each plant the same amount of water today that you gave it yesterday. Also, be sure that you keep each plant in the same location, so that the amount of sunlight it gets stays the same."

• 61. Which one of these is central to an <u>information processing</u> approach to cognitive development?
   a. How children learn from observing others
   b. How children learn from what others tell them
   c. What consequences follow children's behaviors
   d. How mental processes change over time

• 62. An information processing perspective of development portrays cognitive development as:
   a. A series of five distinctly different stages of development
   b. Gradually improving cognitive abilities
   c. Being due primarily to direct instruction about how to think
   d. Something that is influenced largely by hereditarily controlled neurological changes

• 63. The following statements describe the development of information processing abilities as children progress through the elementary school years. Three of the statements are accurate. Which one is <u>not</u>?
   a. Children become increasingly able to pay attention to many different things simultaneously.
   b. Children show an increasing tendency to rehearse information.
   c. Children become increasingly able to determine when they actually know something.
   d. Children become increasingly capable of learning effectively because of their expanding knowledge base.

• 64. Which one of the following statements is most consistent with what we know about the development of attention and its role in learning?
   a. Children become increasingly more distractible during the elementary school years.
   b. Distractibility decreases during the elementary school years but increases briefly at puberty.
   c. Children show an increasing tendency to learn only the things they actually intend to learn.
   d. Young children can pay attention to only one thing at a time; high school students can attend to and learn many things simultaneously.

• 65. Which learning strategy are we most likely to see second graders use?
   a. Rehearsing what they want to remember.
   b. Organizing ideas into categories.
   c. Intentionally elaborating on new material.
   d. Writing down what they want to remember.

• 66. Randy knows more as a tenth grader than he did as a first grader. One result of this increased knowledge base is that Randy:
   a. Can use rehearsal more effectively
   b. Is more easily distracted
   c. Can more easily understand new information
   d. Is more likely to get the different things he knows confused with one another

•• 67. In which one of the following examples is metacognition most clearly illustrated?
   a. Mary knows all the letters of the alphabet before she begins kindergarten.
   b. Fran knows how much of a book she is likely to remember a month later.
   c. Billy can read fourth grade books at the age of six.
   d. Alex has a photographic memory that enables him to remember everything he sees.

• 68. How do young children's estimates of their memory capacity relate to reality?
   a. They usually underestimate how much they can remember.
   b. They usually overestimate how much they can remember.
   c. They are usually fairly accurate in their estimates of how much they can recall.
   d. They don't even try to guess how much they can recall.

• 69. Many children lack metacognitive knowledge. This is reflected in the fact that they:
   a. Don't know very much about how to learn.
   b. Have difficulty with such mathematical concepts as proportions and negative numbers.
   c. Tend to be easily distracted from their schoolwork.
   d. Don't do very well on intelligence test items requiring abstract thought.

• 70. Considering trends in cognitive development from an information processing perspective, which one of the following statements is accurate?
   a. Students generally know the things they know and the things they don't.
   b. Elementary students have a better sense of what they do and don't know than high school students do.
   c. Students tend to know a great many things that they don't realize they know.
   d. Students across the K-12 grade span often think they know things that they really don't know.

• 71. Many theorists believe that people have an innate predisposition to learn language. Three of the following provide sources of evidence that these theorists use to support their belief. Which one is not used to support an inherited predisposition to learn language?
   a. Most languages have certain characteristics in common, such as similar ways of forming negatives.
   b. Children develop increasingly larger and more sophisticated vocabularies as they grow older.
   c. Children sometimes learn a language more easily when they are exposed to it at a young age.
   d. People in the same community learn the same language despite very different experiences with that language.

• 72. Three of the following are examples of expressive language. Which one is an example of receptive language?
   a. Talking on the telephone
   b. Writing an essay
   c. Reading a book
   d. Giving an oral presentation

•• 73. Which one of the following illustrates an <u>overgeneralization</u> error? The words in question are underlined.
   a. Abe knows what the words <u>tall</u> and <u>short</u> mean, but he doesn't realize that one is the opposite of the other.
   b. Ben thinks that all <u>animals</u> have to have fur and four legs; therefore snakes, bumblebees, and people cannot possibly be animals.
   c. Carol says, "I <u>forgetted</u> my homework today."
   d. Donna thinks that whales and dolphins are kinds of <u>fish</u>, when they are actually mammals instead.

•• 74. Maureen vehemently denies that trees are plants. Her understanding of what a <u>plant</u> is reflects which of the following errors?
   a. overregularization
   b. overgeneralization
   c. undergeneralization
   d. a pragmatic error

•• 75. Considering what we have learned from our studies of cognitive development and language development, we should expect elementary school children to have the greatest difficulty understanding the meaning of which one of the following words?
   a. <u>although</u>
   b. <u>somersault</u>
   c. <u>swim</u>
   d. <u>vehicle</u>

• 76. Which strategy is most likely to be effective in promoting semantic development?
   a. Allowing students to make up their own meanings for words to encourage invention and creativity.
   b. Teaching students the meanings of words related to topics they are studying.
   c. Encouraging overgeneralization.
   d. Allowing students to use words incorrectly in the early elementary grades to promote linguistic self-efficacy.

• 77. Knowing which word combinations are grammatically correct reflects knowledge of:
   a. Semantics
   b. Syntax
   c. Generalization
   d. Context

•• 78. Which one of the following sentences reflects <u>overregularization</u> in a child's speech? The words in question are underlined.
   a. I <u>ain't</u> going to school today.
   b. Are you <u>gonna</u> go on the field trip?
   c. The <u>sheeps</u> are in the meadow.
   d. He <u>don't</u> know anything.

•• 79. Given what we know about the language development of elementary school children, three of the following errors might be observed in a class of second graders. Which one is not likely to be observed?
   a. Annie asserts quite adamantly that a penguin is not a bird.
   b. When Benny is shown a doll that has a blindfold and asked if the doll is easy to see, Benny says no.
   c. Connie speaks mostly in "semi-sentences"—i.e., subjects without predicates, and predicates without subjects.
   d. Danny complains that his bicycle is "broked."

• 80. Most children in the early elementary grades think that being a "good listener" means:
   a. Asking the speaker a lot of questions.
   b. Remembering what the speaker says.
   c. Sitting quietly and looking at the speaker.
   d. Being able to tell somebody else what the speaker has said.

• 81. Three of the following aspects of language development appear during the elementary school years or even earlier. Which one are we not likely to see until students are in junior high or high school?
   a. Following accepted social conventions in terms of beginning and ending conversations
   b. Adapting a spoken message to the age of the listener
   c. Using context clues to interpret a speaker's message
   d. Understanding proverbs

•• 82. Which one of the following is the best example of pragmatics in language?
   a. Julie waits until her friend has finished talking before she begins to speak.
   b. Morris understands the underlying meaning of "A stitch in time saves nine."
   c. Sheena knows that the plural of man is men, not mans.
   d. Isaiah recognizes the double meanings in many of the puns he hears.

•• 83. LaWanda understands that a single sentence can sometimes be interpreted in two or more ways. For example, she realizes that the sentence "I know more beautiful women than Miss America" has two possible interpretations: "I know women who are more beautiful than Miss America is" or "I know more beautiful women than Miss America knows." LaWanda's appreciation for the double meanings of some sentences reflects:
   a. Overgeneralization
   b. Metalinguistic awareness
   c. Pragmatics
   d. Expressive language

•• 84. If we were to characterize the language of school-age children, how could we best describe it?
   a. The receptive and expressive language skills of most children are fully developed by second grade.
   b. The receptive and expressive language skills of most children are fully developed by seventh grade.
   c. Receptive language skills are fully developed by second grade, but expressive skills continue to develop at least through seventh grade.
   d. Receptive and expressive language skills continue to develop throughout the elementary and high school years.

• 85. Research regarding learning a second language yields which of the following conclusions?
   a. The ability to learn a second language increases with age until adulthood, when it starts to decline.
   b. The ability to learn a second language increases with age until adolescence, when it starts to decline.
   c. The ability to learn a second language is greatest in the toddler and preschool years.
   d. We do not yet conclusively know if there is a "best" time to learn a second language.

• 86. Based on the textbook's discussion of bilingualism and bilingual children, three of the following statements are true. Which one of the statements is <u>not</u> necessarily true?
   a. Bilingualism is sometimes the result of living in a household in which two languages are spoken regularly.
   b. Learning a second language promotes greater metalinguistic awareness.
   c. Children who learn two languages before the age of four are likely to master less of each language than they would if they learned only one.
   d. Children who learn a second language in addition to their native tongue tend to have a more positive attitude toward people who speak that second language.

• 87. Which approach appears to be most effective for teaching English speakers a second language?
   a. Let them talk with native speakers of the language, who should alternate between using English and the other language.
   b. Teach it to them before kindergarten if possible, because they quickly lose their ability to learn a second language fluently after that.
   c. Immerse them in the second language, having them hear and speak it exclusively in all classroom activities.
   d. Wait until they reach Piaget's formal operations stage so that they can better grasp the subtleties of the new language.

• 88. Three of the following statements accurately describe the diversity we are likely to see in students' cognitive development. Which statement is <u>in</u>accurate?
   a. Some children in a first-grade classroom may show concrete operational thought, whereas others may show signs of preoperational thought.
   b. Students with physical and sensory challenges may have less general knowledge of the world, limiting their ability to relate new experiences to things they already know.
   c. When eighth graders are asked to separate and control variables in a problem about fishing, those who have often fished with family or friends will be more successful than students who have never fished.
   d. Rehearsal is more commonly observed in children who live in developing countries than in children who live in highly urbanized and industrialized ones.

•• 89. Which of the following pairs of students best illustrates the idea of student diversity with respect to different <u>dialects</u>?
   a. Telly was born in Greece, and Fritz was born in Germany. Fritz has an easier time learning English than Telly does because German uses the same alphabet that English does, whereas Greek does not.
   b. Ralph speaks English as it is spoken in rural Mississippi; Kyle speaks the English of inner-city Chicago.
   c. Margaret speaks English fluently; Anna knows fewer words and speaks in simpler sentences because she immigrated from Romania only six months ago.
   d. Elena speaks Spanish and Maria speaks Portuguese—two languages with similar vocabulary and syntax because of their shared Latin roots.

• 90. Which one of the following statements most accurately describes students with <u>limited English proficiency</u> (LED)?
   a. They have greater difficulty than their classmates in understanding what they read and hear in class.
   b. They have difficulty with enunciation, often as the result of birth defects or other physical deformities.
   c. They have normal syntactical development but delayed vocabulary development.
   d. They have normal vocabulary development but delayed syntactical development.

• 91. Some students with special needs have advanced cognitive and linguistic development in comparison to their classmates. Which one of the following characteristics are we <u>least</u> likely to observe with regard to these students?
   a. A more advanced vocabulary
   b. The earlier appearance of formal operational thinking capabilities
   c. More general knowledge about the world
   d. Classroom assignments that are above their zone of proximal development

• 92. Which one of the following statements is true of all three theories of cognitive development we've studied—Piaget's theory, Vygotsky's theory, and information processing theory?
   a. Children are actively involved in their own learning.
   b. Cognitive development involves a series of stages.
   c. Children and adults think in basically the same way.
   d. Development involves both assimilation and accommodation.

• 93. Which one of the following do Piaget, Vygotsky, and information processing theorists all agree is essential for children's cognitive development?
   a. Good feelings about oneself
   b. An environment or situation that presents a challenge
   c. An accepting environment in which children aren't pressured to excel
   d. A rich vocabulary

## Essay Questions

•• 94. Piaget presented his studies of conservation as evidence of the illogical thinking of young children.
   a. What did he mean by the term conservation?
   b. Describe one of his conservation tasks and the kinds of responses that children in the preoperational and concrete operational stages are likely to give.
   c. Describe a specific way in which a child's ability to conserve is essential for learning in either mathematics or science.

•• 95. Describe three characteristics of preoperational children (excluding age) that distinguish them from concrete operational children. Explain how each of these characteristics may interfere with students' ability to learn and perform effectively in the classroom, illustrating your discussion with concrete examples.

• 96. Describe three ways in which students in Piaget's formal operational stage are likely to think differently from those in the concrete operational stage. Illustrate each characteristic with a concrete example of how students in each of the two stages might think or act.

•• 97. Mr. Davis asks his third graders to conduct experiments to examine the effects of water, sunlight, and type of soil on growing sunflowers. He tells them, "I want you to find out which of these three things—water, sunlight, and soil—affect how well sunflowers grow." Here are lots of sunflower seeds, lots of paper cups to grow them in, and two different types of soil. You can give your growing plants lots of sunlight by putting them on the shelf by the window, or you can grow them in a shadier place on the bookshelf behind my desk. And here's a measuring cup you can use to measure the amount of water you give them each day."

   Mr. Davis is assuming his third graders can do at least two things that, from Piaget's perspective, they probably cannot do. What two crucial abilities necessary for conducting appropriate experiments do his students probably not yet have? Justify your answer in a short paragraph.

•• 98. Choose a particular grade level and discuss three important implications of Piaget's theory for teaching students at this grade level. State your three points both in abstract terms and in terms of specific educational practices you would employ.

•• 99. Vygotsky and contemporary Vygotskian theorists have proposed that children's and adolescents' cognitive development is promoted when they work within their zone of proximal development and that scaffolding enables them to do this successfully.
   a. Explain the two concepts underlined above, and give a concrete example of each one.
   b. Choose a topic or skill you might be teaching your students, and explain how you would: (1) scaffold students' efforts, and (2) modify the scaffolding over time.

- 100. The textbook describes a number of trends in the development of information processing skills. Describe at least <u>four</u> ways in which sixth-grade children differ from kindergarten children in their information processing strategies and capabilities.

- 101. Describe at least one limitation elementary school students may have in each one of the following aspects of language, and illustrate each limitation with a concrete example:
  a. Semantics
  b. Syntax
  c. Listening comprehension
  d. Oral communication

- 102. In three short paragraphs, explain the role that <u>challenge</u> plays in each of the theories of cognitive development listed below. In each case, give a concrete example to illustrate your discussion.
  a. Piaget's theory
  b. Vygotsky's theory
  c. Information processing theory

## ANSWER KEY

### Multiple-Choice Questions

1. b
2. a
3. c
4. c
5. d
6. a
7. b
8. a
9. d
10. c
11. b
12. a
13. a
14. d
15. d
16. b
17. c
18. d
19. b
20. b
21. a
22. a
23. b
24. a
25. b
26. d
27. c
28. b
29. c
30. d
31. b
32. d
33. c
34. d
35. a
36. c
37. d
38. a
39. c
40. d
41. b
42. c
43. b
44. b
45. a
46. b
47. d
48. c
49. a
50. c
51. a
52. d
53. b
54. c
55. a
56. d
57. d
58. b
59. a
60. c
61. d
62. b
63. a
64. c
65. a
66. c
67. b
68. b
69. a
70. d
71. b
72. c
73. d
74. c
75. a
76. b
77. b
78. c
79. c
80. c
81. d
82. a
83. b
84. d
85. d
86. c
87. c
88. d
89. b
90. a
91. d
92. a
93. b

## Essay Questions

94. Responses to various parts of the question are as follows:
    a. Conservation is the recognition that if nothing is added or taken away, an amount stays the same regardless of alterations in shape or arrangement.
    b. The student's response might describe conservation of liquid (e.g., the water glasses task), conservation of weight (e.g., the balls of clay task), conservation of number (e.g., the pennies task), or any other conservation task with which they are familiar. Responses of preoperational children reflect a lack of conservation (e.g., "One has more"), whereas those of concrete operational children reflect an awareness that amounts are still the same.
    c. There are a number of possible responses to this question—here are two examples: In mathematics, conservation of number is essential for an understanding of numbers; children must realize that "4 is 4 is 4," no matter how the four items are arranged. In science, students studying the concept of weight must understand that weight stays the same regardless of physical transformations; for example, gas that is heated expands, but it still weighs the same as it did before.

95. Differences between preoperational children and concrete operational children are listed in Table 2.1 in the textbook; the response should describe three of them. For each characteristic of preoperational thought identified, the response should give a plausible explanation and illustration of how it interferes with effective learning or classroom performance—for example: "Due to egocentrism, a student who has been told not to interrupt classmates who are speaking may have trouble understanding why allowing other children to speak is important."

96. Differences between concrete operational and formal operational children are listed in Table 2.2 in the textbook; the response should list three of them. The response should also illustrate each difference with a concrete example of how children in the two stages might think or behave differently; possibilities are listed in Table 2.2, but other plausible examples are acceptable as well.

97. Mr. Davis is assuming that his students can <u>formulate and test multiple hypotheses</u> and can <u>separate and control variables</u>. According to Piaget, these are abilities that emerge in formal operations. However, Mr. Davis's students, being about eight or nine years old, are probably still in concrete operations.

98. Students' responses to this item are likely to vary considerably. A response should list three implications derived either from Piaget's general assumptions (see the section entitled "Piaget's Basic Assumptions") or from characteristics of the stage in which the age group is likely to be in (see the section entitled "Piaget's Stages of Cognitive Development"). Each implication should be described in both general, abstract terms, and as one or more specific, concrete teaching practices.

99. Responses to the two parts of the question are as follows:
    a. The zone of proximal development is the range of tasks that a child can do only with the assistance of a more competent individual. Scaffolding is the structure that the more competent individual provides to help a child perform a difficult task successfully; this structure is gradually removed over time as the child becomes more skillful. The response should include a concrete example of each of these concepts.
    b. Students' responses will vary considerably depending on the topics and specific form of scaffolding they choose. A response should include both an appropriate form of scaffolding (see the bulleted list in the section "Scaffolding" for possibilities) and a description of how the scaffolding is gradually removed over time.

100. From an information processing theory perspective, sixth graders differ from kindergartners in the following ways (the response should address at least four of these):
    - They are less distractible; for example, they can work more effectively in a noisy classroom.
    - They are more likely to learn only the specific things they intend to learn.
    - They are more likely to rehearse the information that they want to learn.
    - They are more likely to organize the information that they want to learn.
    - They have more knowledge to which they can relate new information.
    - They have a better integrated knowledge base—one in which pieces of information are interrelated rather than isolated.
    - They have a more realistic idea of how much they can learn and remember; kindergartners tend to be overly optimistic.
    - They have more knowledge about effective learning strategies; for example, they are more likely to realize that if you don't learn something the first time, you need to study it again.
    - They are more likely to know when they have effectively learned something and when they have not.

101. Elementary school students may have limitations such as these (the response should include at least one bulleted item in each of the four areas below, with each item being illustrated with a concrete example):

   a. Semantics
      - Limited vocabulary
      - Incomplete understanding of words (e.g., undergeneralization or overgeneralization)

   b. Syntax
      - Overregularization
      - Limited understanding of complex syntactical structures (e.g., passive sentences, sentences with two or more clauses)

   c. Listening comprehension
      - Belief that good listening means sitting still and being quiet rather than understanding what is being said
      - Belief that it is inappropriate to ask for clarification when a message isn't understood
      - Overreliance on context clues when interpreting a spoken message

   d. Oral communication
      - Pronunciation difficulties
      - Difficulty taking the characteristics of the listener into account
      - Limited pragmatic skills (i.e., limited knowledge about the social conventions of spoken language)

102. Piaget proposed that children modify schemes and develop new ones only when they cannot interpret new experiences in light of existing schemes. Vygotsky proposed that children are most likely to develop when they perform tasks within their zone of proximal development—tasks for which they need the assistance of someone more skilled. Information processing theorists propose that children develop more sophisticated learning strategies only when their current ones are not effective.

# Chapter 3

# PERSONAL, SOCIAL, AND MORAL DEVELOPMENT

| CHAPTER OUTLINE | RELEVANT TEST BANK ITEMS |
|---|---|
| INFLUENCE OF HEREDITY AND ENVIRONMENT ON PERSONAL, SOCIAL, AND MORAL DEVELOPMENT<br>Temperamental Differences<br>Effects of Parenting<br>Effects of Culture<br>Peer Influences | Multiple-Choice 1–9 |
| DEVELOPMENT OF A SENSE OF SELF<br>Factors Influencing the Development of Self-Views<br>Developmental Changes in Students' Self-Views | Multiple-Choice 10–35<br>Essay 89–90 |
| SOCIAL DEVELOPMENT<br>Peer Relationships<br>Social Cognition<br>Fostering Social Skills<br>Promoting Social Interaction Among Diverse Groups | Multiple-Choice 36–58<br>Essay 91 |
| MORAL AND PROSOCIAL DEVELOPMENT<br>Development of Moral Reasoning: Kohlberg's Theory<br>Possible Gender Differences in Moral Reasoning: Gilligan's Theory<br>Emotional Components of Moral Development<br>Determinants of Moral Behaviors<br>Promoting Moral Development in the Classroom | Multiple-Choice 59–81<br>Essay 92 |
| CONSIDERING DIVERSITY IN PERSONAL, SOCIAL, AND MORAL DEVELOPMENT<br>Accommodating Students with Special Needs | Multiple-Choice 82–83 |
| THE BIG PICTURE<br>Personal Development<br>Social Development<br>Moral Development<br>Characteristics of Different Age Groups<br>General Themes in Personal, Social, and Moral Development | Multiple-Choice 84–88<br>Essay 93 |

| The items in the "Integrative Questions" chapter of this Test Bank integrate the content of two or more textbook chapters. Within that chapter, the items listed to the right are relevant to Chapter 3. | Multiple-Choice 1-5<br>Essay 19, 21–23, 39 |
|---|---|

## Multiple-Choice Questions

• 1. Which one of the following most accurately describes the concept temperament?
   a. The ways that individuals have learned to react to environmental stimuli as a result of their past experiences
   b. An inherited predisposition to interact with one's environment in certain ways
   c. The extent to which people are either outgoing (extroverted) or withdrawn (introverted)
   d. The extent to which people either like or dislike themselves

•• 2. Which one of the following fifth graders clearly shows signs of attachment as developmental psychologists define the term?
   a. Miranda seems withdrawn and frightened much of the time.
   b. Mike seems unusually preoccupied with an attractive young actress who stars in a popular television show.
   c. Shelly has no friends and behaves aggressively toward the other girls in her class.
   d. Jeffrey is self-confident and often likes to work independently.

• 3. Authoritative parents can best be characterized as having which type of relationship with their children?
   a. High expectations, loving support, and shared decision-making
   b. Few expectations, loving support, and considerable freedom for children to make their own decisions
   c. Little emotional support or interest in their children's needs
   d. High expectations, strict rules, and little give-and-take in decision-making

• 4. Which student has probably come from a home in which his or her parents exhibit an authoritative parenting style?
   a. Rhoda is anxious and unhappy.
   b. Margaret is impulsive and disobedient.
   c. Frank is well-behaved and self-confident.
   d. Patrick is selfish and unmotivated.

• 5. Three of the following statements about parenting are accurate. Which one is inaccurate?
   a. When parents are abusive, their children are more apt to be aggressive.
   b. How parents treat their children is somewhat dependent on their children's temperaments.
   c. Very permissive parents tend to have children who are highly motivated and self-directed.
   d. Very controlling parents tend to have children who are uptight and socially inept.

•• 6. If we extend research findings regarding effective parenting styles to the classroom, teachers would be well advised to:
  a. Insist on strict obedience, with immediate punishment for infractions.
  b. Establish fair rules and high expectations, and provide loving support.
  c. Allow students to make their own decisions regarding how they should and should not behave in the classroom.
  d. Reward good behavior and ignore inappropriate behavior.

• 7. The process that molds children to become productive adults in the culture in which they live is known as:
  a. Decentration
  b. Personal development
  c. The imaginary audience
  d. Socialization

•• 8. Which one of the following best illustrates a <u>norm</u> that children acquire through the socialization process?
  a. To sit quietly in class
  b. To eat when hungry
  c. To keep others from doing their work
  d. To turn and look at the source of a loud noise

•• 9. Three of the following teachers are socializing their students in the way that schools typically do. Which teacher is <u>not</u> socializing students in a typical fashion?
  a. Ms. Allen insists that her students complete their independent seatwork before they go to recess.
  b. Ms. Bernetti has her students go to lunch by rows, letting the quietest rows go first.
  c. Ms. Castanza does not permit her students to talk back to her in a disrespectful fashion.
  d. Ms. Dobson suggests that Sean bang his fist against the wall a few times whenever he gets frustrated.

•• 10. Given what we know about people's self-concepts, three of the following are likely scenarios. Which scenario is <u>not</u> likely to occur?
  a. Daniel knows he has many friends, but he wishes he were a better student.
  b. Mike vacillates between thinking of himself as being very smart and as being extremely stupid.
  c. Aaron thinks that kids his age don't like him, so he spends most of his spare time with his parents.
  d. Rex knows he's good in math and science but thinks of himself as a complete klutz when it comes to sports.

•• 11. Students usually have feelings about their competence in three general areas: cognitive, social, and physical. Which one of the following is an example of social competence?
  a. Perry thinks that his teacher likes him because he is the best speller in his class.
  b. Teresa prefers to do her math problems in cooperative groups rather than alone.
  c. Betty likes her classmates and knows that they like her.
  d. Devin doesn't think he does very well in physical education, but his teacher thinks he is a capable athlete.

•• 12. Which one of the following best illustrates self-efficacy rather than self-concept or self-esteem?
   a. Anne is pretty sure she can win a spot on the school's dance squad if she practices her routine regularly.
   b. Brandi thinks of herself as being more intelligent than most of her classmates.
   c. Connor has little faith in his academic abilities, and so he does whatever he can to avoid doing assigned classroom tasks.
   d. Darvin is convinced that no one likes him, even though most people do.

•• 13. Which one of these examples best reflects the role that self-concept typically plays in achievement and school behavior?
   a. Melissa thinks of herself as physically fit, so she doesn't think she needs to participate in sports or other physical activities.
   b. Kim doesn't want to take any more math classes because she knows she's already good at math.
   c. Nettie doesn't think she is very popular, so she smiles at others and tries to talk to them so they will like her.
   d. Linda knows she is a good reader, so she takes an extra reading class as an elective.

•• 14. On average, students who attend schools for gifted children have lower self-esteem than students of equal intelligence who attend regular schools with students of widely varying abilities. If we consider research about factors affecting self-concept and self-esteem, we can explain this finding in the following way:
   a. Children who attend gifted programs typically have more assertive parents, and such parents tend to undermine their children's self-concepts.
   b. Having a label of any kind—even the label "gifted"—tends to lower self-esteem.
   c. Identifying a child as gifted requires an intensive evaluation, and evaluations inevitably lower self-esteem.
   d. Children form their self-concepts in part by comparing their own performance to the performance of those around them.

• 15. Children's self-concepts become increasingly stable, and therefore increasingly more difficult to change, as they grow older. Which one of the following is the most likely explanation for the increasing stability of the self-concept over time?
   a. Maturational factors play a major role in the formation of the self-concept; these factors continue to unfold throughout childhood.
   b. Research studies indicate that the self-concept has a strong genetic component.
   c. Most of a student's teachers and classmates behave in ways that consistently lower the student's self-concept.
   d. Children will behave in ways consistent with their self-concepts, thereby reaffirming their views of themselves.

• 16. The formation of children's self-concepts is most strongly influenced by:
   a. Their inherited temperaments
   b. Their physical attractiveness
   c. How other people treat them
   d. The self-concepts of their parents

•• 17. The four teachers below are hoping to improve their students' self-concepts and self-esteem. Which one will probably be <u>least</u> effective in doing so?
   a. Mr. Anderson helps his students be successful at math word problems.
   b. Ms. Berry tells her students how wonderful they are.
   c. Mr. Carrera helps his students improve their creative writing skills.
   d. Ms. D'Amato helps her students throw a softball farther.

•• 18. Sharon is a student who does not believe that she can be academically successful. Considering the textbook's discussion of factors that promote a positive self-concept, you should:
   a. Tell her at least once a day that she is smarter than she thinks she is.
   b. Tell her that social skills are more important than academics anyway.
   c. Put her in situations in which she will experience academic success.
   d. Foster a friendship between Sharon and a student who is academically gifted.

• 19. As students grow older, they are more likely to:
   a. Hold themselves to unrealistically high standards for performance
   b. Be satisfied with low levels of performance
   c. Evaluate their own performance in terms of how it compares with that of their classmates
   d. Evaluate their own performance in terms of how much improvement it shows over time

• 20. We can most effectively enhance students' self-concepts and self-esteem when we:
   a. Hold high yet achievable expectations for their performance
   b. Hold expectations for performance that we know they can achieve with little or no effort
   c. Encourage them to think more positively about themselves
   d. Talk about the advantages of having a positive self-concept

• 21. With the textbook's discussion of negative feedback and self-concept in mind, choose the statement that most accurately reflects the appropriate use of negative feedback in a school setting.
   a. Negative feedback should be vague and general, to avoid hurting a student's feelings.
   b. Negative feedback should be given in front of classmates, who can then learn by example.
   c. Negative feedback should never be given in a school setting.
   d. Negative feedback should be given within the context of a warm, respectful relationship.

• 22. Which one of the following best describes Erik Erikson's theory of psychosocial development?
   a. A series of stages, each of which has a unique developmental task to be dealt with
   b. A process of growing increasingly self-confident through the years as one's competence improves
   c. A series of stages in which people develop increasingly more sophisticated social skills
   d. A progression of increasingly more abstract understandings of social situations

• 23. According to Erik Erikson, students' ability to trust those around them stems from:
   a. Early experiences with teachers
   b. Experiences with adults during infancy
   c. Peer behaviors during the elementary years
   d. Friendships formed during the teenage years

• 24. One of the most important stages in a child's early years is Erikson's stage of <u>initiative vs. guilt</u>, in which children learn to:
   a. Control their bodily functions so they don't feel guilty about having "accidents."
   b. Take initiative in feeding and dressing themselves.
   c. Plan and carry out some of their own activities.
   d. Persevere at difficult tasks.

• 25. At which of Erikson's stages do children realize that they can obtain the recognition of teachers and parents by producing things?
   a. Industry vs. inferiority
   b. Identity vs. role confusion
   c. Initiative vs. guilt
   d. Generativity vs. stagnation

•• 26. Jules is discovering that by being able to write all his letters, he is winning the approval of his teacher. Without knowing anything else about Jules, the best guess is that he is in Erikson's stage of:
   a. Trust vs. mistrust
   b. Autonomy vs. shame and doubt
   c. Initiative vs. guilt
   d. Industry vs. inferiority

• 27. If we consider Erikson's theory of personal development, then which one of the following issues would we expect secondary students to be <u>most</u> concerned about?
   a. Wanting to form a close and intimate relationship with another human being.
   b. Trying to decide who they really are and the role they will play in adult society.
   c. Needing to gain the recognition of parents and teachers through their academic activities and achievements.
   d. Finding a way to wiggle out of doing difficult tasks.

•• 28. Which one of the following best illustrates Erikson's stage of <u>identify vs. role confusion</u>?
   a. Arnold is always wishing things were different than they are.
   b. Beth can't keep a steady boyfriend.
   c. Craig is trying to decide what he wants to be when he grows up.
   d. Dawn underestimates her ability to learn mathematics.

• 29. Given what we know about changes in children's and adolescents' self-esteem over the years, which teachers should be especially careful to help students feel good about themselves and their abilities to succeed?
   a. Third- through fifth-grade teachers
   b. Kindergarten and first-grade teachers, and junior high school teachers
   c. High school teachers who teach advanced courses
   d. High school coaches and physical education teachers

•• 30. Which one of the following examples illustrates how the imaginary audience can be a factor in the adolescent's developing self-concept?
   a. Annette talks to an imaginary friend when she is having problems and feels she has no one else to turn to.
   b. Bernita feels as if everyone must be looking at her when she walks down the hall with her friends.
   c. Candy feels detached, as if she has no life of her own but is only watching everyone else live their lives.
   d. Dora feels self-conscious when she has to get up in front of her class and give a speech from memory.

•• 31. Which one of the following illustrates developmental theorists' notion of the personal fable?
   a. Olivia becomes very popular with her peers when she makes up a story that she is from another country and has royal blood in her family.
   b. Wendy has trouble getting along with teachers because she believes herself to be especially vulnerable to illness and injury.
   c. Jonathan feels he is just like everyone else—a nobody—so he isn't very popular.
   d. William feels he is invincible, immortal, and immune to the problems others face.

•• 32. Which one of the following best illustrates a sense of identity?
   a. Carlos takes pride in his Mexican American heritage.
   b. Shea knows she could be a better dancer if she practiced more often.
   c. Drew wonders whether she should be a doctor or a lawyer.
   d. Noah feels confident that he will make new friends when he moves to a new school district next year.

•• 33. Sixteen-year-old Reynelda has known since she was four years old that she will become a teacher. Her grandmother was a teacher, and her mother and two aunts are teachers. She's never really even thought about any other occupation. Reynelda can best be described as showing:
   a. identity diffusion
   b. foreclosure
   c. moratorium
   d. identity achievement

•• 34. As a 17-year-old high school senior, Julian has no sense of direction. Over the past year he has dabbled in auto mechanics, photography, and Buddhism, but nothing has held his interest for more than a month or so. Julian can best be described as showing:

a. identity diffusion
b. foreclosure
c. moratorium
d. identity achievement

•• 35. Three of the following teachers are using strategies that should promote their students' self-esteem. Which one probably will <u>not</u>?

a. Mr. Abrams tells Susan, "The short story you wrote yesterday was a really good start. The main character seems a little flat, though. Let's sit down and brainstorm some ideas as to how you might give her more life."
b. Ms. Barnes hopes to motivate her students to succeed by having them participate in various academic competitions.
c. Ms. Crumb tells her students she fully expects that all of them will be able to succeed in her class if they work hard and seek her help when they need it.
d. When Matthew is hospitalized with a broken leg, Ms. Danetta comes by to see how he is doing and to bring him some assignments to do during his absence from class.

• 36. Peer relationships, like parent-child relationships, are essential to a child's development. Which one of the following is <u>not</u> one of the ways that peer relationships influence the developing child?

a. Peer relationships provide opportunities to develop and practice social skills.
b. Peers are the first individuals to whom a child becomes truly attached.
c. Peers can be a source of emotional support during difficult times.
d. Peers provide information about which behaviors are desirable and which are not.

• 37. Which one of the following statements is most accurate about the effects of peer groups and peer pressure?

a. Peer pressure is strongest in the primary grades, when children first enter school.
b. Peer pressure is strongest during the late high school years, as students approach graduation.
c. Peer groups may encourage either desirable qualities (e.g., honesty) or undesirable qualities (e.g., violence).
d. When a particular peer group discourages academic achievement, members of that group will always achieve lower class grades than they are capable of achieving.

• 38. The textbook suggests that the effects of peer pressure have been overrated. Three of the following are factors that ameliorate, or "soften," the potential effects of peer pressure. Which statement is <u>not</u> necessarily accurate?

a. Students may give an outward impression of acting "cool" or "going along with the crowd" while secretly behaving in accordance with their own standards.
b. Students tend to hang out with peers whose values and interests are similar to their own.
c. Students retain some of the values they have acquired from their families.
d. Most adolescents have developed abstract moral principles that guide their daily decision making.

• 39. Friendships are especially important in social development because children and adolescents:
   a. Can practice cooperation and reciprocity only with people they care deeply about
   b. Are deeply committed to those relationships and will develop the skills needed to maintain them
   c. Develop high self-esteem only if they participate in enjoyable recreational activities at least twice a week (on average)
   d. Develop internal standards for behavior only when friends reinforce such standards

•• 40. Julie, a sixth grader, nearly always eats lunch with the same five or six girls. They usually spread out at the table so no other girls can sit with them. Sometimes they even plan together what they will wear to school the next day. Julie's group is an example of:
   a. A clique
   b. A subculture
   c. A norm group
   d. A gang

• 41. A larger social group in which the members show strong loyalty to each other, have strict rules, and often have some sort of initiation rites is known as:
   a. A clique
   b. A subculture
   c. A norm group
   d. A gang

•• 42. Which one of the following romantic relationships would be <u>most typical</u>?
   a. Didi, a third grader, feels as if she's the only girl in her class without a boyfriend.
   b. Jake, a fifth grader, has taken Andrea to the movies several times and thinks about her constantly.
   c. Sonia, a seventh grader, has a crush on her science teacher and giggles with her friends whenever he walks by.
   d. Sally, an eighth grader, has a sexually intimate relationship with her boyfriend Brad.

•• 43. Many of the students at Buchanan Junior High know that John and Sara have been "going out" for the past two months. Given what we know about students' early dating habits, it is <u>most likely</u> that John and Sara:
   a. Have confided in each other about very personal and private matters
   b. Have many of the same interests and greatly enjoy each other's company
   c. Find each other attractive but don't know each other very well
   d. Have begun to experiment in sexually intimate ways

• 44. When asked which students they would most like to do things with, most middle school students choose classmates who:
   a. Are cooperative and sensitive
   b. Are the best athletes
   c. Enjoy teasing others
   d. Always like to be in charge

• 45. Most days Marnie keeps to herself at school, and her classmates don't even seem to be aware that she is nearby. Marnie can best be described as a:
   a. Student at Kohlberg's preconventional level
   b. Neglected student
   c. Student at Kohlberg's conventional level
   d. Rejected student

•• 46. Which one of the following is the best example of <u>social cognition</u>?
   a. Max refuses to do the tasks his teacher assigns because he doesn't want to look foolish when he fails at them.
   b. Julie and Isabelle giggle as they try to imitate the haughty snobbishness of the obnoxious head cheerleader.
   c. Rhonda needs to be around other people all the time; she gets bored when she has to entertain herself.
   d. Luke tries to anticipate how Sheila might respond if he backs out of doing the science project the two friends have agreed to do together.

•• 47. Luanne has only recently begun to understand that good friendships involve give-and-take on both sides to make them work. Considering Selman's work regarding the stages of perspective taking and the ages at which they occur, Luanne is probably at what grade level?
   a. In preschool
   b. In the early elementary grades
   c. In middle school
   d. In her junior or senior year of high school

•• 48. Dallas and his friends think that Billy is "stuck up" simply because he never says anything to them. They don't consider other possible reasons why Billy isn't more outgoing. Considering Selman's work regarding the stages of perspective taking and the ages at which they occur, Dallas and his friends are probably at what grade level?
   a. In the early elementary grades
   b. In middle school
   c. In their junior or senior year of high school
   d. In college

• 49. If we want to promote perspective taking in our students, probably the best strategy is to:
   a. Encourage them to keep an open mind about things
   b. Have them work closely with, and perhaps tutor, children at a younger grade level
   c. Have them listen to one another's points of view about an issue
   d. Punish students when they act in an extremely self-centered fashion

• 50. Which one of the following best illustrates a <u>hostile attributional bias</u>?
   a. Howard thinks that other students will like him better if he projects a "tough guy" image.
   b. When Isaac accidentally brushes by Janine in the hall, she assumes that he is intentionally trying to hurt her.
   c. Kenneth gets a thrill out of threatening children younger than himself and watching them squirm.
   d. Linda spreads malicious gossip whenever she hears it; on some occasions, she starts unkind rumors herself.

• 51. Danny is a quiet eleven-year-old who usually stays to himself. Some of the other boys in class like to tease him when the teacher isn't looking because they know they can provoke him to fight, and then Danny will get in trouble. The type of aggression that Danny exhibits is called:
   a. Proactive aggression
   b. Prosocial aggression
   c. Action-reaction aggression
   d. Reactive aggression

•• 52. Three of the following statements describe typical behaviors of children who are predisposed to aggressive behavior. Which one is <u>not</u> a typical description?
   a. Jordan pushes Lisa because she is sure that Lisa bumped into her on purpose.
   b. Other children always give in to Bobby's demands because they are afraid he will push them down if they don't, but Bobby thinks the other students respect him for his actions.
   c. Derek wants to join in the soccer game in progress on the playground, so he runs into the middle of the field and trips Nathan so he can get the ball.
   d. Carrie throws her pencil at Jack because she thinks he is laughing at her, but is immediately sorry and tells him so.

•• 53. Three of the following are examples of <u>prosocial behavior</u>. Which one is <u>not</u>?
   a. Ashley lends a shoulder to cry on when Sarah breaks up with her boyfriend.
   b. Bruce shares his lunch with a classmate who forgot hers.
   c. Carla and Suellen cooperate on their history project.
   d. Dustin asks Morris for help on his homework.

•• 54. Anita's idea of how to interact with her classmates is to tease or insult them. Not surprisingly, she has few friends. Her teacher can best help her by:
   a. Doing nothing, because her peers are the most effective teachers of what she needs to know
   b. Asking the principal to move Anita to a different classroom
   c. Encouraging classmates to reciprocate by teasing and insulting <u>her</u>, so she will know how such treatment feels
   d. Teaching her more productive social interaction skills

•• 55. Three of the following strategies should foster the development of students' social skills. Which strategy, although possibly beneficial in other ways, will not foster more appropriate social skills?

a. Ms. Ackerman sees two students having a minor disagreement and decides to let them work it out for themselves.
b. When the school principal visits Mr. Brightman's fifth-grade class seeking volunteers to work at the school library fundraiser on Friday afternoon, Mr. Brightman says to his students, "You have always been a very thoughtful and helpful class. How many of you can spare a couple of hours after school on Friday?"
c. During an important district-wide test, Ms. Chambers reminds her students to keep their eyes on their own papers.
d. Mr. Dunn will not tolerate sexist or racist jokes in his classroom and openly tells his students so.

• 56. Three of the following strategies should encourage positive interactions among students with diverse backgrounds or needs. Which strategy is unlikely to do so?

a. Letting students choose their own seats in the classroom.
b. Forming cooperative learning groups that include students from different ethnic backgrounds.
c. Encouraging all students to participate in extracurricular activities.
d. Teaching students about the nature of the specific disabilities that some of their classmates may have.

•• 57. Four students with special educational needs are listed below. Identify the student that nondisabled students are least likely to accept and/or be tolerant of in the classroom. As you make your choice, keep in mind the textbook's discussion of how well nondisabled students understand students with various kinds of special needs.

a. Adam is hyperactive and often disruptive.
b. Beth is totally deaf and communicates primarily through sign language.
c. Chris can no longer walk because of a car accident.
d. David is blind.

• 58. Fourteen-year-old Wayne has a history of aggressive behavior toward other students, and so his classmates have naturally kept their distance from him over the years. But Wayne has worked extensively with the school counselor in recent months, and his interpersonal behavior has improved dramatically. Wayne's teachers must remember, however, that:

a. Such improvement is likely to be short-lived
b. Other students will continue to reject Wayne unless they can be convinced that he has changed
c. Wayne's self-esteem regarding his ability to succeed at academic tasks is likely to have decreased in the meantime
d. Wayne's aggressive behavior is likely to reappear whenever he is placed in a competitive situation

• 59. How did Lawrence Kohlberg study the moral development of children?
   a. By asking them to imagine being in another person's situation.
   b. By asking them to respond to situations with no obvious right or wrong answers.
   c. By observing how they acted in real-life situations calling for moral behavior.
   d. By comparing their moral beliefs with their moral behavior.

•• 60. If we consider Kohlberg's theory of moral development, we could best characterize children's moral development as a process of:
   a. Progressing through a series of stages from self-centeredness to increasing concern about the needs and rights of others.
   b. Learning to obey the rules that society, government, and religion have established.
   c. Remaining extremely self-centered until well into adolescence.
   d. Being almost exclusively a function of how directly students have been instructed about morality and moral issues.

•• 61. If we look at children's moral development from the perspective of Lawrence Kohlberg's stage theory, then we see which of the following trends?
   a. Preschool children have little idea of what behaviors are likely to be punished. As they proceed through the school years, they show an increasing tendency to avoid punishment by behaving appropriately.
   b. In the late elementary years (fifth and sixth grade), we see a temporary reversal to the immoral behavior of the preschool years.
   c. Children become increasingly more "religious" in how they define "right" and "wrong" (e.g., by defining "right" as obeying the Ten Commandments).
   d. Children become increasingly more likely to define "right" and "wrong" in terms of what behaviors will help society run smoothly.

• 62. Students at Kohlberg's <u>preconventional</u> level of moral reasoning are likely to define "right" behavior in terms of:
   a. What people expect of them
   b. Society's standards regarding what's right or wrong
   c. What they can get away with
   d. Abstract principles of morality

•• 63. Which one of the following statements reflects Kohlberg's <u>preconventional</u> moral reasoning?
   a. "It's okay to cheat on this exam because the teacher isn't watching me."
   b. "It isn't fair to the students who studied hard if I cheat."
   c. "Cheating is against school rules, so I shouldn't do it."
   d. "The most popular boy in school cheats all the time, so I guess I can too."

•• 64. Which one of the following individuals is in Kohlberg's <u>law and order</u> stage of moral reasoning?
   a. Adam does what the teacher says because he knows he will be punished if he doesn't.
   b. Barbara obeys the teacher because she wants the teacher to think nice things about her.
   c. Clara obeys the teacher because she understands that the only way schools can run smoothly is if students behave appropriately.
   d. Don obeys the teacher because the rules say he must obey, and it is his duty to obey.

•• 65. Which one of the following individuals is in Kohlberg's <u>social contract</u> stage of moral reasoning?
   a. Adam does what the teacher says because he knows he will be punished if he doesn't.
   b. Barbara obeys the teacher because she wants the teacher to think nice things about her.
   c. Clara obeys the teacher because she understands that the only way schools can run smoothly is if students behave appropriately.
   d. Don obeys the teacher because the rules say he must obey, and it is his duty to obey.

•• 66. The parents of students in your fifth-grade class want you to include moral issues in your classroom curriculum. A few who have read Kohlberg's theory of moral development want you to help the students progress to postconventional moral reasoning. You should reply by pointing out that:
   a. There is nothing you can do to promote moral development before students reach adolescence.
   b. This is a good idea because postconventional reasoning will promote abstract thought.
   c. Research studies indicate that most students have already reached the postconventional level by fifth grade.
   d. Postconventional reasoning is an unrealistic goal for fifth graders.

• 67. In what way do Kohlberg's stages of moral development relate to Piaget's stages of cognitive development?
   a. Certain stages of cognitive development are a prerequisite to certain stages of moral reasoning.
   b. Certain stages of moral reasoning are a prerequisite to certain stages of cognitive development.
   c. Piaget's and Kohlberg's stages are both based on Erikson's stages of psychosocial development.
   d. Piaget's and Kohlberg's stages are both heavily dependent on physiological maturation.

• 68. From Kohlberg's perspective, how can you best promote students' moral development?
   a. By being a good example through word and deed
   b. By presenting reasoning one stage above their current stage
   c. By consistently presenting postconventional explanations
   d. By letting it unfold naturally

•• 69. Your students are reasoning at Kohlberg's second stage of moral reasoning. In a discussion of people who are homeless, you present reasoning at Kohlberg's fifth stage. From Kohlberg's perspective, what influence are your remarks likely to have on your students' moral reasoning?

a. It will help move them to Stage 3.
b. It will help move them to Stage 5.
c. It will make them move back to Stage 1.
d. It will have little effect on their moral development.

• 70. Three of the following are accurate statements about the shortcomings of Kohlberg's theory of moral reasoning. Which one is <u>inaccurate</u>?

a. Most elementary school children distinguish between two kinds of "wrong" behaviors—those that are morally wrong and those that violate cultural standards.
b. The same person may reason at different levels depending on the situation.
c. Children may show conventional thinking for several years and then revert back to preconventional thinking when they reach adolescence.
d. Young children are not as influenced by consequences and the dictates of authority figures as Kohlberg suggested.

•• 71. Which one of the following most accurately reflects how research links moral behavior and moral reasoning?

a. Connie reasons at a Stage 1 level, but she behaves at Stage 4 when she is taught Stage 4 behavior.
b. Eddie behaves at Stage 2 when under stress, although he is capable of reasoning at Stage 3.
c. Louise reasons at Stage 5, but usually behaves at Stage 1 or 2.
d. Albert reasons at a postconventional level, but his behavior shows no morals at all.

• 72. Carol Gilligan's theory of moral development differs from Lawrence Kohlberg's theory in that it:

a. Focuses more on a "human rights" perspective of moral development
b. Focuses more on the development of caring and compassion
c. Proposes that boys exhibit more rapid moral development than girls
d. Proposes that girls exhibit more rapid moral development than boys

• 73. When we see signs that a student feels ashamed or guilty about something that he or she has done, we can reasonably conclude that the student

a. Has generally low self-esteem
b. Will become socially withdrawn unless we intervene
c. Will show a temporary increase in aggressive behavior
d. Has developed a sense of right and wrong

• 74. Feelings of <u>empathy</u> are especially important for the development of

a. What Erik Erikson calls "industry"
b. What Erik Erikson calls "initiative"
c. Prosocial behavior
d. Self-esteem

• 75. Considering Eisenberg's research regarding the development of prosocial behavior, at what age level do most students begin to show genuine empathy regarding the well-being of others?
   a. In preschool
   b. In the early elementary grades
   c. In the late elementary grades
   d. In junior high or high school

• 76. Three of the following statements accurately describe how motivation influences moral behavior. Which statement is not necessarily accurate?
   a. Children become less generous with age, apparently because they gain greater appreciation for the value of money.
   b. Some adolescents incorporate a commitment to helping others into their self-concepts.
   c. Students are more likely to behave morally if doing so does not cause them much inconvenience.
   d. Students are more likely to behave morally if they know they will gain others' approval by doing so.

•• 77. At a Parent Teacher Association (PTA) meeting at your school, several parents complain about the moral decline of today's youth and argue that the school should be giving regular lectures about the importance of honesty, loyalty, generosity, and so on. If the teachers and school administrators are up to date on research regarding moral development, they should respond by saying that such lectures:
   a. Can be effective only if parents urge their children to take the lectures seriously
   b. Would do little if anything to promote moral behavior
   c. Are likely to be effective for junior high and high school students but not for elementary school students
   d. Are likely to be effective for elementary school students but not for junior high and high school students

• 78. Three of the following strategies are likely to promote moral development. Which one, although possibly appropriate in certain situations, is unlikely to promote students' moral development?
   a. Giving students reasons why some behaviors are unacceptable
   b. Having students discuss moral issues related to classroom subject matter
   c. Making sure that students know who is "boss" in the classroom
   d. Modeling morally appropriate behavior

• 79. Three of the following strategies may foster growth in students' moral reasoning. Which one probably will not?
   a. Making sure all students eventually come to agreement about how best to deal with a moral dilemma.
   b. Encouraging students to volunteer their individual perspectives on a moral issue.
   c. Asking students to consider their reasons for making the moral decisions that they do.
   d. Encouraging students to consider all sides of a moral issue.

• 80. Three of the following strategies should promote students' moral development. Which one probably will <u>not</u>?
   a. Getting students involved in community service projects
   b. Asking students to wrestle with difficult moral issues
   c. Engaging in moral behavior yourself
   d. Describing how good boys and girls should behave

•• 81. Which one of the following statements is most likely to promote students' moral development?
   a. "Your behavior is not allowed in this classroom. As a consequence, you'll have to stay after school today."
   b. "You mustn't take Ruthie's paper, or I won't like you any more."
   c. "If you don't help with clean-up, you don't get to go out on recess."
   d. "You destroyed Martha's paper, and now she has to stay late to finish rewriting it."

• 82. Three of the following statements accurately describe the diversity that we are likely to see in our students' personal, social, and moral development. Which statement is <u>not</u> accurate?
   a. Students who have lived in isolated areas and so have not had opportunities to develop friendships may be lacking some social skills.
   b. Some students from diverse ethnic backgrounds may have a strong sense of ethnic identity; others may prefer to blend in with the mainstream culture.
   c. Students from some cultures may believe that lying is a legitimate way of saving face.
   d. Some cultures promote an "every man for himself" attitude and never teach the importance of helping others.

• 83. Three of the following statements accurately describe the personal, social, and/or moral development of students with special needs. Which statement is <u>not</u> accurate?
   a. Overly aggressive students are likely to have difficulty seeing situations from someone else's perspective.
   b. Most students with advanced cognitive development (e.g., students who are gifted) have poor social skills.
   c. Students with a history of academic difficulty often have low self-esteem.
   d. Students with mental retardation have less awareness of appropriate social behavior than their classmates.

• 84. How can we best characterize the moral reasoning and behavior of <u>elementary school students</u>?
   a. They understand that people's behaviors are the results of many factors and have a desire to help those in need. However, they have rigid notions of right and wrong.
   b. They are postconventional in their moral reasoning. However, they are still very self-serving in their moral behavior and can take no one's perspective except their own.
   c. They are preconventional in their moral reasoning. They do show some interest in helping other people but have stereotypic ideas about what helping actually involves.
   d. Thanks to their newly acquired formal operational thought and the idealism that accompanies it, they have a truly abstract understanding of human rights and morality.

• 85. How can we best characterize the moral reasoning and behavior of high school students?

a. They understand that people's behaviors are the results of many factors and have a desire to help those in need. However, they have rigid notions of right and wrong.

b. They are postconventional in their moral reasoning. However, they are still very self-serving in their moral behavior and can take no one's perspective except their own.

c. They are preconventional in their moral reasoning. They do show some interest in helping other people but have stereotypic ideas about what helping actually involves.

d. Thanks to their newly acquired formal operational thought and the idealism that accompanies it, they have a truly abstract understanding of human rights and morality.

• 86. Which one of the following variables is essential for personal, social, and moral development (i.e., for all three)?

a. Social interaction

b. Moral dilemmas

c. Withdrawal of love for inappropriate behavior

d. Postconventional reasoning

•• 87. Which one of the following teacher behaviors illustrates an important factor in the social and/or moral development of children?

a. Ms. Grice allows her fourth graders to fight with the class bully so he will learn from their negative feedback.

b. Mr. Freeman takes his sixth-grade class to see a violent film and then stresses the importance of not engaging in such violence.

c. Ms. Little isolates those students who can't get along with others so they don't promote discord in the classroom.

d. Mr. Tutwiler describes the prosocial behaviors he expects of his students and gives concrete examples of such behaviors.

•• 88. Which teacher is doing the most to foster the overall development of his students?

a. Mr. Bakewell ensures that his students will obey all of his strict rules by imposing severe consequences for failure.

b. Mr. Mecham gives his students complete freedom in the classroom so that they will learn to cooperate with one another.

c. Mr. Poller conveys the message that he likes his students and wants them to succeed in the classroom.

d. Mr. Winters treats well-behaved students with warmth and kindness and ignores unruly students.

**Essay Questions**

• 89. Students' self-concepts and self-esteem related to school subject matter affect their learning and performance in the classroom. Imagine that you have several students with extremely low self-esteem regarding their ability to perform in your class. Simply giving them encouragement—for example, "You can do it if you try!"—may not be especially effective. Keeping in mind the factors that affect self-concept and self-esteem, describe <u>three different strategies</u> that you might use to enhance your students' confidence that they can succeed in school. Describe each of these strategies in terms of specific things that you might do in the classroom.

• 90. Specify the grade level at which you expect to be teaching, and identify which one of Erikson's psychosocial stages your students are likely to be in. Discuss the implication of this stage for your own teaching practice, illustrating your discussion with a concrete example of what you might do.

•• 91. Imagine that you are teaching at a school that serves students from diverse ethnic backgrounds. The students tend to congregate in groups along ethnic lines, to the point where they are quite "clique-ish" and exclusive, and hostilities are building up between ethnic groups. Using guidelines presented in the textbook, describe three strategies that you and your fellow teachers might use to foster positive interaction and friendships across the groups. Describe each strategy in a separate paragraph, and be specific about what you might do.

•• 92. Students' moral development is affected not only by their family and friends, but by their school experiences as well. Whether you intend to or not, you will undoubtedly be teaching your students moral values as well as academic content. With this in mind:

a. Describe the types of experiences that, according to researchers and theorists, are likely to help students develop morally. Within your discussion, identify <u>three different</u> factors that promote moral development.

b. Identify a moral issue that may arise either within a specific content area you will be teaching or within the general classroom situation. Explain what you, as a teacher, might specifically do to promote moral growth as you deal with the moral issue you just identified.

•• 93. Identify a specific grade level at which you hope to be teaching. Then, drawing on Kohlberg's, Selman's, and Eisenberg's stages, describe the prosocial and moral reasoning abilities your students are likely to have. Give a concrete example to illustrate your discussion.

## ANSWER KEY

### Multiple-Choice Questions

1. b
2. d
3. a
4. c
5. c
6. b
7. d
8. a
9. d
10. b
11. c
12. a
13. d
14. d
15. d
16. c
17. b
18. c
19. c
20. a
21. d
22. a
23. b
24. c
25. a
26. d
27. b
28. c
29. b
30. b
31. d
32. a
33. b
34. a
35. b
36. b
37. c
38. d
39. b
40. a
41. d
42. c
43. c
44. a
45. b
46. d
47. c
48. a
49. c
50. b
51. d
52. d
53. d
54. d
55. c
56. a
57. a
58. b
59. b
60. a
61. d
62. c
63. a
64. d
65. c
66. d
67. a
68. b
69. d
70. c
71. b
72. b
73. d
74. c
75. d
76. a
77. b
78. c
79. a
80. d
81. d
82. d
83. b
84. c
85. a
86. a
87. d
88. c

### Essay Questions

89. Strategies for enhancing self-concept and self-esteem include the following (the response should identify at least one concrete strategy related to three of them):
    - Promote success in school tasks (e.g., gear assignments to students' current knowledge and ability levels).
    - Minimize opportunities for students to judge themselves unfavorably in comparison with their peers (e.g., competitive situations).
    - Give positive and specific feedback about what students do well.
    - Provide negative feedback within the context of overall positive regard.
    - Hold realistically high expectations for students' performance.
    - Communicate an interest in students' well-being.

90. Preschool students will probably be in the initiative vs. guilt stage, elementary school students will be in industry vs. inferiority, and secondary school students will be in identity vs. role confusion. Implications for teaching students in the various stages are the following:
    <u>Initiative vs. guilt</u>
    • Support students in their efforts to plan and carry out activities.
    <u>Industry vs. inferiority</u>
    • Encourage students to make and do things.
    • Praise students for their accomplishments.
    <u>Identity vs. role confusion</u>
    • Provide opportunities to explore various career options.
    • Provide opportunities to explore a variety of social and/or political belief systems.
    The response should include a concrete strategy that reflects a recommendation for the appropriate age level, or something equally justifiable from the standpoint of Erikson's description of the relevant stage.

91. The response should include three strategies, with each one being described in a separate paragraph. The following strategies are identified in the section "Promoting Social Interaction Among Diverse Groups":
    • Set up situations in which students can form new friendships (e.g., assign cooperative learning activities, periodically change seat assignments).
    • Minimize or eliminate barriers to social interaction (e.g., teach the native languages of other students).
    • Encourage and facilitate participation in extracurricular activities.
    • Help change the reputations of formerly antisocial students.
    • Encourage a general feeling of respect for others.
    Also give credit for other strategies that are clearly justified by concepts or research presented in the textbook. For instance, strategies described in the section on moral development may be relevant here.

92. Responses to the two parts of the question are as follows:
    a. Experiences that promote moral development include these (the response should describe at least three):
       • An environment that is warm and supportive yet holds high expectations for behavior (i.e., an authoritative environment)
       • Challenges to moral thinking (disequilibrium), especially from individuals reasoning at the next higher stage
       • Hearing reasons why certain behaviors are unacceptable (induction); for example, becoming aware that an action causes physical pain or inconvenience for someone else
       • Practice in identifying the emotional states of others
       • Seeing models demonstrate moral and/or prosocial behavior
       • Encountering and discussing moral issues and dilemmas
       • Participation in community service activities
    b. Responses to this question will vary. The response should identify a specific issue that might arise within a classroom setting. It should also describe a specific strategy for promoting moral development that is consistent with one of the bulleted items in part *a* above.

93. Responses will vary, depending on the specific grade level identified. The discussion should include at least one stage- or level-related characteristic described by Kohlberg, Selman, and Eisenberg (see Tables 3.1, 3.2, and 3.3 for guidance), with at least one concrete example to illustrate the discussion. In many cases, it will be appropriate to mention that the students at a particular grade level are likely to be heterogeneous in terms of moral development, so they may be in two or more stages or levels.

# Chapter 4

# INDIVIDUAL AND GROUP DIFFERENCES

| CHAPTER OUTLINE | RELEVANT TEST BANK ITEMS |
|---|---|
| KEEPING INDIVIDUAL AND GROUP DIFFERENCES IN PERSPECTIVE | Multiple-Choice 1 |
| INTELLIGENCE<br>Measuring Intelligence<br>How Theorists Conceptualize Intelligence<br>Heredity, Environment, and Group Differences<br>Being Optimistic About Students' Potential | Multiple-Choice 2–19<br>Essay 58–59 |
| CREATIVITY<br>Fostering Creativity in the Classroom | Multiple-Choice 20–25<br>Essay 60 |
| CULTURAL AND ETHNIC DIFFERENCES<br>Navigating Different Cultures at Home and at School<br>Examples of Ethnic Diversity<br>Creating a More Multicultural Classroom Environment | Multiple-Choice 26–35<br>Essay 61 |
| GENDER DIFFERENCES<br>Origins of Gender Differences | Multiple-Choice 36–45<br>Essay 62 |
| SOCIOECONOMIC DIFFERENCES<br>Factors Interfering with School Success<br>Working with Homeless Students<br>Fostering Resilience<br>Building on Students' Strengths | Multiple-Choice 46–51 |
| STUDENTS AT RISK<br>Characteristics of Students at Risk<br>Why Students Drop Out<br>Helping Students at Risk Stay in School | Multiple-Choice 52–55<br>Essay 63 |

| TAKING INDIVIDUAL AND GROUP DIFFERENCES INTO ACCOUNT<br>Accommodating Students with Special Needs | Multiple-Choice 56–57 |
|---|---|
| The items in the "Integrative Questions" chapter of this Test Bank integrate the content of two or more textbook chapters. Within that chapter, the items listed to the right are relevant to Chapter 4. | Essay 22, 24 |

## Multiple-Choice Questions

• 1. Which one of the following is the most accurate statement about group differences among students?
   a. When we have knowledge about typical group differences, we have a very good idea of how individual students are likely to perform in the classroom.
   b. We can make fairly accurate predictions about individual students when we know their ethnic background, but not when we know their gender.
   c. We can make fairly accurate predictions about individual students when we know their gender, but not when we know their ethnic background.
   d. The average for one group may be different than for another group, but variability within each group keeps us from predicting individual performance.

• 2. Psychologists believe that intelligence is culture-specific—that "intelligent" behavior in one culture is not necessarily intelligent behavior in a different culture. Three of the following are aspects of intelligence <u>regardless</u> of the culture in which it is found. Which one is probably related to intelligence in some cultures but not in others?
   a. Applying prior knowledge to new situations.
   b. Doing well in academic classroom activities.
   c. Learning how to perform a new task quickly.
   d. Adapting readily to new situations.

•• 3. Judging from what you have learned about how intelligence is typically measured, which one of the following would you be <u>least</u> likely to find on an intelligence test?
   a. If all jerps are loobs, and if all loobs are rengs, are all jerps also rengs?
   b. How many friends do you have?
   c. What does the word <u>candid</u> mean?
   d. In what way are a tree and a flower alike?

• 4. Which one of the following is a true statement about IQ scores?
   a. They are calculated from this formula: (MA/CA) x 100.
   b. They are calculated from this formula: (CA/MA) x 100.
   c. They reflect the percentage of typical "adult-level" intelligence that a person has acquired.
   d. They are derived from comparisons with the test performance of others.

•• 5. Which one of the following is a correct interpretation of a high school student's IQ score of 115?
   a. It will remain constant for that student for a period of at least five to six years.
   b. The student has acquired 84% of the average adult's intellectual capabilities.
   c. The student has performed better on an intelligence test than the majority of students of the same age.
   d. The student is probably not "college material."

•• 6. Lily is ten years old. She gets a score of 97 on an IQ test. What does this tell us about her intellectual ability?
   a. Lily must be a very smart girl—100 is a perfect score.
   b. Lily is brighter than two-thirds of her age-mates, as IQ scores go up to about 150.
   c. Lily's score is in the bottom fifth of the population.
   d. Lily's score is about average for her age group.

• 7. The original purpose of intelligence tests is still their main purpose today—that is, to:
   a. Assess students' ability to solve abstract problems.
   b. Measure students' innate ability to adapt to a complex environment.
   c. Identify students who may require special educational services.
   d. Predict how well students are likely to perform in various professional careers.

• 8. Which one of the following statements most accurately describes the relationship between IQ scores and classroom performance?
   a. IQ scores obtained in the early elementary years are excellent predictors of high school success.
   b. On average, students with higher IQ scores do better in school than students with lower IQ scores.
   c. Students with IQ scores above 110 perform better when they are placed one or two grade levels ahead of where their age-mates are.
   d. Because intelligence tests measure inherited potential, IQ scores are unrelated to school achievement, which is influenced primarily by environmental factors.

•• 9. The teacher of a sixth grade class is concerned about the poor academic performance of a 12-year-old student named Nancy. The teacher looks through Nancy's school records and discovers that Nancy got an IQ score of 80 when she took an intelligence test in preschool. Considering the textbook's discussion of IQ scores, the teacher should conclude that:
   a. Nancy's IQ is mostly an inherited characteristic, so there is little the teacher can do to improve her learning potential.
   b. Nancy's IQ is mostly due to environmental conditions; given proper stimulation, instruction, and curricular materials, it can probably be raised as much as 30 points over the next school year.
   c. Nancy's IQ score in preschool is not necessarily a good reflection of her capability in sixth grade.
   d. Nancy may still be at Piaget's preoperational stage of cognitive development.

• 10. Three of the following are accurate statements about the limitations of intelligence tests. Which one is not an accurate statement?
  a. Some students may have little motivation to perform at their best.
  b. They may yield somewhat different scores for the same student on different occasions.
  c. They focus more on the kinds of things females are likely to know and so are biased against males.
  d. They focus on skills important in mainstream Western culture and ignore some skills more important in other cultures.

•• 11. Four high school teachers have just learned that Ralph, one of their students, has scored extremely well on an intelligence test. Which teacher appears to believe in Spearman's concept of g in intelligence?
  a. Mr. Hudson says, "No wonder Ralph performs consistently well in all of his classes!"
  b. Ms. Crawford says, "Ralph is an exceptional writer, but from what I've observed, his math skills are only average."
  c. Ms. Wyman says, "I agree that Ralph writes very well, but his spelling is atrocious."
  d. Mr. Grant says, "Ralph has trouble remembering basic math facts, but he's very good when it comes to solving challenging math problems."

•• 12. Sam is a very talented dancer; he also shows considerable creativity in art class. He finds math and science classes very difficult, but he loves to read and tell stories to his many friends. Which view of intelligence is best reflected in Sam's abilities?
  a. Sternberg's triarchic theory
  b. Gardner's multiple intelligences
  c. Piaget's theory of cognitive development
  d. Distributed intelligence

•• 13. Marissa seems to be a "born leader." As president of the school service club, she can often persuade her classmates to get involved in school and community service activities. Given this information, we could conclude that Marissa has a strength in which one of Gardner's multiple intelligences?
  a. Spatial
  b. Naturalistic
  c. Bodily-kinesthetic
  d. Interpersonal

• 14. Which one of the following statements best reflects Sternberg's triarchic theory of intelligence?
  a. Intelligent behavior is a function of how well people draw on their prior experiences and cognitively process information in order to adapt to their particular environmental situation.
  b. Intelligence is due to heredity, environment, and a complex interaction between the two; ultimately, these three things can never be isolated by researchers.
  c. Intelligent behavior evolves in three stages: concrete thought, abstract thought, and automaticity.
  d. To be truly intelligent, one must show competence in creativity and social skills as well as in traditional academic tasks.

•• 15. Which one of the following best illustrates automaticity?
   a. Knowing more about dinosaurs than most people your age.
   b. Playing a musical piece on the piano easily and effortlessly.
   c. Helping two friends resolve their differences and make amends.
   d. Sculpting a lifelike model of the human hand.

• 16. Which one of the following statements most accurately reflects the concept of distributed intelligence?
   a. How "intelligent" children become is, to some extent, a function of the number of siblings they have; children from larger families tend to have slightly lower IQ scores.
   b. How "intelligent" students are is, to some extent, a function of class size; students achieve at lower levels when they are in larger classes.
   c. Students almost invariably perform at higher levels in some academic subject areas than they do in others.
   d. Students will behave more intelligently when they can use outside resources as well as their minds.

•• 17. Which one of the following teachers is using a strategy that reflects the concept of distributed intelligence?
   a. Mr. Arvis asks students to exchange and grade one another's homework assignments.
   b. Mr. Baker encourages his students to use their calculators when solving algebraic word problems.
   c. Mr. Chinn gives easy writing assignments at the beginning of the year and raises his expectations as the school year progresses.
   d. Mr. Devlin encourages his students to relate what they are learning in social studies to their own personal experiences.

• 18. In 1994, Richard Herrnstein and Charles Murray published The Bell Curve. What does the textbook conclude about this book?
   a. That the book inappropriately attributes racial differences in IQ to genetics.
   b. That approximately 50% of IQ is due to heredity and 50% is due to one's environment.
   c. That heredity plays a stronger role in group differences than The Bell Curve would have us believe.
   d. That people's IQ scores are determined almost entirely by the environments in which they have been raised.

• 19. If we consider both Gardner's and Sternberg's views of intelligence, we would be most likely to conclude that:
   a. We can bring about dramatic improvements in students' IQs in a year or two if we provide a stimulating classroom environment.
   b. Regardless of cultural background, students with high intelligence will do well in school.
   c. Most of our students are likely to be "intelligent" in one way or another.
   d. Students who are fluent in two or three languages will be more intelligent than students who are fluent in just one.

•• 20. Which one of the following behaviors meets both of the essential criteria for creativity?
  a. Modeling himself after a popular TV character, Al shaves all the hair off his head with the hope that he will win the admiration of the girls in his class.
  b. Rick finds a new use for an ice cream scoop: He uses it to mold perfectly round tops for the towers on his snow castle.
  c. Trina douses her running shoes in perfume to keep them from smelling after gym class; although they're too soggy to wear for the rest of the week, they do smell better.
  d. Kevin decorates his room with posters and black lights in a manner similar to how his friend Alex has decorated his room.

•• 21. Creativity often involves divergent thinking. Which one of the following is the best example of divergent thinking?
  a. Lacking any wooden blocks to build an arch for his toy soldiers to march under, Thomas builds an arch using upside-down paper cups.
  b. Frank solves several multiplication problems using a strategy he has learned for solving "9's" problems.
  c. Marsha builds a bookcase by following directions she has found in a hobby magazine.
  d. After reading in a library book about what hamsters like to eat, Jennifer gives the class hamster a diet of vegetables, fruit, and hamster pellets to help him grow faster.

•• 22. Meshawn is thinking about the many different ways in which the concept of a <u>lever</u> might be applied to everyday problems. Meshawn is exhibiting:
  a. Intrapersonal intelligence
  b. Bodily-kinesthetic intelligence
  c. Convergent thinking
  d. Divergent thinking

•• 23. As a sixth grader, Mario shows exceptional creativity in his art class when using pastels for the first time. Which one of the following predictions is most warranted from this information?
  a. When his class is asked to invent a device to help keep the classroom cool on hot days, he will develop one of the most creative solutions.
  b. He is likely to show artistic creativity when using watercolor paints as well.
  c. He will include many vivid descriptions of people and places in the short stories he writes.
  d. If he is taught to play a musical instrument, he will probably show creativity in how he plays it.

• 24. Three of the following strategies should promote students' creative behavior. Which one is <u>unlikely</u> to promote creativity?
  a. Introducing a subject in class and then intentionally stopping when students have only a partial understanding of it.
  b. Reminding students that occasional failures are an inevitable part of the creative process.
  c. Encouraging students to feel proud of their creative accomplishments.
  d. Asking questions that get students thinking about classroom material in a different way than they might otherwise.

•• 25. Which one of the following classes is most likely to foster students' creativity?
   a. Mr. Lester's class, where students are allowed to dabble freely in whatever subject area they want during a ten-minute creativity break at the end of each school day.
   b. Ms. Patrick's class, where students are drilled until they memorize specific facts word for word.
   c. Ms. Francisco's class, where students are expected to perform quickly yet creatively in order to get a good grade.
   d. Mr. Logan's class, where students are allowed to spend a 45-minute block of time every week experimenting with the artistic medium of their choice.

•• 26. Three of the following are likely to give you reasonable clues about a student's cultural background and/or ethnic group membership. Which one is probably <u>least</u> dependable as an indicator of a student's cultural background and ethnicity?
   a. The ethnicity of the student's parents
   b. The color of a student's skin
   c. The cultural and religious activities in which a student regularly participates
   d. A language other than English spoken as the primary language at home

•• 27. Rani has just moved here from a Middle Eastern country where most women remain at home serving their husbands and taking care of their children. She seems confused when she is asked to perform the same school tasks that her male classmates are. Rani's situation illustrates:
   a. The value of public conversation
   b. The influence of counterstereotypical information
   c. Cultural mismatch
   d. The importance of wait time

• 28. You have several students in your class who speak a dialect other than Standard English. If you follow the textbook's recommendation for handling this situation, you will:
   a. Teach them to speak and write Standard English exclusively, and as quickly as possible.
   b. Allow them to use their own dialect or version of English exclusively in all school classes and activities.
   c. Strongly discourage them from speaking their dialect, even when they are off school grounds.
   d. Ask them to use Standard English in formal situations (e.g., oral reports) but encourage them to use their own dialect in other situations.

• 29. What impact does teacher wait time have on students' classroom performance?
   a. When wait time is three seconds or longer, students are more likely to answer questions.
   b. If wait time is increased beyond two seconds, students will be embarrassed by the awkward silence and not answer.
   c. Wait time of about one second is optimal. If it is much longer, students will get distracted and forget the question.
   d. Increased wait time is only necessary when working with low-ability learners. Average and above-average learners don't need much wait time.

- 30. Three of the following are differences that teachers may find among children from some cultural backgrounds. Which behavior is probably not the result of a student's cultural background per se?
    a. Some students may look down at their feet as a way of showing respect for authority figures.
    b. Some students may feel that teachers' personal questions are intrusive and perhaps have been specifically taught not to answer certain kinds of questions.
    c. Some students may be accustomed to "talking back" to authority figures when they disagree.
    d. Some students may have been taught that artistic expression in areas such as art, dance, and music is of greater importance than academic achievement.

- 31. Which one of the following statements is accurate regarding individual achievement and competition in many Hispanic and Native American communities?
    a. Students from these communities have a greater need to achieve individual recognition, so they may be strongly tempted to cheat in competitive situations.
    b. Students from these communities may compete with each other for the lowest grade in class, and intentionally fail their tests.
    c. Students from these communities are uncomfortable with competition and may prefer to help their classmates rather than compete with them.
    d. Students from these communities may get so caught up in competition that they become hostile and aggressive toward their classmates.

- 32. When we say that different cultural and ethnic groups have different world views, we mean that
    a. Their basic assumptions about how the world operates may be different.
    b. They tend to think of their country of origin as being the best possible place in which to live.
    c. They may have little understanding of geographic regions other than their own.
    d. Their native language inevitably distorts how they think about their physical and social environments.

- 33. Which one of the following teaching strategies best reflects the textbook's definition of multicultural education?
    a. Ensuring that all classes include students from diverse cultures
    b. Fostering ongoing communication (e.g., through "pen pal" letters or e-mail messages) with students from other countries
    c. Considering the perspectives of different cultures groups regularly throughout the school year
    d. Devoting at least one month of each school year to an intensive exploration of diverse cultures

•• 34. Three of the teachers below are using strategies appropriate for a culturally diverse classroom. With the textbook's discussion of student diversity in mind, identify the teacher who is probably <u>not</u> promoting the classroom success of some of her students.

a. Ms. Andreas forms small, multicultural groups in which students describe and compare their perspectives about a recent international conflict.
b. Ms. Boynton uses competitive activities to get all students motivated to do their best.
c. Ms. Champas explores the ways in which children from different backgrounds are alike as well as different.
d. Ms. Delaney makes sure she presents both the American and Mexican views of the Mexican-American War.

• 35. The textbook author stresses the importance of <u>equity</u> in her discussion of strategies for creating a multicultural classroom environment; in other words, she stresses the importance of:

a. Making sure that all students achieve the same objectives
b. Tailoring instruction to meet the unique needs of each student
c. Helping students to understand how a democratic society functions
d. Helping students to discover one another's unique strengths

• 36. Numerous research studies have examined gender differences in verbal, visual-spatial, and mathematical abilities. These studies lead to which of the following conclusions?

a. In terms of math achievement, we can expect that the top 50% of students in a class will be almost all boys, and the bottom 50% will be mostly girls.
b. Girls show better visual-spatial ability in the preschool years, but boys begin to show better visual-spatial ability around second grade.
c. During the elementary years, girls are ahead of boys in verbal skills by almost two grade levels.
d. Any gender differences in these abilities are so small that we would not notice them in the classroom.

•• 37. Ms. Youmans has a class of 24 sixth graders—12 girls and 12 boys. Given what we know about gender differences in verbal ability and visual-spatial ability, which one of the following is Ms. Youmans justified in concluding about her students?

a. Her highest reading group will have almost all girls, and her lowest reading group will have mostly boys.
b. All of the boys should do better than all of the girls on a test of visual-spatial ability (in other words, there is no overlap between the two groups).
c. About 80% of the boys should do better than 80% of the girls on a test of visual-spatial ability.
d. Ms. Youmans probably won't notice differences in the average abilities of boys and girls.

• 38. Three of the following are accurate statements about differences between boys and girls. Which statement is <u>not</u> accurate?

a. Boys are physically stronger than girls beginning at birth.
b. Girls are more aware of people's subtle "body language."
c. Boys are more physically aggressive than girls.
d. Girls are more likely to form close, intimate friendships.

•• 39. Marietta is a high school student. Considering research related to gender differences in motivation, and without knowing anything else about Marietta, in which area would you expect her to have the highest motivation to achieve?
  a. Auto mechanics
  b. Body building
  c. Cooking
  d. Engineering

• 40. Research on gender differences in self-esteem tells us that:
  a. Boys almost always have higher self-esteem than girls.
  b. Girls almost always have higher self-esteem than boys.
  c. Both boys and girls tend to have higher self-esteem in "gender-appropriate" activities.
  d. Boys and girls have more or less equal levels of self-esteem in virtually all areas.

•• 41. Tim and Sally are both fifth-grade students at an elementary school science fair. They both receive an A on their science projects. Considering gender differences in students' explanations for success, how are the two students likely to explain their good grades?
  a. Tim will think, "I got an A because I'm really good in science." Sally will think, "I got an A because I worked really hard on my project."
  b. Tim will attribute his A to his many nights of hard work. Sally will think, "I got an A because I'm good in science."
  c. Tim will think that he is lucky when it comes to projects like this. Sally will think that she succeeded because her father is a scientist and she must have inherited his ability.
  d. Tim will think, "My project got an A because I had a lot of help from my friends." Sally will think, "I got an A because I'm smarter than the other kids."

•• 42. Mark and Francie are two eighth-grade students who have just failed a math test. Considering gender differences in students' explanations for failure, how are the two students likely to explain their poor test performance?
  a. Mark will think that he failed because he "just can't do math." Francie will think, "I got an F because I didn't work hard enough on this subject—I could have studied more."
  b. Mark will attribute his failure to a lack of effort, thinking, "I didn't study hard enough, 'cause I don't need to get good grades." Francie will think, "I'm just not very good at math."
  c. Mark will think that he isn't very lucky when it comes to tests, and Sally will think that she failed because she didn't have her friends to help her study.
  d. Mark will think, "I got an F because I'm not smart enough to do this math." Francie will think, "I failed because the teacher hates me and the test wasn't fair."

• 43. Three of the following describe environmental factors that contribute to gender differences we see in school-age children. Which statement is <u>not</u> an accurate description of how the environment contributes to gender differences?
   a. Most characters in books and television shows behave in a gender-stereotypical fashion.
   b. Parents have higher expectations for their daughters regarding the level of education they should obtain.
   c. Boys' typical games are more likely to foster visual-spatial skills.
   d. Girls' typical toys are more likely to promote the development of social skills.

•• 44. Three of the following situations reflect how peer relationships often exacerbate gender differences. Which situation is <u>not</u> typical?
   a. Molly says to Danielle, "Wow, what a great Barbie doll collection you have!"
   b. Ed says to Trudy, "We need to get this lab experiment done. You read what we need to do, and I'll do it."
   c. Helen says to Vicki, "Oh, there's Sherry. Don't talk to her—she's a real math nerd."
   d. Fred says to Mike, "Did you really sign up for a sewing class? What a great idea! Maybe I'll sign up, too."

•• 45. Considering research on gender differences, what is the likely result when Ms. Wolf assigns small-group work in her seventh-grade science class?
   a. Kevin and Bill will sit back and watch, making Amelia and Sally do all the work.
   b. Steven will set up the samples, Roger will do the measurements, Jennifer will take notes, and Ruth will watch.
   c. James will write down the results and John will watch while Millie sets up the samples and Linda measures them.
   d. Miranda will measure, Donna will direct the activities, and Jeff and Scott will alternate taking notes and watching.

•• 46. Poor nutrition is a problem for many children who live in poverty. Which one of the following situations is likely to be associated with poor nutrition?
   a. Hilda has problems with mathematics but is otherwise a bright and attentive student.
   b. Even though Yvonne tries hard in school and pays attention most of the time, she has difficulty learning anything abstract.
   c. Lonnie learns things easily but does not work very hard in class. He is often too busy socializing to pay attention in class.
   d. Jill appears to have trouble remembering things and does not seem motivated to achieve in school.

• 47. Three of the following are more common for students from middle-income homes than for students from low-income homes. Which one is <u>not</u> necessarily more common for middle-income students?
   a. An emotionally supportive home environment
   b. Early exposure to reading materials
   c. Parental involvement in school activities
   d. Regular interaction with other children of the same age

•• 48. Three of the following depict challenges that children from lower-income homes are likely to face. Which situation is <u>least</u> typical?

a. Theresa is sometimes late for school because her father and mother are fighting about overdue bills and so are preoccupied when it is time to take her to school.
b. Thomas's only meal of the day is the free lunch he gets at school.
c. Timothy is often late to class because he must wait for his mother to get home from her night job before he can leave his baby sister.
d. Trina is unable to attend school because her parents take her with them when they go on long car trips to visit family members in distant cities.

• 49. Which one of the following characteristics are teachers <u>least</u> likely to see in students who are homeless?

a. Gaps in academic skills
b. A short attention span
c. Inappropriate classroom behaviors
d. Eagerness to go to school

• 50. The school principal tells you that Mary, a new student who just joined your classroom this morning, is currently residing at a homeless shelter. Which one of the strategies below does the textbook <u>not</u> recommend for helping Mary succeed in your classroom?

a. Pair Mary with a classmate who can show her around the school building and introduce her to other students.
b. Find some school supplies, including a clipboard to write on, that Mary can use to do her homework at the shelter.
c. Ask Mary's parents to meet with you in your classroom after school.
d. Enlist the aid of volunteers to provide tutoring for Mary at the shelter.

• 51. All of the following strategies are certainly beneficial, but only one is likely to foster resilience in students who live in difficult and challenging circumstances (e.g., extreme poverty, abusive family members). Which strategy is known to foster <u>resilience</u>?

a. Take a personal interest in students' welfare and show them that they can turn to you in times of need.
b. Show students how academic tasks are relevant to their personal lives.
c. Give students both positive and negative feedback when it is appropriate to do so.
d. Be an active and visible participant in community programs in students' neighborhoods.

• 52. Which one of the following descriptions best reflects how educators typically define <u>students at risk</u>?

a. Students unlikely to acquire the basic academic skills necessary for success in the adult world.
b. Students with a strong probability of becoming long-term substance abusers.
c. Students who show a pattern of criminal-like behavior by the age of fourteen.
d. Students who have had numerous encounters with the criminal justice system.

•• 53. Which one of the following students best fits the pattern associated with being <u>at risk</u>?

   a. Sal started kindergarten a year later than his peers because his parents wanted to be sure he was ready for school.
   b. Wesley has recently failed sophomore algebra, and he is frustrated because he now has to go to summer school.
   c. André isn't doing very well in any of his classes; he will have to pull up his grades or he won't be allowed to continue to participate in varsity football.
   d. Evan is doing poorly in all of his classes because of repeated absenteeism and failure to turn in assignments.

•• 54. Three of the following students show warning signs of being at risk. Which student is <u>least</u> likely to be at risk?

   a. Ann never stays after school for extracurricular activities, and she seems to have no friends at school.
   b. Barbara is so busy with student government, cheerleading, and varsity sports that her grades have gone from As to Cs and Ds.
   c. Carol is fourteen years old and still in sixth grade, so she has little in common with her classmates.
   d. Donna has gotten low achievement test scores since elementary school.

• 55. Three of the following strategies are likely to help students at risk stay in school. Which one is <u>unlikely</u> to do so?

   a. Discourage them from participating in extracurricular activities so they can focus on getting their grades up.
   b. Communicate your expectation that they can do well and that you will help them achieve school objectives.
   c. Provide opportunities for them to form friendships with their classmates.
   d. Identify them as early as possible and provide the academic support they need to succeed.

• 56. Three of the following statements are true with regard to gender differences in students with special educational needs. Which statement is <u>false</u>?

   a. General delays in cognitive and social functioning (e.g., mental retardation) are more often found in males than in females.
   b. Males are more likely than females to be socially withdrawn.
   c. Learning disabilities are more common in males than in females.
   d. Males are more likely to demonstrate overt classroom misbehaviors.

• 57. Three of the following statements accurately describe gender differences in students with advanced cognitive development (i.e., gifted students). Which statement is <u>not</u> necessarily true?

   a. In some cultures, females are more likely to show giftedness in mathematics than their male counterparts.
   b. Gifted females have fewer role models than gifted males do.
   c. Gifted females are less self-confident about their abilities than is true for gifted males.
   d. In some cultures, gifted females are discouraged from acting too "intelligently" relative to their male peers.

## Essay Questions

•• 58. Many intelligence tests yield a single IQ score. Explain whether this practice is theoretically consistent or inconsistent with:

a. Spearman's concept of g
b. Gardner's theory of multiple intelligences
c. Sternberg's triarchic theory of intelligence

•• 59. Explain what psychologists mean by the term distributed intelligence. Describe at least three different teaching and/or assessment strategies you might use that would be consistent with this concept.

•• 60. One of your objectives for the coming school year is to foster your students' creative thinking and/or behavior in a subject area you will be teaching. Basing your discussion on at least four different factors known to influence creativity, describe four strategies you might use to promote such creativity. Illustrate each strategy with a concrete example of what you might do.

•• 61. The textbook speaks of a cultural "mismatch" that may interfere with a student's ability to succeed in a traditional classroom. Describe the types of mismatches that might occur related to each of these traditional educational practices:

a. The daily school time schedule
b. The use of Standard English
c. Whole-class question-answer sessions
d. Classroom competition

• 62. Describe how similar or different the boys and girls in your classroom are likely to be, on the average, in each of the following areas:

a. Scholastic abilities
b. Physical and motor skills
c. Self-esteem
d. Explanations for success and failure
e. Expectations for themselves

• 63. Some of your students may be at risk for academic failure; if they do fail, they are likely to be ill-equipped to become productive citizens in the adult world. With the typical characteristics of students at risk in mind, identify five strategies you might use to help such students succeed at school. For each one, describe what you would do in specific and concrete terms.

## ANSWER KEY

### Multiple-Choice Questions

| | | | | |
|---|---|---|---|---|
| 1. d | 13. d | 25. d | 37. d | 49. d |
| 2. b | 14. a | 26. b | 38. a | 50. c |
| 3. b | 15. b | 27. c | 39. c | 51. a |
| 4. d | 16. d | 28. d | 40. c | 52. a |
| 5. c | 17. b | 29. a | 41. a | 53. d |
| 6. d | 18. a | 30. c | 42. b | 54. b |
| 7. c | 19. c | 31. c | 43. b | 55. a |
| 8. b | 20. b | 32. a | 44. d | 56. b |
| 9. c | 21. a | 33. c | 45. b | 57. a |
| 10. c | 22. d | 34. b | 46. d | |
| 11. a | 23. b | 35. b | 47. d | |
| 12. b | 24. a | 36. d | 48. d | |

### Essay Questions

58. Responses to various parts of the question are as follows:
    a. A single IQ score is consistent with Spearman's idea that there is a general factor (g) that underlies people's performance on many different measures of intelligence.
    b. A single IQ score is inconsistent with Gardner's theory of multiple intelligences. Gardner proposes that people may be more or less intelligent in eight different areas. A single IQ score cannot reflect all eight of these simultaneously.
    c. A single IQ score is inconsistent with Sternberg's triarchic theory. This theory proposes that intelligent behavior is a function of the environmental context, one's prior experiences, and the cognitive processes brought into play; thus, intelligence will vary from situation to situation and cannot be reflected by a single IQ score.

59. The concept of distributed intelligence reflects to the idea that people behave more intelligently when they have the support of their physical and/or social environments and the use of symbolic systems that others have developed. Possible strategies based on this concept are:
    - Letting students use a dictionary when writing
    - Letting students use calculators during math or science
    - Letting students use resource materials when taking a test
    - Having students work in pairs or small groups to solve difficult problems
    - Having students find experts who can give them information they are seeking
    - Letting students use formulas or diagrams to help them solve problems

    Other strategies that clearly show students using tools, other people, or symbolic systems to help them tackle difficult tasks are also acceptable.

60. The textbook identifies six factors that appear to influence creativity, underlined in the list below. The response should include strategies listed under four of the six factors; each strategy should be illustrated by a concrete example.

    Valuing creativity
    - Encourage and reward unusual ideas.
    - Look for answers and behaviors that, although not what we had in mind, are legitimately correct.
    - Engage in creative behavior ourselves.

    Focus on internal rewards
    - Provide opportunities to explore special interests.
    - Downplay the importance of grades.
    - Focus students' attention on the internal satisfaction that creative efforts bring.

    Mastery of a subject area
    - Help students master course content.

    Thought-provoking questions
    - Ask higher-level questions (e.g., those that require divergent thinking).

    Freedom to take risks
    - Have students engage in some activities without being evaluated on them.
    - Encourage students to think of their mistakes as an inevitable part of creative behavior.

    Time
    - Give students time to experiment, correct mistakes, and/or refine their work.

61. Responses to various parts of the question are as follows:
    a. Schools typically run on a rigid time schedule—a time to be at school, a time to go to lunch, etc. Some students have been raised in cultures where punctuality in terms of specific clock time is not expected.
    b. Some students have been raised in a community that speaks either a dialect different from Standard English or a different language altogether. In the case of dialect differences, grammatical structures and vocabulary that are perfectly acceptable at home may not be acceptable in school. In the case of language differences, students may have a difficult time understanding instruction provided solely in English. (The response should include a discussion of either dialect differences or language differences; only one is necessary for credit on this item.)
    c. At least three kinds of cultural mismatch may occur in question-answer sessions (the response should mention at least one of them). Some students are used to interacting with adults in private, one-on-one contexts rather than in a more public setting such as a classroom. Some students may wait before responding (respecting the wait time that their culture dictates), giving their teacher the impression that they don't know the answer. Some students may not be accustomed to asking the kinds of questions teachers often ask in school.
    d. Many cultures encourage children to work cooperatively with others. This cooperative spirit is inconsistent with the competitive environment of many classrooms.

62. Responses to various parts of the question are as follows:
    a. Boys and girls tend to be similar in terms of IQ scores and school achievement. Small differences sometimes exist for language-based tasks (girls have the advantage) and visual-spatial skills (boys have the advantage). Also, small differences appear in different aspects of mathematics. (The response does not need to include a discussion of the small gender differences just listed; an overall statement that boys and girls are similar should be sufficient here.)
    b. Gender differences in physical and motor skills are quite small in the elementary grades. After puberty, boys have the advantage in skills requiring height or strength.
    c. Boys have greater self-esteem regarding their ability to control the world and solve problems. Girls have greater self-esteem regarding their capabilities in social situations. Both genders have greater self-esteem in gender-stereotypical activities (e.g., boys have higher self-esteem related to science and mathematics).
    d. Boys tend to attribute their successes to ability and their failures to a lack of effort. Girls tend to attribute their successes to effort and their failures to a lack of ability.
    e. Boys have higher expectations for themselves, especially in gender-stereotypical activities.

63. Strategies for helping students at risk include these (the response should describe, in specific and concrete terms, at least five strategies reflecting the ideas below):
    - Identify them and intervene as early as possible.
    - Incorporate their interests into the curriculum.
    - Show them how the curriculum is relevant to their personal needs.
    - Encourage them to set high yet realistic goals.
    - Focus their attention on short-term, specific goals.
    - Provide extra support for academic success.
    - Help them recognize that they are personally responsible for their classroom successes.
    - Use instructional techniques that promote active involvement in class (e.g., class discussions, cooperative learning).
    - Establish close, trusting relationships with them.
    - Encourage participation in extracurricular activities.
    - Involve them in school policy and management decisions.
    - Give them positions of responsibility at school.
    - Provide rewards for good attendance records.

# Chapter 5

# STUDENTS WITH SPECIAL EDUCATIONAL NEEDS

| CHAPTER OUTLINE | RELEVANT TEST BANK ITEMS |
|---|---|
| Introduction | Multiple-Choice 1 |
| EDUCATING STUDENTS WITH SPECIAL NEEDS IN GENERAL EDUCATION CLASSROOMS<br>Historical Overview of the Inclusion Movement<br>Public Law 94-142: The Individuals with Disabilities Education Act (IDEA)<br>Is Inclusion in the Best Interest of Students?<br>The Current Conception of Inclusion | Multiple-Choice 2–20<br>Essay 75 |
| GENERAL CATEGORIES OF STUDENTS WITH SPECIAL NEEDS<br>Using People-First Language<br>An Overall Organizational Scheme | Multiple-Choice 21–22<br>Essay 76 |
| STUDENTS WITH SPECIFIC COGNITIVE OR ACADEMIC DIFFICULTIES<br>Learning Disabilities<br>Attention-Deficit Hyperactivity Disorder (ADHD)<br>Speech and Communication Disorders<br>General Recommendations for Students with Specific Cognitive or Academic Difficulties | Multiple-Choice 23–32<br>Essay 77 |
| STUDENTS WITH SOCIAL OR BEHAVIORAL PROBLEMS<br>Emotional and Behavioral Disorders<br>Autism<br>General Recommendations for Students with Social or Behavioral Problems | Multiple-Choice 33–42 |
| STUDENTS WITH GENERAL DELAYS IN COGNITIVE AND SOCIAL FUNCTIONING<br>Mental Retardation | Multiple-Choice 43–47 |

| | |
|---|---|
| STUDENTS WITH PHYSICAL AND SENSORY CHALLENGES<br>Physical and Health Impairments<br>Visual Impairments<br>Hearing Loss<br>Severe and Multiple Disabilities<br>General Recommendations for Students with Physical and Sensory Challenges | Multiple-Choice 48–57<br>Essay 78 |
| STUDENTS WITH ADVANCED COGNITIVE DEVELOPMENT<br>Giftedness | Multiple-Choice 58–67<br>Essay 79 |
| CONSIDERING DIVERSITY WHEN IDENTIFYING AND ADDRESSING SPECIAL NEEDS | Multiple-Choice 68–69 |
| THE BIG PICTURE<br>Inclusion<br>Categories of Students with Special Needs<br>Strategies for Helping All Students with Special Needs | Multiple-Choice 70–74 |
| The items in the "Integrative Questions" chapter of this Test Bank integrate the content of two or more textbook chapters. Within that chapter, the item listed to the right is relevant to Chapter 5. | Multiple-Choice 6 |

## Multiple-Choice Questions

• 1. In which of the following ways are students with special needs different from their classmates?
   a. Any student who learns best when classroom instruction is adapted to accommodate his or her abilities probably has special needs.
   b. There is a typical profile of academic, social and physical strengths and weaknesses for students at a particular grade level, and students with special needs are those who don't fit that profile.
   c. Students with special needs are students who cannot reach their full potential in a general education classroom unless special instructional modifications are made.
   d. Students with special needs are students whose appearance or behavior is noticeably different from that of their classmates.

• 2. In the United States, most students with special needs are educated at least partially in general education classrooms because:
   a. Federal law supports inclusive education for students with special needs.
   b. Grouping students by ability is less popular today than it used to be.
   c. Most schools can no longer afford to maintain enough special educators and other resources to educate them in self-contained classrooms anymore.
   d. Many institutions that used to serve students with special needs have closed or cut back their services.

• 3. Which one of the following is an example of a self-contained classroom?
   a. Mrs. Ferdinand has two students with physical disabilities among her 28 fifth graders.
   b. Mrs. Jefferson has a class of 24 first graders; none of them has been identified as having special needs.
   c. In her first-period high school English class of 20 students, Ms. Nivens has five students with recent IQ scores of 120 or higher.
   d. Miss Rosser's class consists of seven students with emotional and behavioral disorders.

• 4. Three of the following statements represent reasons for the rise of the inclusion movement. Which one of the following was <u>not</u> a reason for the inclusion movement?
   a. Ethnic minority groups were over-represented in self-contained classrooms for students with special needs.
   b. Students taught in special classes seldom did better and often did worse then those with similar needs in general classes.
   c. Students educated separately lost out on chances to make friends with students in general classrooms.
   d. Most students with special needs were found to benefit more from social interaction with peers than from academic instruction.

•• 5. <u>Mainstreaming</u> was a common approach to special education during the 1970s and 1980s. Which one of the following best illustrates this approach?
   a. Because of her learning disability, Julie receives individualized instruction in a resource room every morning, but she spends the afternoon in a regular first-grade classroom.
   b. Rafael has Down's Syndrome and is in fifth grade. During math class, his peers use various manipulatives to explore fractions, while he uses them to practice counting and identifying shapes.
   c. Jean-Paul, who has hearing and speech problems, is in a class with other students who have hearing loss and is taught entirely through American Sign Language.
   d. Rama attends a special school for students with mental retardation, but an important part of her program involves venturing into the general community to practice the social skills she is learning.

•• 6. Which one of the following best illustrates <u>inclusion</u> as it is defined by special educators?
   a. Amy, who has dramatic mood swings, joins a regular classroom on the days when she is well-behaved.
   b. Alice, who has multiple physical disabilities, has a special classroom where she and a student with severe cerebral palsy are taught.
   c. Alex, who has mental retardation, is taught in a general education classroom, where his teacher and a specialist both design and deliver instruction.
   d. Andrew, who is deaf, joins a regular class when it goes to art and physical education.

- 7. What is the primary purpose of the Individuals with Disabilities Education Act (IDEA)?
    a. It ensures that all public schools comply with building codes that make them accessible to students with physical disabilities.
    b. It provides funding for grants to schools that demonstrate excellence in their special education programs.
    c. It guarantees an education to students with cognitive, emotional and physical disabilities and outlines educational policies for that purpose.
    d. It declares that schools have a responsibility to educate all students about the civil rights of people with disabilities as part of the curriculum.

- 8. In the United States, Public Law 94-142, also known as the Individuals with Disabilities Education Act (IDEA), provides several specific guarantees for students with disabilities. Which of the following is <u>not</u> one of the PL 94-142's guarantees?
    a. Instruction is tailored to meet students' unique educational needs.
    b. Educational decisions are made by a multidisciplinary team.
    c. Education occurs entirely within the context of the regular classroom.
    d. A fair, nondiscriminatory evaluation is conducted to determine the student's specific educational needs.

•• 9. Juliana is a five-year-old who is paralyzed and cannot speak. To act in accordance with IDEA's concept of a <u>free and appropriate education</u>, her local school district:
    a. Probably will not enroll Juliana because she cannot participate in school activities in a typical way, but it will pay for her enrollment in any private school that will accept her.
    b. Should make sure its classrooms are wheelchair accessible, hire an aide to take care of Juliana's personal needs, and find ways to modify the curriculum so she can participate.
    c. Will accept Juliana for enrollment, but because she cannot move or speak, she will not be expected to participate in classroom activities or follow an instructional plan.
    d. Probably will not enroll Juliana, but if her parents decided to try home-schooling her, the school will provide them with textbooks and other materials.

•• 10. Which one of the following is the best example of a fair and nondiscriminatory evaluation, as defined by IDEA?

a. Greg's teachers are concerned that he is slow to learn the material that his classmates learn easily. They ask the school psychologist to administer an IQ test, and Greg scores a 65. On that basis, he is coded as having mild mental retardation so that he can begin receiving special services.

b. Niki has always had a tendency to get in trouble at school, but in eighth grade her behavior turns violent. She is often heard threatening classmates, and her teachers find her behavior impossible to manage. They are certain she must have an emotional and behavioral disability. After reviewing her record of misconduct, the school administration agrees.

c. Brandon does well in most subject areas but is failing to master basic arithmetic. His teacher consults the special educator (who tests Brandon to evaluate his abilities in math and related areas) and the school psychologist (who administers an intelligence test). The interdisciplinary team meets to discuss Brandon's test results and classroom performance and determines that Brandon has a learning disability.

d. Holly seems inattentive and often fails to hear her teacher's instructions. There is a history of hearing loss in Holly's family. Her teacher contacts her family, and they make an appointment to see a hearing specialist. In the meantime, Holly is enrolled in the special education program so she won't miss out on instruction while waiting for a diagnosis.

• 11. IDEA's requirement that students with disabilities be educated in "the least restrictive environment" means that:

a. Students should be included in general classrooms as long as they can do the same work that is assigned to everyone else and as long as they do not present behavior problems.

b. Students should be included in general classrooms as long as their presence does not restrict the advancement of their peers.

c. Students should be included in general classrooms as long as they do not pose a danger to themselves or others and as long as, given specially adapted instruction, they are able to make reasonable progress toward their educational goals.

d. Students with emotional and behavioral disorders should not be put in physical restraints, except as a last resort.

•• 12. Which example best illustrates the concept of the "least restrictive environment"?

a. Jerry, who uses a wheelchair, is educated in a classroom with no desks or other furniture to constrain his movement around the room.

b. Rudy, who has emotional and behavioral problems, is allowed to attend classes or not, as he wishes.

c. Kevin, who has a hearing impairment, receives education in a class where there are no grades, achievement requirements, or other limits on his freedom.

d. Sheila, who is visually impaired, attends a general education class but has special copies of the textbooks written in Braille.

• 13. A student with special needs is guaranteed an individualized education program. Who among the following is least likely to be involved in developing this program?
   a. A representative from the superintendent's office
   b. The student's parents
   c. The student's classroom teacher
   d. A specialist in the student's area of need

•• 14. The individualized education program of a special needs student typically has several components. With these components in mind, choose the statement that you are least likely to see in an IEP.
   a. "The student has a tested IQ of 85."
   b. "The student will successfully solve two-digit subtraction programs that require borrowing."
   c. "The student will meet with the speech therapist for 30 minutes once a week."
   d. "The student's progress will be assessed by teacher-made tests twice a month."

•• 15. Three of the following concerns would be addressed in an individualized education plan. Which one would probably not be addressed?
   a. Mr. Rodriguez knows that his son, Rodney, has a learning disability, and he knows that Rodney feels badly about not being as "smart" as his older sister. Rodney's frustrations about school are starting to put a strain on family dynamics. What can be done to improve Rodney's relationship with various members of his family?
   b. Mr. Hansen is a new fourth-grade teacher this year. He isn't sure what to expect from any of the children in his class. How will he know how to make appropriate modifications for children with special needs while still challenging them to achieve all that they can?
   c. Mrs. Dawson worries for her daughter, who has cerebral palsy and is now in high school. What kind of work will she be qualified to do, and how will she make the transition from a school environment to the outside world?
   d. Mrs. Shaw knows that Courtney has some individual goals which are different from those other children are working toward. How should she best evaluate Courtney's efforts in that area, and how often should she update Courtney's parents on her progress?

•• 16. Three of the following parents are acting within their rights as defined by IDEA. Which one is not?
   a. Ms. Osowski walks into the school office and asks to see all of her daughter Macy's records.
   b. Mr. Bournewood has been told repeatedly that his son Jeremy's reading skills are well below grade level and that Jeremy may have a disability. Still, Mr. Bournewood refuses to allow the school to evaluate Jeremy to see if he could benefit from special services.
   c. Ms. Frothingham is incensed that her son Nathan's teacher is disregarding the goals and modifications spelled out in his IEP. She calls the school and reminds them that Nathan's educational program cannot be changed without her knowledge or consent.
   d. Mr. Jones feels that his daughter Louisa is not receiving enough individual attention in the general classroom. He instructs the school to teach her in a segregated setting for the remainder of the year.

•• 17. Which one of the following practices is most consistent with the spirit of IDEA?
   a. Educating a student with a disfiguring birth defect in a self-contained classroom where other students are less likely to see her.
   b. Allowing a visually impaired student to attend classes with a parent who knows his specific needs.
   c. Giving a student paralyzed from the waist down a specially adapted chair to sit in.
   d. Excusing a student with cerebral palsy from taking a test because he cannot write.

• 18. Three of the following questions reflect common sources of concern or controversy about the effectiveness of inclusion. Which one is <u>not</u> a particular source of concern or controversy?
   a. Do students with special needs get enough individualized instruction to reach their full potential within general classroom settings?
   b. Is the inclusion movement based more on philosophical beliefs than on empirical research?
   c. Is it possible for students with such varying cognitive and physical abilities to form friendships?
   d. Is current research on inclusion applicable to students with all kinds of disabilities and across all grade levels?

• 19. Three of the following are the results of the changing conceptualization of inclusion in recent years. Which one is <u>not</u>?
   a. Teachers are individualizing instruction for all students, not just those identified as having special needs.
   b. Some general classroom teachers now teach cooperatively with special educators in the classroom.
   c. Teachers are taking a critical look at traditional curriculum materials and educational practices as they pertain to all students.
   d. Special educators are rarely involved in the day-to-day instruction of children with special needs.

•• 20. Which one of the following best characterizes the recent trend in how specialists are involved in the education of students with special needs?
   a. Schools are hiring fewer specialists who work with only one type of disability or special need; instead, they are hiring more special educators who can work with all students who have special needs.
   b. Schools are hiring fewer general special educators; instead, they are hiring more specialists who each work with only one type of disability or special need.
   c. Schools are moving away from having students leave the classroom to meet with specialists; instead, they are providing more special services within the classroom.
   d. Schools are moving away from providing special services within the classroom; instead, they are more frequently having students meet with specialists outside the classroom.

• 21. Three of the following statements describe advantages of categorizing special needs students. Which one has not necessarily been shown to be an advantage of categorizing these students?
   a. Students need to know what their limitations are in order to develop high self-esteem.
   b. Teachers and parents can access special interest groups and publications to enhance students' learning.
   c. Federal funding for special education depends on students being identified as having a particular disability.
   d. Students in a given special needs category are similar in certain ways, so they may sometimes benefit from similar instructional strategies.

•• 22. Which one of the following statements uses people-first language?
   a. Carl is a mentally retarded fifth grader with two older sisters.
   b. Saloni loves fiction, but she has a learning disability that affects her ability to read.
   c. Autistic children like Jeb need extra help in learning social skills.
   d. Ms. Ravinsky has two learning disabled children in her class.

•• 23. Which one of the following students is likely to be classified as having a learning disability?
   a. Marcus, who has trouble learning abstract information and cannot easily adapt to new situations
   b. George, who gets average scores on intelligence tests but has difficulty with certain kinds of memory tasks and is well below average in reading and writing
   c. Justine, who performs well on academic tasks but has a poor self image and has difficulty behaving appropriately in the classroom
   d. Melissa, who has no problem with reading and writing, but refuses to speak out to answer questions in class

•• 24. Three of the following children have a learning disability. Which one probably does not?
   a. Five-year-old Jodi spends hours trying to imitate her older sister's drawings. No matter how she tries, Jodi's art lacks proportion and perspective.
   b. Fifteen-year-old Peter has trouble following oral directions. Unless he has them in writing, he gets them mixed up or forgets important steps.
   c. Twelve-year-old Josh teases Sam about his new glasses. Sam grows silent and looks away but doesn't say anything. Later, Josh is quite surprised to find out that he has hurt Sam's feelings.
   d. Ten-year-old Katrina has a good oral vocabulary, but when she writes she tends to put letters in the wrong order, even when spelling common words.

• 25. Students with learning disabilities may have difficulty in three of the following areas. In which area do they not experience particular difficulty?
   a. Finding corrective lenses (glasses) that provide 20/20 vision
   b. Understanding the subtle social signals that others send them
   c. Understanding and remembering what other people tell them
   d. Paying attention

•• 26. Todd is an elementary school student with a learning disability in reading. His motor skills are poor, and he has trouble staying on task. Based on the experience of most children with learning disabilities, what might you expect to happen when Todd reaches high school?

   a. He will continue to exhibit poor motor skills, and this will prevent him from playing sports and participating in physical education.
   b. His attention span and motor skills will improve, but his reading skills may be inadequate to understand many of his textbooks.
   c. His reading skills will improve as a result of early intervention, but his attention span will still be as short as it was when he was in elementary school.
   d. He will improve dramatically in all areas and probably will not require specialized instruction by the time he reaches high school.

•• 27. Three of the following examples illustrate specific strategies that can be effective in helping students with learning disabilities learn classroom material. Which strategy has <u>not</u> been shown to be effective with these children?

   a. Josie's teacher gives her special memory tricks to help her remember how to spell certain words (e.g., "The principal is my pal").
   b. Nattie's teacher looks at the errors Nattie makes when she solves long division problems for clues about what Nattie might be doing incorrectly.
   c. Russell's teacher suggests that he listen to his favorite radio station while he studies for tomorrow's spelling test.
   d. Vern's history teacher loans Vern a videotape that depicts some of the historical events about which the class is reading.

•• 28. Three of the following children have been diagnosed with attention-deficit hyperactivity disorder. Which one is <u>least</u> likely to have ADHD?

   a. Eva daydreams in class a lot. She tends to stare at books without reading them, and her teacher often needs to repeat the same instructions several times.
   b. Martin rarely stays in his seat for more than ten minutes, and his hands are always fidgeting with something. He needs frequent reminders to get back on task, and transitions are challenging for him.
   c. Caroline turns her head toward every sound she hears. The sound of a pencil dropping catches her attention as easily as a fire alarm. Often she is so engrossed in listening to happenings in the hall or across the room that she does not hear someone speaking directly to her.
   d. Ben's favorite times of day are recess and gym, and he takes full advantage of them, running circles around the other kids. It's hard for him to sit still on rainy afternoons when he hasn't had a chance to burn off some energy, but he does get his work done.

• 29. Mrs. Fredericks has three students with attention-deficit hyperactivity disorder in her class this year. She wants to make some changes to increase their chances for success. Three of the following strategies are consistent with the textbook's recommendations for students with ADHD. Which one is <u>not</u>?

   a. Reading a story to the class after lunch to help them settle down and regain their focus.
   b. Asking students to make eye contact with her whenever she gives instructions.
   c. Helping them establish a daily routine for completing classroom assignments.
   d. Asking the three students to jog in place or do jumping jacks every time they exhibit off-task behavior.

• 30. Zack is a high school student with a speech disorder. Which one of the following characteristics is least likely to be associated with his disability?
   a. Zack's reading skills are among the lowest in his class.
   b. When asked to speak in front of a group, Zack blushes and looks uncomfortable.
   c. Zack shows no interest in contemporary music; in fact, he doesn't even listen to the radio.
   d. Zack has difficulty with writing assignments.

• 31. How can we best help students with speech and communication disorders?
   a. By refraining from having them speak in front of their classmates, as doing so might embarrass them.
   b. By calling on them frequently, so they will get used to speaking in front of others.
   c. By finishing their sentences for them when they begin to stutter.
   d. By asking them to clarify any parts of a message that we don't understand.

• 32. Only one of the following strategies is consistent with the textbook's recommendations for helping students with cognitive or academic difficulties succeed in your classroom. Which one?
   a. Spend time clarifying instructions and expectations, and check to make sure they know what they are supposed to do.
   b. Maintain high expectations when it comes to reading. Challenge students who have reading difficulties to read the same materials as their peers. This will motivate them to improve their skills.
   c. At the end of each day, talk to students about the areas in which they did not succeed that day. Ask them to concentrate on improving in those areas tomorrow.
   d. Keep students in from recess for extra instructional time if they do not maintain a C average or better.

•• 33. Which one of the following students is most likely to be identified as having an emotional or behavioral disorder?
   a. Lana, who has no friends and seems to be constantly depressed
   b. Rory, who stutters whenever he has to speak in front of his classmates
   c. Luke, who gets easily frustrated with his mathematics problems
   d. Janeen, who is constantly misinterpreting spoken directions and so is seldom doing what she is supposed to at any given time

•• 34. Which behavior is most likely to indicate that a student has a possible emotional or behavioral disorder?
   a. Betty's mind is often on her boyfriend rather than on classroom discussions.
   b. Eliza sometimes forgets to do her homework assignments, even though she really likes her teacher and wants to please him.
   c. Harrison is often more interested in socializing with his friends than in paying attention to his teacher.
   d. Jeff is usually somber and uncommunicative; the only time he speaks to other students is to insult them.

•• 35. Which one of the following students is exhibiting an <u>externalizing behavior</u>?

a. Tanya, who weighs 93 pounds but has stopped eating lunch and cut back on other meals because she thinks she's too fat.
b. Roberto, who has been overindulging in alcohol and making frequent comments about killing himself.
c. Natasha, who has been unable to sleep through the night for months because she cannot stop worrying about her life.
d. Peter, who has been stealing small items from his classmates' desks and publicly accusing others of taking them.

• 36. Only one of the following statements is true about emotional and behavioral disorders. Which one is true?

a. If a student exhibits only internalizing behaviors (rather than externalizing behaviors), she or he probably does not need to be evaluated for special services because she or he is not a danger to others.
b. It is possible to be genetically predisposed toward having an emotional or behavioral disorder but not show signs of a disorder until adolescence.
c. There is a high dropout rate for students with emotional and behavioral disorders because they often come from families who make them work to support themselves at an early age.
d. Almost all emotional and behavioral disorders are due to environmental factors.

•• 37. Mr. Jones is concerned about one of his students, Todd, who has been recently identified as having an emotional and behavioral disorder. Which one of the following is a good strategy for Mr. Jones to use with Todd?

a. Mr. Jones avoids talking to Todd about his problems. That's what the school psychologist is for, and besides, Todd might become too reliant on Mr. Jones for help.
b. Because Todd exhibits defiant behavior, Mr. Jones takes every opportunity to exert his own authority in the classroom. It's the only way he can keep control of the situation and not lose face with the other students.
c. Mr. Jones is developing his next history unit around the building of the first transcontinental railroad to appeal to Todd's interest in trains.
d. Mr. Jones encourages his other students to avoid interacting with Todd in order to reduce the number of fights Todd gets into in the classroom.

• 38. Three of the following are common signs that a student is contemplating suicide. Which one is <u>least</u> likely to be indicative of suicidal thoughts?

a. Gracie has become quite interested in looking and dressing like a popular rock star.
b. Erik has stopped hanging out with his friends and refuses to take their telephone calls.
c. After being seriously depressed for several weeks, Larinda is suddenly quite happy.
d. Oscar is giving away many of his most prized possessions.

•• 39. Three of the following students have autism. Which student is <u>least</u> likely to have autism?

a. Danny becomes visibly frustrated whenever class assemblies disrupt the regular schedule.
b. Faye seldom interacts with other children in class except by repeating things she hears them say.
c. Billy falls on the playground and hurts himself, but he pulls away when the teacher tried to help and comfort him.
d. Candace prefers to work alone rather than in groups. She doesn't have close friends in class, but she seems really attached to her teacher.

• 40. Which one of the following strategies is <u>most</u> likely to help students with autism?

a. Convey information in a lecture format and use the same key phrases repeatedly. Children with autism tend to repeat those phrases to themselves and so remember them better.
b. Keep the classroom environment stable and predictable. Don't rearrange classroom furniture, and keep the classroom schedule constant.
c. Do not let children with autism know ahead of time about unusual events such as fire drills and assemblies, as they will be unable to focus on anything else until the events occur.
d. Rotate the seating arrangement occasionally so that children with autism will get to know other members of the class. Otherwise, they are unlikely to have the skills and confidence to approach their peers.

•• 41. Three of the following teachers are using effective strategies to help students with emotional and behavioral disorders and students with autism. Which one is <u>not</u>?

a. When Chris has an emotional outburst, Ms. Wong does whatever she needs to do in order to pacify him. She is afraid that his behavior might get progressively worse if she does otherwise.
b. Mr. Connelly records everything that is happening when Karen has an emotional outburst. He hopes to find a pattern in this log which will help him anticipate problems and make modifications to help Karen.
c. Mrs. Parks spends time at the beginning of each year defining expectations for behavior in the classroom and outlining consequences of good and bad behavior. That way, when problems arise, she can specifically tell children which rule they are breaking and be consistent in administering consequences.
d. When Mr. Dove sees students using good interpersonal skills to work together or resolve conflicts, he praises them and identifies the specific behaviors he is praising them for.

•• 42. Three of the following teachers are using strategies that are likely to be effective with students who have social or behavioral problems. Which one is <u>not</u> using an effective strategy?

a. Mr. Green rewards his students for such appropriate behaviors as smiling, speaking pleasantly, and cooperating.
b. Ms. Walsenburg allows students to be verbally aggressive with classmates on occasion as long as they don't become physically aggressive.
c. Ms. DuBois asks Harry, "Do you want to talk about it?" when he seems especially upset.
d. Mr. Moreno makes it clear that he will not allow his students to get up and leave the classroom whenever they feel like it.

• 43. In addition to low general intelligence and poor academic performance, what other characteristic must be present to classify students as having mental retardation?
   a. A genetic condition such as Down Syndrome
   b. A discrepancy between intelligence and academic achievement
   c. Distractibility and an inability to focus on the details of a particular task
   d. Difficulty functioning in age-appropriate ways in the social environment

• 44. Three of the following are characteristic of students with mental retardation. Which one is <u>not</u> necessarily associated with mental retardation?
   a. Below-average academic achievement
   b. Immature social behavior
   c. Disruptive classroom behavior
   d. Poor performance on intelligence tests

•• 45. You have referred the following four students to the school psychologist for evaluation. Which one is the psychologist most likely to identify as having mental retardation?
   a. Matthew is having difficulty in mathematics but is performing at grade level in reading and spelling.
   b. Lacy shows low achievement in all areas and prefers to play with younger children.
   c. Wanda is hyperactive and frequently expresses her boredom with class material.
   d. Mark is a low achiever in all areas; he is a leader of a local neighborhood gang.

•• 46. Three of the following teachers are using strategies that are appropriate for students with mental retardation. Which teacher is <u>not</u> using an appropriate strategy?
   a. Ms. Akers uses many manipulatives to make new concepts concrete for students.
   b. Mr. Britton gives students explicit instructions, such as, "Hang up your coat, then come sit at your desk and take out a pencil."
   c. Ms. Chang teaches basic math facts but does not teach students how to use them in real-life situations.
   d. Mr. DiStefano presents new material at a slower pace than he does for his nondisabled students.

•• 47. Mr. Wilson will have a student with mental retardation included in his class for the first time this fall. Her name is Susan, and Mr. Wilson is considering what changes he should make to his style of teaching to promote her success. Which one of the following strategies is <u>least</u> likely to be helpful?
   a. Mr. Wilson will structure his lesson plans so that all of the children can work at their own pace as much as possible. This will allow Susan to go as slowly as she needs to in order to succeed.
   b. Mr. Wilson will use the Golden Rule ("Do unto others as you would have them do unto you") to define acceptable behavior in the classroom. It will be easier for Susan to remember this rule than a more specific list, and it should apply to any unexpected problems that might arise.
   c. When teaching math, Mr. Wilson will set up real life scenarios such as going to the store or balancing a checkbook. That will help Susan know when to apply the skills she learns.
   d. Mr. Wilson will make an effort to give Susan complete instructions, step by step, and not assume that she will understand directions he doesn't make explicit.

•• 48. Kristen has large scars on her neck from surgeries she has received to correct a problem with her esophagus. In the past she has been fed with a tube, but now she is learning to eat through her mouth. Her doctor wants her to snack throughout the day to increase her calorie intake. According to the guidelines set forth by IDEA, the most appropriate school response would be to:

a. Educate Kristen in a self-contained classroom so that she won't be subjected to other children staring at her scars and so that she can eat on a different schedule.
b. Ask Kristen's parents to hire someone to come in and oversee her meal and snack times.
c. Excuse Kristen from having to do homework in light of the fact that she is going through so much outside of school.
d. Allow Kristen to break for snacks in class and to provide whatever accommodations she needs in the classroom to do this.

• 49. A characteristic that students with physical and health impairments and those with visual impairments share is:

a. Fewer educational experiences outside the home
b. Reduced mental alertness, requiring longer time for processing information
c. Psychological denial that they have a disability
d. Limited opportunities to converse with others and develop language

•• 50. Three of the following children have visual impairments that qualify them for special services. Which one does <u>not</u> have a qualifying condition?

a. Rita has a restricted field of vision. She can only see what's straight in front of her.
b. Dan wears an extremely strong prescription to bring his eyesight to 20/20. Without his glasses, he can't function in a classroom.
c. Tracey has been blind since she was born due to an inherited condition.
d. Gustafo lost his eyesight in a terrible car accident.

• 51. Whereas students with good vision often learn things by seeing them firsthand, students with visual impairments must learn many of those same things by hearing about them instead. One drawback of having to listen to a description of something rather than seeing it directly is that:

a. Listening takes more time because information is received just one piece at a time.
b. Auditory attention is more difficult to maintain than visual attention.
c. Students with visual impairments usually have difficulties in auditory perception as well.
d. It is difficult to develop an abstract understanding of things that are heard rather than seen.

- 52. Mr. McDonald is making accommodations for Emily, who has a visual impairment. Which one of the following strategies is consistent with the textbook's recommendations for students with visual impairments?
    a. Because Emily can see objects if they are large and distinct, Mr. McDonald lets her walk around the room to watch other students as they work.
    b. Mr. McDonald always thanks Emily for her patience when he shows other students visual material.
    c. Mr. McDonald gives Emily full credit for any assignments she cannot accomplish because of her disability.
    d. Mr. McDonald asks another student to paint country boundaries with nail polish on a map so that Emily can feel them.

- 53. Which one of the following characteristics are we <u>most</u> likely to find in students with hearing loss?
    a. Delayed language skills
    b. Emotional problems
    c. Poor motor coordination
    d. Low self-esteem

- 54. Nota was born with a severe hearing loss. She is now in second grade, and her teachers are concerned because she has less developed reading skills than her peers. Also, although she has learned to sign, she seems to express less general knowledge about the world than her peers. Which of the following explanations for Nota's difficulties is most likely to be true?
    a. Because she has had less exposure to oral communication than her classmates, Nota's development in these areas has been delayed.
    b. Nota's general intelligence was probably affected by the same condition that caused her hearing loss.
    c. In addition to having a hearing loss, Nota probably has a language-related learning disability.
    d. Nota is probably depressed about her disability and is therefore less motivated to learn than her peers.

- 55. Students with hearing loss may not be able to fully understand oral communication, even when they are not totally deaf. Which one of the following is the most appropriate strategy that teachers can use to increase their understanding of what is going on in the classroom?
    a. Speak louder than usual, so that students who are only partially hearing impaired will be able to hear better.
    b. Try to stand in front of a window or other light source so that students will be able to read the teacher's lips.
    c. Supplement auditory presentations with visual presentations of the same material.
    d. Rather than trying to talk to the student directly, talk to a third person who can interpret for the student.

• 56. Which one of the following should you keep in mind when teaching students with severe and multiple disabilities?
   a. Students with multiple and severe disabilities can participate in a meaningful way in almost all classroom activities if you think creatively about accommodating their needs.
   b. Most students with severe and multiple disabilities are unable to adapt to a new environment. Therefore, you should be prepared for them to misbehave frequently in your classroom.
   c. Students with multiple and severe disabilities are working on more basic skills than others in the class. Nevertheless, asking them to work together with peers who do not have special needs would only hurt their self esteem and hamper other children's progress.
   d. When teaching a student with severe and multiple disabilities, it is more important to concentrate on development of interpersonal skills than on academic skills.

•• 57. Which one of the following teachers is using a strategy recommended in the textbook for working with students with physical and sensory challenges?
   a. Mr. Nishamura keeps an eye on Sarah so he can anticipate when she needs help. By offering help before she has to ask, he saves her considerable embarrassment.
   b. Ms. Sadatmand builds new supply shelves so that Harvey can access all classroom materials from his wheelchair.
   c. Mrs. Solomon always gives Yolanda a reduced workload. Although Yolanda is capable of doing all the work, she tires easily.
   d. Mr. Christensen allows Jamal, who is unable to speak, to use an augmentative communication device during language arts but not at other times of day. He does not want Jamal to become overly dependent on technology.

•• 58. Three of the following students exemplify characteristics of giftedness described in the textbook. Which one does not?
   a. When twelve-year-old Angela tells a story, she captivates her audience with her vivid character portrayals and rich vocabulary.
   b. Sixteen-year-old Barry is extraordinarily sensitive to the feelings and needs of others. Not only is he a keen observer of people, but he also has a knack for responding in the best possible way.
   c. Fourteen-year-old Calvin is an extremely hard worker; in addition to doing well in his schoolwork, he is an excellent babysitter.
   d. Ten-year-old Debbie learns more quickly than her classmates and is already demonstrating aspects of formal operational thought.

• 59. Which one of the following is a legitimate reason for not relying solely on intelligence tests when we identify gifted students?
   a. Because of the culture-dependent nature of intelligence, we may overlook gifted students from an ethnic minority group.
   b. Because intelligence tests measure innate intelligence, we may overlook students whose giftedness is due to an enriched environment.
   c. Because intelligence test results are so difficult to interpret, we are likely to identify many nongifted students as gifted.
   d. Because high achievement is a more important criterion than high intelligence when we identify gifted students, we should focus on achievement test results instead.

- 60. Which one of the following is most likely to be a problem when identifying students who are potentially gifted?
    a. Some students will resist being tested because gifted programs have a reputation for being too difficult.
    b. Some students will do poorly on intelligence tests because they consistently misinterpret the questions.
    c. The parents of most gifted students do not want special educational services for their children.
    d. Some students may intentionally perform poorly in order to hide their talents from their classmates.

- 61. On average, how do children who are gifted compare to their peers in social and emotional development?
    a. They tend to be loners, preferring such solitary activities as reading or computer games.
    b. They tend to be less mature than their peers and more prone to emotional problems.
    c. They tend to be above average in social development, and most are emotionally well adjusted.
    d. They tend to be about the same as their peers in emotional adjustment and social development.

- 62. Of the following, which one has been the most common argument against providing special programs for the education of children who are gifted?
    a. Students who are gifted are able to meet normal school objectives without outside help.
    b. Students who are gifted are typically not motivated and would not take full advantage of special opportunities.
    c. The public school system should concentrate its efforts on students of average ability, not those outside the norm.
    d. All students are gifted in some way, so special programs would have to be offered to everyone.

- 63. Within the context of Vygotsky's perspective of cognitive development, why do students who are gifted often not benefit from regular classroom instruction?
    a. Because they are typically more distractible than their nongifted peers.
    b. Because they aren't working within their zone of proximal development.
    c. Because they're too preoccupied by their own self-talk.
    d. Because they're too busy thinking about things they learned from their outside reading to want to learn material presented in the classroom.

- 64. The textbook recommends three of the following strategies for adapting instruction for students who are gifted. Which one does it <u>not</u> recommend?
    a. Ask students to be patient while their classmates master instructional objectives.
    b. Form study groups of students with similar interests and abilities.
    c. Encourage students to set high goals for themselves.
    d. Find outside resources through which students can pursue their interests.

• 65. Which is the most likely result of forming a study group of several gifted students who share common interests?
  a. They will become frustrated in the company of other gifted students because they are no longer the smartest ones in the room.
  b. Because they usually prefer learning independently, they will resist the group learning approach.
  c. They will learn from other group members only if everyone is at the same grade level.
  d. They will be less apt to hide their talents in the company of others who share those talents.

• 66. Which one of the following strategies best describes an enrichment approach to gifted education?
  a. Teaching students complex thought processes like problem solving and creativity, which they can then apply to any situation.
  b. Allowing students to do more in-depth work on the same subject that the rest of the class is studying.
  c. Allowing students to work with more advanced textbooks in a subject area of their own choosing.
  d. Bringing in outside help or resource persons to teach students about new topics that may be of interest to them.

•• 67. Which one of the following students is participating in an acceleration approach to gifted education?
  a. Victor studies the same concepts as his peers, but he works on more challenging problems.
  b. Barbara usually finishes her work early, so her teacher gives her extra problems to keep her occupied while her classmates catch up.
  c. Jenabeth is working on the same curriculum as her peers, but because she is working at her own pace, she is two months ahead of the rest of the class.
  d. Hugo does the same work as the rest of his class, but his teacher is working with him on special skills like speed reading.

• 68. A disproportionate number of students identified as having cognitive, social, or physical disabilities come from low-income families or from certain ethnic minority backgrounds. As educators, we can best address this situation by:
  a. Thinking of any labels (e.g., "mental retardation") as being temporary classifications that can help students get the special services they need to enable them to improve
  b. Realizing that students are apt to improve more when they are placed in self-contained classrooms that are specialized to meet their needs
  c. Placing priority on meeting students' physical and medical needs; working on academic and social needs only after their health improves
  d. Campaigning for resources that will allow us to teach these students in a residential setting

• 69. Students from diverse cultural backgrounds won't necessarily show their exceptional gifts and talents on traditional intelligence tests. Three of the following characteristics may be indicative of giftedness in such students. Which characteristic is least likely to indicate giftedness?

a. Solving problems in unique and creative ways
b. Insisting on perfection at all times
c. Seeing connections between two very different topics
d. Learning quickly

• 70. Three of the following strategies are recommended for teaching students with special needs. Which strategy is not recommended?

a. Using methods of instruction that are tailored to each student's unique needs.
b. Obtaining as much information as possible about each student.
c. Encouraging students with and without disabilities to work together on cooperative projects.
d. Making it clear to everyone that you have different expectations for different students.

•• 71. Three of the following teachers are using strategies that are recommended for teaching students with special needs. Which one is using a strategy that is not recommended?

a. Mr. DeWolfe stays in close touch with Katie's parents so that they can be consistent in their expectations for her at school and at home
b. Ms. Gagnon begins each year by focusing on getting to know each of her students and their strengths, weaknesses, and interests. This helps her to adapt her instruction to the unique needs of each student.
c. Mr. Hartell makes sure that at least once a month, his students with special needs get a chance to make some choices about what goal they will work on and what topic they will study.
d. Ms. Toor develops a different set of general expectations for her students with special needs than for the rest of her class at the beginning of each year. By anticipating their limitations, she ensures that they will feel successful about everything they are asked to do.

• 72. Three of the following strategies should help students with special needs become more socially integrated with their classmates. Which strategy is not recommended?

a. Teach students with special needs how to initiate conversations with others.
b. Assign one or more student "partners" to each student with special needs—partners who can provide assistance in their area of difficulty.
c. Emphasize to nondisabled classmates that students with special needs have thoughts and emotions very different from their own.
d. Have toys and classroom equipment that require the cooperation of several students in order to be used.

•• 73. To promote positive interactions between students with and without disabilities, which one of the following techniques is likely to be most effective?
   a. Ms. Crow encourages her students who have special needs to become active in extracurricular activities. By participating in more activities outside of the classroom, these students have more opportunities to establish friendships with their peers.
   b. One of Mr. Grondin's students, Pamela, has a physical disability. Mr. Grondin refrains from assigning any cooperative group work in class. This way, he eliminates the chance that other students will become frustrated about working with Pam and so will be more likely to feel positively about her.
   c. Miss Williamson encourages other students learn to be patient with Rodney's misbehavior and try to remember that he doesn't have the same ability to control himself that they do.
   d. When Mike's classmates ask Mr. Rogers about Sidney's differences, he says things like, "Some people are just different."

• 74. Which one of the following strategies does the textbook recommend as the most effective way to help students with special needs blend in with their classmates?
   a. Give students with special needs the same instruction that other students receive so that they don't appear to be getting special treatment.
   b. Provide all students with individualized instruction so that students with special needs are not singled out.
   c. Remove students with special needs from the regular classroom when special instruction must be provided.
   d. Provide individualized instruction to students with special needs when their classmates go to art, music, or physical education.

## Essay Questions

• 75. Public Law 94-142 (the Individuals with Disabilities Education Act) guarantees five things for students with disabilities:
   a. A free and appropriate education
   b. A fair and nondiscriminatory evaluation
   c. Education in the least restrictive environment
   d. An individualized education program
   e. Due process

   In five short paragraphs, explain the implications of each of these for educational practice.

• 76. Attaching labels to students with disabilities ("mental retardation," "learning disability," etc.) has often been criticized for stigmatizing children unnecessarily. Despite this concern, educators continue to categorize and label students who have special needs. In three short paragraphs, discuss three reasons why categories of special needs continue to be used.

- 77. Even if you are a teacher in a general education classroom, you will probably find one or more students with specific or general cognitive difficulties in your classroom. List five strategies that may be useful as you work with such students. For each one, (1) describe in specific and concrete terms what you might do, and (2) identify the kinds of special needs your strategy will address.

- 78. Even if you are a regular classroom teacher, you will probably find one or more students with physical and sensory challenges (physical and health impairments, visual impairments, hearing loss) in your classroom. List three strategies that may be useful as you work with such students. For each one, (1) describe in specific and concrete terms what you might do, and (2) identify the kinds of special needs your strategy will address.

- 79. As a teacher, you may find that some of your students have exceptional gifts or talents in the subject matter you are teaching.
    a. Describe three behaviors that may lead you to believe that one or more of your students is potentially eligible for special services for the gifted.
    b. Identify three different strategies you might use to provide educational experiences suitable for students who are gifted. For each strategy, describe what you might do in specific, concrete terms.

## ANSWER KEY

### Multiple-Choice Questions

| | | | | |
|---|---|---|---|---|
| 1. c | 16. d | 31. d | 46. c | 61. c |
| 2. a | 17. c | 32. a | 47. b | 62. a |
| 3. d | 18. c | 33. a | 48. d | 63. b |
| 4. d | 19. d | 34. d | 49. a | 64. a |
| 5. a | 20. c | 35. d | 50. b | 65. d |
| 6. c | 21. a | 36. b | 51. a | 66. b |
| 7. c | 22. b | 37. c | 52. d | 67. c |
| 8. c | 23. b | 38. a | 53. a | 68. a |
| 9. b | 24. a | 39. d | 54. a | 69. b |
| 10. c | 25. a | 40. b | 55. c | 70. d |
| 11. c | 26. b | 41. a | 56. a | 71. d |
| 12. d | 27. c | 42. b | 57. b | 72. c |
| 13. a | 28. d | 43. d | 58. c | 73. a |
| 14. a | 29. d | 44. c | 59. a | 74. b |
| 15. a | 30. c | 45. b | 60. d | |

### Essay Questions

75. Responses to various parts of the question are as follows:
    a. We must provide an educational program designed to meet the specific needs of each student with a disability.
    b. Evaluation methods must provide a complete and accurate assessment of each student's unique educational needs. For example, evaluation instruments must be administered by individuals trained in their use, and evaluation procedures must take the student's background and any suspected physical or communication difficulties into account.
    c. Every student with special needs is entitled to education in the most typical and standard educational environment that can reasonably meet his or her needs.
    d. An IEP must be developed and described in written form for each student identified as having a disability. This is reviewed and revised on an annual basis.
    e. IDEA mandates several practices that ensure that a student's rights, as well as those of parents acting on the student's behalf, are preserved throughout the decision making process.

76. The textbook identifies three reasons why categories of special needs continue to be used (the response should include all three). (1) Students in the same category have some characteristics in common and may benefit from similar instructional strategies. (2) Special interest groups have developed to help students in specific categories, resulting in specialized organizations, journals, research programs, and political lobby groups. (3) Federal funding for special services is available only when a student has been identified as having a particular disability.

77. The question encompasses many students with special needs, including those with learning disabilities, ADHD, speech and communication disorders, and mental retardation. Accordingly, a response may include strategies for accommodating instruction for students in any of these categories. Appropriate strategies include the following:

    Strategies for students with learning disabilities
    - Minimize distractions.
    - Use a variety of modalities to present information.
    - Analyze errors for clues as to why students are having difficulty.
    - Provide specific strategies (e.g., mnemonics) for learning and remembering things.
    - Provide study aids.

    Strategies for students with ADHD
    - Modify students' schedules and work environments.
    - Teach attention-focusing strategies.
    - Teach strategies for controlling hyperactivity and impulsivity.
    - Provide outlets for excess energy.
    - Teach strategies for organizing and using time effectively.
    - Teach and encourage appropriate classroom behaviors.

    Strategies for students with speech and communication disorders
    - Encourage students to talk, but don't force them to do so.
    - Listen patiently if students have difficulty expressing themselves.
    - Ask students to clarify things you don't understand.

    General strategies for students with specific cognitive or academic difficulties
    - Promote success on academic tasks.
    - Communicate clear expectations for classroom performance.
    - Take students' reading skills into consideration when assigning reading materials, assessing achievement, etc.
    - Take steps to enhance self-confidence and motivation.

    Strategies for students with mental retardation
    - Pace instruction at an appropriate level.
    - Explain tasks concretely, specifically, and completely.
    - Provide scaffolding to facilitate effective cognitive processing.
    - Teach vocational and general life skills.
    - Encourage independence.

    You may also want to give credit for some of the strategies listed in the section "The Big Picture." The response should identify five strategies, illustrate each strategy with a concrete example of what a teacher might do, and specify which students are likely to benefit from the strategy.

78. Strategies appropriate for students with physical and sensory challenges include these:

    Strategies for students with physical and health impairments
    - Accommodate specific physical needs (e.g., giving an oral test rather than a written one).
    - Know what to do in emergencies.
    - Educate classmates about the nature of the disability.

    Strategies for students with visual impairments
    - Orient students to the physical layout of the classroom.
    - For partially sighted students, use visual materials with sharp contrast, and give frequent breaks when using them.
    - Transmit information through nonvisual modalities.
    - Allow extra learning time.

    Strategies for students with hearing loss
    - Minimize irrelevant noise.
    - Supplement auditory presentations with visual information and hands-on activities.
    - Maximize students' ability to use whatever hearing ability they have (e.g., use a natural speaking voice).
    - Make sure students can see you clearly.
    - Occasionally check for understanding when presenting information auditorially.
    - Address any deficiencies in reading and language.
    - Teach signing to other class members.

    General strategies for students with physical and sensory challenges
    - Provide access to the same educational opportunities that other students have.
    - Treat students as normally as possible.
    - Provide assistance only when students really need it.
    - Use technological innovations.

    You may also want to give credit for some of the strategies listed in the section "The Big Picture." The response should identify three strategies, illustrate each strategy with a concrete example of what a teacher might do, and specify which students are likely to benefit from the strategy.

79. Responses to the two parts of the question are as follows:
    a. Behaviors that indicate possible giftedness include these (the response should include at least three):
        - Exceptionally high achievement (e.g., test scores, classroom assignments)
        - Ability to learn things quickly
        - Greater flexibility in thinking and behavior
        - Appearance of formal operational thought processes at an earlier age than normal
        - Positive self-concept related to academic tasks
        - Above-average social development and emotional adjustment
        - Ability to generalize to other, seemingly unrelated tasks
        - Originality and resourcefulness
        - Exceptional communication skills
        - Unusual sensitivity to the needs and feelings of others
        - Large vocabulary
        - Extensive knowledge and expertise in certain areas
        - More advanced cognitive and/or metacognitive skills
        - High motivation to achieve on challenging tasks
        - Boredom for easy tasks
        - Unusually high standards for performance
    b. Strategies for addressing the needs of gifted students include these (the response should identify at least three strategies and explain each one in concrete terms):
        - Individualize instruction.
        - Form study groups.
        - Teach complex cognitive skills within the context of specific topics.
        - Provide opportunities for independent study.
        - Encourage students to set high goals.
        - Seek outside resources (e.g., mentors) through which students can develop special talents.

    You may also want to give credit for some of the strategies listed in the section "The Big Picture."

# Chapter 6

# LEARNING AND COGNITIVE PROCESSES

| CHAPTER OUTLINE | RELEVANT TEST BANK ITEMS |
|---|---|
| LOOKING AT LEARNING FROM DIFFERENT PERSPECTIVES<br>Learning as a Change in Behavior<br>Learning as a Change in Mental Associations<br>Learning and the Brain<br>Keeping an Open Mind about Theories of Learning | Multiple-Choice 1–11 |
| BASIC ASSUMPTIONS OF COGNITIVE PSYCHOLOGY | Multiple-Choice 12–15 |
| BASIC TERMINOLOGY IN COGNITIVE PSYCHOLOGY | Multiple-Choice 16–19 |
| A MODEL OF HUMAN MEMORY<br>The Nature of the Sensory Register<br>Moving Information to Working Memory: The Role of Attention<br>The Nature of Working (Short-Term) Memory<br>Moving Information to Long-Term Memory: Connecting New Information with Prior Knowledge<br>The Nature of Long-Term Memory<br>Critiquing the Three-Component Model | Multiple-Choice 20–39<br>Essay 93–94 |
| LONG-TERM MEMORY STORAGE<br>The Various Forms That Knowledge May Take<br>How Declarative Knowledge is Learned<br>How Procedural Knowledge is Learned<br>Prior Knowledge and Working Memory in Long-Term Memory Storage<br>Using Mnemonics in the Absence of Relevant Prior Knowledge | Multiple-Choice 40–72<br>Essay 95–98 |
| LONG-TERM MEMORY RETRIEVAL<br>The Nature of Long-Term Memory Retrieval<br>Factors Affecting Retrieval<br>Why People Sometimes "Forget" | Multiple-Choice 73–88 |

| | |
|---|---|
| GIVING STUDENTS TIME TO PROCESS: EFFECTS OF INCREASING WAIT TIME | Multiple-Choice 89–91 |
| ACCOMMODATING DIVERSITY IN COGNITIVE PROCESSES<br>Facilitating Cognitive Processing in Students with Special Needs | Multiple-Choice 92 |
| The items in the "Integrative Questions" chapter of this Test Bank integrate the content of two or more textbook chapters. Within that chapter, the items listed to the right are relevant to Chapter 6. | Multiple-Choice 7–8, 11–13<br>Essay 25–31, 39 |

## Multiple-Choice Questions

• 1. Three of the following reflect components of learning common to both behaviorist and cognitive definitions of learning. Which one is not common to the definitions of both perspectives?
   a. The fact that learning involves a change.
   b. The importance of thought processes in learning.
   c. The relative permanence of whatever is learned.
   d. The role of experience in learning.

•• 2. Three of the following are examples of learned behavior. Given the textbook's definitions of learning, which behavior probably does not reflect learning?
   a. Abigail cries when she feels sad.
   b. After many hours of heated debate, Brian begins to modify his religious beliefs.
   c. Cara suddenly recognizes how the division fact "24 ÷ 4 = 6" is related to the multiplication fact "6 x 4 = 24."
   d. David has been running away from German shepherds ever since he was bitten by a German shepherd two years ago.

•• 3. Reynelda has trouble tracing a complex shape with a pencil when she is in kindergarten, but she can do it quite well by the time she is in second grade. Is this an instance of learning?
   a. Yes, because her behavior has changed.
   b. No, because the circumstances are too dissimilar.
   c. Maybe, although the change may be due to physiological maturation rather than experience.
   d. Maybe, but only if she is being reinforced for tracing accurately.

•• 4. A fellow teacher says to you, "I never believe my students have learned anything until I see their behavior change." Without knowing anything else about this teacher, you can guess that he or she agrees with the ___________ perspective of learning.
   a. behaviorist
   b. social cognitive
   c. cognitive
   d. Piagetian

• 5. Behaviorists define learning differently than cognitive psychologists do. Which one of the following statements best describes that difference?
   a. Behaviorism focuses on temporary changes; cognitive psychology focuses on relatively permanent changes.
   b. Behaviorism focuses on relatively permanent changes; cognitive psychology focuses on temporary changes.
   c. Behaviorism focuses on internal mental changes; cognitive psychology focuses on external behavioral changes.
   d. Behaviorism focuses on external behavioral changes; cognitive psychology focuses on internal mental changes.

• 6. Which one of the following statements best describes the view of early behaviorists about how learning can best be studied?
   a. Psychologists can determine how learning occurs only if they can identify its physiological basis.
   b. Introspection—reporting what and how one is thinking—is likely to yield the most accurate results.
   c. To study learning scientifically, researchers must confine their investigations to animal research in a laboratory setting.
   d. The study of learning will be more objective and scientific if only observable events are considered.

•• 7. Mr. Loosigian is worried about Jerri, a girl who is struggling in his seventh grade class. He thinks about several different reasons why she might be having so much difficulty with her schoolwork. Which one of the possible reasons that he considers is consistent with a <u>behaviorist</u> perspective of learning?
   a. "Maybe she isn't paying attention as much as she should be."
   b. "Maybe I don't praise her enough when she does something well."
   c. "Maybe she has trouble understanding the things she reads."
   d. "Maybe she has trouble remembering things from one day to the next."

• 8. Which one of the following statements best characterizes a <u>cognitive</u> approach to learning?
   a. Students' learning is a function of how stimuli in the environment are organized and sequenced.
   b. Students learn through a series of either-or decisions similar to how computers operate.
   c. Students' learning is a function of what they do, mentally, with the information they receive.
   d. Students are most likely to learn the things they think they will be reinforced for learning.

• 9. Early behaviorists argued that thinking cannot be observed so it cannot be studied objectively and scientifically. How would a cognitive psychologist be most likely to respond to this argument?
   a. "Modern technology allows us to study thought processes in a very precise manner."
   b. "By studying people's responses to various stimuli, we can draw inferences about the thought processes that underlie those responses."
   c. "We study mental events, which are not necessarily the same thing as 'thinking.'"
   d. "We can determine what people are thinking simply by asking them what they are thinking. The things they say are observable behaviors that we can measure objectively."

•• 10. Which one of the following researchers is drawing an inference about thinking from her observations of behavior?
   a. Dr. Aragon discovers that students remember more when new concepts are illustrated by pictures as well as being verbally described; she concludes that visual imagery helps learning and memory.
   b. Dr. Burger finds that students who learn information word for word don't remember it for very long; she concludes that requiring students to learn information verbatim isn't an effective teaching strategy.
   c. Dr. Cooper finds that students who listen to an organized lecture remember more information than students who listen to an unorganized lecture; she concludes that organized material promotes better learning.
   d. Dr. Delgado finds that students who listen to foreign language tapes while sleeping don't remember what they've heard; she concludes that being awake is necessary for learning to occur.

• 11. Which one of the following best describes our current knowledge about the brain and learning?
   a. We know that learning is associated with the formation of new synapses.
   b. We know that large doses of certain vitamins promote brain growth and lead to more rapid learning.
   c. We know that "left-brained" individuals are, on average, more effective learners than "right-brained" individuals.
   d. We know that the long-term memories of rapid learners are about 20% larger than the long-term memories of slow learners.

•• 12. Which one of the following teaching strategies best reflects the perspective of cognitive psychology?
   a. Mr. Atherton plans classroom activities that are likely to elicit desirable student behaviors.
   b. Mr. Birleffi makes sure that he performs classroom tasks the same way that he wants his students to do them.
   c. Mr. Camacho shows his students exactly what they should and should not do as they use the equipment in his chemistry lab.
   d. Mr. Darwin has students recall personal experiences related to the concepts they are studying.

• 13. Three of the following assumptions underlie cognitive perspectives of learning. Which one does <u>not</u>?
  a. People may learn different things from the same experience if they process it differently.
  b. People don't just passively absorb knowledge like a sponge; instead, they actively construct it.
  c. People learn in ways that are similar to how other species learn.
  d. People's existing beliefs about a topic influence the new things they learn about the topic.

• 14. As human beings, we encounter a great many stimuli at any one time. Which one of the following most accurately reflects cognitive psychologists' perspective about how we respond to all these stimuli?
  a. By learning to use effective long-term memory storage processes, we can eventually begin to remember almost everything we encounter.
  b. We must select the things we think are most important to learn and remember, and ignore the rest.
  c. We remember virtually everything we experience, but we have difficulty retrieving most of it.
  d. We cannot remember everything, and we have little control over the things that we <u>do</u> remember.

• 15. Which one of the following statements best describes the idea that learning involves a process of <u>construction</u>?
  a. Students must learn certain things very well before they can begin to understand other things.
  b. Students must learn ideas in a concrete form before learning them as abstractions.
  c. Students use pieces of information about a topic to develop their own understanding.
  d. Students' thought processes become increasingly complex and sophisticated as they grow older.

• 16. When cognitive psychologists talk about the process of "putting" things in memory, they often use the term:
  a. retrieval
  b. selectivity
  c. inference-drawing
  d. storage

•• 17. As his teacher reads a story, Wesley pictures the main characters the way he thinks they must look. By forming visual images based on the verbal descriptions his teacher reads, Wesley is ______ those descriptions.
  a. encoding
  b. retrieving
  c. organizing
  d. using verbal mediation to learn

•• 18. Which one of the following is the best example of <u>encoding</u> while learning state capitals?
   a. Abe tries to learn Atlanta, Georgia by thinking, "The Atlantic Ocean is gorgeous."
   b. Bernice tries to learn St. Paul, Minnesota by repeating "St. Paul, Minnesota" over and over to herself.
   c. Corey tries to learn Austin, Texas by making sure he is relaxed before he studies it.
   d. Darcy tries to learn Sacramento, California by having a tape recorder play "Sacramento, California," over and over while she sleeps.

• 19. During a lecture about World War II, Mr. Cochran tells his class about some of the major leaders of the countries involved in the war. He then asks Kathy to identify the leader of Great Britain during World War II, and she correctly responds, "Winston Churchill." At the time she answers the question, Kathy is exhibiting:
   a. storage
   b. retrieval
   c. elaboration
   d. proactive interference

•• 20. Which one of the following statements best describes the three-component model of memory presented in the textbook?
   a. All information that reaches the sensory register also reaches working memory, but only a small percentage of this information is stored in long-term memory.
   b. Information that must be remembered for a long time goes directly from the sensory register to long-term memory; less important information is stored in working memory.
   c. The three components of memory are used to store different kinds of information: visual images are stored in the sensory register, most numerical information is stored in working memory, and verbal information is stored in long-term memory.
   d. All information that enters long-term memory must first pass through the sensory register and working memory.

• 21. Which one of the following statements best describes the <u>sensory register</u>?
   a. It stores everything that is sensed in a relatively unencoded fashion.
   b. It stores information primarily in terms of its underlying meaning.
   c. It stores only a small amount of information, selecting things that will probably be important to know.
   d. It stores only a small amount of information, selecting things more or less at random.

•• 22. Which one of the following best reflects the use of the <u>sensory register</u> component of memory?
   a. You can remember a tune for several hours, even though you don't remember the words.
   b. You can remember something you heard for a second or two even though you weren't paying attention.
   c. You can remember the name of a person just long enough to introduce her to someone else.
   d. You can remember the concept of <u>reinforcement</u> because you are able to relate it to your own experiences.

• 23. Which one of the following statements best characterizes the duration of the sensory register?
   a. Information can last indefinitely in the sensory register if the visual or auditory image is retrieved occasionally.
   b. Meaningless information fades quickly, but meaningful information may remain for hours.
   c. Visual information lasts less than a second, with auditory information lasting a bit longer.
   d. Information remains for about ten seconds regardless of its nature.

•• 24. Mr. Wagner stands in front of the class explaining the process of evolution. Ellen is sitting in the front row, but her mind is on the fight she had with her best friend just before class. Based on this information, how far in Ellen's memory system did Mr. Wagner's lecture get?
   a. It reached the sensory register.
   b. It reached working memory.
   c. It reached long-term memory.
   d. It never got into the memory system at all.

• 25. Learning theorists often emphasize the importance of <u>attention</u> in the learning process. From the perspective of the three-component model of memory, why is attention so important?
   a. It gets information into the sensory register.
   b. It moves information from working memory into long-term memory.
   c. It moves information from the sensory register into long-term memory.
   d. It moves information from the sensory register into working memory.

•• 26. Which one of the following examples best reflects the <u>cocktail party phenomenon</u>?
   a. Students become overwhelmed when too much is going on in the classroom at once.
   b. Students working in a small group can hear what one student is saying even though students in other groups are also talking.
   c. When a dog walks into the classroom, students' attention is temporarily distracted from their independent seatwork assignment.
   d. Students pay more attention when they are enjoying themselves.

•• 27. Considering what cognitive psychologists tell us about attention, identify the pair of activities that most people would have trouble doing simultaneously.
   a. Thinking about what to cook for dinner while combing one's hair
   b. Watching the evening news on television while studying for an exam
   c. Carrying on a conversation about the meaning of life while walking down the street
   d. Mentally planning a weekend camping trip while jogging

• 28. Three of the following students' behaviors indicate that they are paying attention. Which one does <u>not</u> necessarily show that students are paying attention?
   a. Students correctly answer questions about the material just presented.
   b. Students are taking good notes on the material being presented.
   c. Students are solving problems using the material just presented.
   d. All students' eyes are clearly directed at their teacher.

• 29. The textbook recommends a number of strategies for increasing students' attention in the classroom. Which one of the following, while possibly beneficial for other reasons, is not necessarily recommended as a strategy for increasing attention?
   a. Follow a predictable routine every day.
   b. Vary classroom presentation methods.
   c. Place students near the teacher if their minds tend to wander.
   d. Show enthusiasm for classroom subject matter.

• 30. Which one of the following statements best characterizes working memory (sometimes known as short-term memory)?
   a. It holds information for several hours and includes only things that we know we will need later on.
   b. It holds information for only a second or two unless we engage in maintenance rehearsal.
   c. It actively processes a small amount of information, typically holding it for less than a minute.
   d. It holds processed information for several days or weeks, but probably not forever.

•• 31. Susan hears her teacher say, "Seven times nine is sixty-three," and immediately repeats this math fact to herself three times. Five minutes later, Susan cannot respond correctly when her teacher asks, "What is seven times nine?" Based on this information, how far in Susan's memory system did the math fact probably get?
   a. It reached the sensory register.
   b. It reached working memory.
   c. It reached long-term memory.
   d. It never got into the memory system at all.

•• 32. Which one of the following situations reflects the typical duration of working memory?
   a. Arnie remembers his locker combination through the entire school year. After summer vacation, however, he has forgotten it.
   b. Barney looks up the correct spelling of the word "fossil," repeats the letters once, and closes the dictionary. By the time he finds a piece of paper on which to write the word, he has forgotten how to spell it.
   c. Carol remembers most of the information that she has been learning about World War II in class this week, but she remembers very little of what she learned about World War I two weeks ago.
   d. At noon, Darrell makes a mental list of the five homework assignments he needs to complete that night. At 3:00 he checks himself and realizes that he still remembers all five. However, by 7:00 p.m. he cannot remember two of the five assignments.

•• 33. Eunice had trouble learning the formula for calculating the area of a circle, so she is saying it to herself over and over again while the teacher passes out the geometry test. Eunice is demonstrating:
   a. storage in the sensory register
   b. retrieval from working memory
   c. the use of maintenance rehearsal
   d. the use of verbal mediation

• 34. It is difficult to think about too many things all at the same time—a fact that reflects:
  a. The nature of the sensory register
  b. The limited capacity of working memory
  c. The constructive nature of long-term memory
  d. The concrete nature of visual imagery

•• 35. Only one of the following teaching practices is consistent with what we know about working memory. Which one?
  a. Mr. Adamson tells his students that, with practice, they will be able to do complicated long division problems in their heads.
  b. Ms. Borelli tells her students that they should try to focus on main ideas rather than try to remember every detail.
  c. Ms. Constas suggests that students in her Russian class listen to Russian tapes while they sleep.
  d. Mr. Dominowski urges his students to put information for tomorrow's test in their "short-term memories."

• 36. Three of the following statements are accurate descriptions of long-term memory. Which one is not?
  a. Information can last for a lengthy period of time, although not necessarily forever.
  b. The more information it contains, the less room it has for new material.
  c. Many of the items stored there are stored in terms of their meanings.
  d. Retrieval of information from long-term memory is sometimes difficult.

•• 37. To prepare for his test on Tuesday morning, Harry studied on Monday night. He remembered the information long enough to do well on the test on Tuesday but could not remember it for a surprise quiz a week later. Based on this information, how far in Harry's memory system did the information get?
  a. It reached the sensory register.
  b. It reached working memory.
  c. It reached long-term memory.
  d. It never got into the memory system at all.

•• 38. Gretchen thinks about Christopher Columbus, which reminds her of Spain, which in turn reminds her that she needs to do her homework for her Spanish class. Which one of the following does Gretchen's train of thought best illustrate?
  a. The interconnectedness of long-term memory
  b. Elaboration in working memory
  c. Reconstruction error in retrieval
  d. Encoding during long-term memory storage

• 39. Which one of the following statements best describes an activation model of memory?
  a. Information is more effectively encoded when it is acted out (for example, through role playing) at the time of storage.
  b. What you are thinking about is activated; other things stored in your memory are in an inactive state.
  c. You must repeat information several times if it is to be stored effectively.
  d. Different pieces of information in memory interact with one another, so that you often remember something differently than the way in which you stored it.

• 40. Which one of the following statements best describes how information is stored in long-term memory?
   a. Mostly as images—how things look, sound, feel, or smell
   b. Almost entirely as underlying meanings, or semantic codes
   c. Mostly in terms of the words of the first language a person has learned
   d. In a variety of possible forms

•• 41. You know what a computer is, and you may also know how to send an e-mail message using a computer. The difference between these two kinds of knowledge can best be characterized as a difference between:
   a. declarative knowledge vs. procedural knowledge
   b. visual imagery vs. elaboration
   c. rehearsal vs. organization
   d. long-term memory vs. working memory

•• 42. A biology teacher wants students to remember the various components of a <u>cell</u> (nucleus, cytoplasm, cell membrane). Considering what research tells us about encoding and retrieval, the teacher would be well advised to help students encode information about the cell:
   a. Primarily in a visual form, because visual images usually remain vivid in memory for a long period of time
   b. Primarily in a verbal form, because language underlies much of human learning
   c. In both visual and verbal forms, because multiple forms of encoding increase the likelihood of retrieval
   d. In a relatively unencoded form for a few days, to allow for greater flexibility in encoding later on

• 43. Nicole learns the formula "$E = mc^2$" by repeating it to herself over and over again. Which one of the following processes is Nicole most clearly demonstrating?
   a. Elaboration
   b. Meaningful learning
   c. Rehearsal
   d. Internal organization

• 44. Three of the following statements accurately characterize <u>rote learning</u>. Which statement is <u>not</u> true of rote learning?
   a. Few if any connections are made to existing knowledge.
   b. Information is learned in a relatively meaningless fashion.
   c. Repetition is the main strategy used during storage.
   d. Information is stored as one or more visual images.

•• 45. To learn how to spell "rhinoceros," Paula repeats the letters of the word over and over again without really thinking about what she is saying. Considering research findings about the effectiveness of rehearsal, we can predict that Paula's strategy will be:
   a. highly effective
   b. effective only if she says the letters in a very loud voice
   c. effective only if she says the letters slowly (e.g., at a rate of one letter per second)
   d. relatively ineffective

•• 46. Four students are storing this fact: "St. Augustine, Florida was settled in 1565." Based on the following information, which student is probably going to have the <u>most difficult</u> time retrieving the information from long-term memory a few days later?

a. Alexander repeats the fact to himself ten times in a row.
b. Blondie once visited the fortress there and recalls that it was several hundred years old.
c. Cookie realizes that 1565 was more than four hundred years ago.
d. Dagwood is amazed to learn that the Spanish settled in Saint Augustine, Florida, before the Pilgrims landed at Plymouth.

•• 47. In which of these situations is information most likely to be stored effectively in long-term memory?

a. Abby looks up the correct spelling of "independence" and immediately writes it down.
b. Bob repeats "Comment allez vous?" after his teacher five times in a row.
c. Corinne realizes that <u>receive</u> follows the "I before E except after C" rule.
d. David stares at a page in his textbook trying to form a photographic image of the page in his mind.

•• 48. Travis realizes that the year World War II ended—1945—is the same year that his father was born. Which one of the following processes is Travis most clearly demonstrating?

a. A mnemonic
b. Rehearsal
c. Meaningful learning
d. Imagery

• 49. According to the textbook, students often engage in rote learning rather than meaningful learning of school subject matter because:

a. It is human nature to do so unless taught otherwise.
b. Rote learning is characteristic of preoperational and concrete operational thought.
c. Information learned at a rote level is stored in working memory more quickly.
d. Classroom teaching and testing practices often encourage it.

• 50. Three of the following conditions are necessary for meaningful learning to occur. Which one of the following is <u>not</u> an essential condition for meaningful learning?

a. Being emotionally involved with the information being studied
b. Intending to learn information in a meaningful fashion
c. Knowing something about the topic already
d. Being aware that prior knowledge is related to the topic being studied

•• 51. Which one of the following students definitely has a <u>meaningful learning set</u>?

a. Annie practices calculating the area of a triangle by completing her 20 homework problems.
b. Benny memorizes the fact that 0.5 is equivalent to 1/2.
c. Connie knows that she will eventually learn the multiplication tables if she practices them enough times.
d. Danny is trying to figure out the logic behind the process of long division.

•• 52. Students in a fifth grade classroom are studying dinosaurs. With the three conditions for meaningful learning in mind, choose the student who is most likely to engage in meaningful learning.

a. When the teacher introduces the topic, Arthur vaguely remembers reading a book about dinosaurs several years ago, although he can't seem to recall much about it.
b. When the teacher describes the tremendous size of some of the dinosaurs, Becky remembers a huge brontosaurus skeleton she saw at a museum.
c. When the teacher writes the word "protoceratops" on the board, Connor writes it down, being sure to copy the word accurately.
d. When the teacher introduces the terms "meat-eaters" and "plant-eaters," Donna repeats both terms to herself several times.

•• 53. Three of these teachers will probably promote meaningful learning in their students. Which one is unlikely to do so?

a. Mr. Pulos shows how the area of a triangle (area = $^1/2$ base x height) is half of something they already know—the area of a rectangle.
b. Ms. Rubenstein asks her students to define peninsula in their own words.
c. Mr. Warner encourages his third graders to practice their cursive letters at least once every day.
d. Ms. Elms points out that the German word krank (meaning "sick") might be related to the English word cranky.

• 54. When you are studying for a test, you may often try to find interrelationships among the new pieces of information you are learning. Cognitive psychologists call this process:

a. Facilitative interference
b. Organization
c. Reconstruction in retrieval
d. Automaticity

•• 55. To help herself learn the early explorers of the New World, Jessica makes a chart that lists the Spanish explorers together, the Portuguese explorers together, the French explorers together, and so on. Which one of the following processes is Jessica most clearly demonstrating?

a. Elaboration
b. Meaningful learning
c. Rehearsal
d. Organization

•• 56. Cordell is trying to remember the various rocks he has been studying in his earth science class (granite, sandstone, limestone, obsidian, marble, etc.). He finally decides it would be easiest if he studied them as three groups: sedimentary, igneous, and metamorphic. Considering research regarding this strategy, Cordell should:

a. Have an easier time remembering them because he's organizing them
b. Have a more difficult time remembering them because he must remember the three groupings as well as the rocks themselves
c. Have an easier time remembering them only if he also looks at pictures of each kind of rock
d. Have a more difficult time remembering them because he's only using rehearsal to learn them

• 57. Which one of the following alternatives best characterizes the process of elaboration of new information?

a. Paying careful attention to the most important aspects of new information
b. Failing to notice significant aspects of new information
c. Constructing meaning by adding something already known to new information
d. Remembering the order in which several pieces of new information are received

•• 58. Tyler learns that Christopher Columbus's first voyage across the Atlantic was financed by Queen Isabella of Spain. He thinks to himself, "She probably thought she would make a profit on her investment." When he stops to consider the queen's motives, Tyler is demonstrating which one of the following processes?

a. Elaboration
b. Meaningful learning
c. Rehearsal
d. Organization

•• 59. Which one of the following teaching practices is most likely to encourage students to elaborate as they study new material?

a. Help them locate Berlin on a map of Europe.
b. Ask them how they might apply the principle that gas expands when heated.
c. Ask them, "Who remembers what the chief exports of Japan are?"
d. Say, "Yesterday we learned the safe way to hand a pair of sharp scissors to someone else. Who can show us how we learned to do that?"

•• 60. As Jane reads about General Custer's last stand, she pictures him as he must have looked, with long blonde hair and a full mustache, riding tall and proud on the open plain just before he was attacked. Considering research findings regarding the effectiveness of visual imagery, we can predict that Jane will:

a. Get confused by the vividness of her visual image
b. Remember the information better than she might otherwise
c. Store the information in her working memory rather than her long-term memory
d. Remember her image perfectly for a year or longer

•• 61. These four teachers claim to be practicing principles from cognitive psychology. Based on the following information, which one is not actually doing so?

a. Ms. Anthony, a high school biology teacher, draws a hierarchy on the board showing how mammals, fish, birds, reptiles, and amphibians are all vertebrates, and how vertebrates and invertebrates are both animals.
b. Mr. Bottenberg, a fourth grade teacher, suggests that his students try to learn their spelling words by thinking about similarly spelled words that they already know.
c. Ms. Conrad, a third grade teacher, introduces her class to the topic of multiplication by showing them how it relates to addition.
d. Mr. Danforth, a junior high school soccer coach, asks his players to practice passing the ball to one another as they run down the field and then openly praises those players who are passing skillfully.

•• 62. Three of the following teachers are using strategies that should help students learn information effectively. Which one is <u>not</u> necessarily promoting effective cognitive processing?

a. Mr. Ayotte helps students identify important ideas in their textbooks.
b. Ms. Bertinelli has students repeat definitions of new vocabulary words out loud.
c. Mr. Canton makes sure that students are paying attention before he begins class.
d. Ms. Darwin talks about how famous battles in history are in some ways similar to the fights students sometimes have on the playground.

•• 63. Three of the following mathematics teachers are using techniques that should help their students remember information. Which one is using a relatively <u>in</u>effective technique?

a. Mr. Allen uses wooden blocks to help students understand how the volume of a cube is calculated.
b. Ms. Batchelder asks students to think of real-life problems requiring the use of multiplication.
c. Mr. Constanza shows his students how division is simply the reverse of multiplication.
d. Ms. Davenport asks her students to memorize definitions of eight geometric figures.

• 64. Which one of the following statements best describes how learners often acquire <u>procedural knowledge</u>?

a. Learners first learn it as declarative knowledge; with time and practice, it gradually becomes procedural knowledge.
b. Learners first learn it initially as one or more auditory images; eventually, they recode it into visual images.
c. Learners initially acquire it in an automatic, "unthinking" form; eventually, it evolves into knowledge that they can talk about and describe.
d. Learners are able to bypass working memory; the knowledge goes immediately from the sensory register into long-term memory.

•• 65. Mr. Gaydos wants to teach his students how to perform the Heimlich maneuver. Three of the following strategies should help his students learn the maneuver more effectively. Given what we know about teaching procedural knowledge, which strategy is <u>least</u> likely to be effective in helping students learn the procedure correctly?

a. Mr. Gaydos can give his students an opportunity to practice the maneuver on a realistic human dummy.
b. Mr. Gaydos can show his students pictures of the various steps involved in the maneuver.
c. Mr. Gaydos can describe Dr. Heimlich's medical background and his motivation for developing the procedure.
d. Mr. Gaydos can encourage his students to talk themselves through the procedure as they perform it.

• 66. In general, students with more prior knowledge about a topic learn new information about that topic more easily. Three of the following statements provide reasons why this is so. Which one of the following is <u>not</u> a reason?
   a. Prior knowledge facilitates meaningful learning.
   b. Prior knowledge facilitates elaboration.
   c. Prior knowledge gives students a better idea of what they should pay attention to.
   d. Prior knowledge enhances students' ability to use rehearsal effectively.

•• 67. Three of the following are examples of <u>mnemonics</u>. Which one is <u>not</u> a mnemonic?
   a. To learn how to drive a car with a standard transmission, Bart practices the various parts of the task (e.g., steering, shifting, and braking) separately.
   b. To learn the letters identifying the spaces on the treble clef (F A C E), Annabelle simply remembers the word "face."
   c. To learn that the Spanish word <u>pájaro</u> means "bird," Corey pictures a bird wearing pajamas.
   d. To learn that the Spanish word <u>navidad</u> means "Christmas," Dorene thinks of the word "nativity."

•• 68. Norman is studying Chinese and needs to remember that the word for "exit" is <u>chu</u>, so he remembers the sentence, "The choo-choo train is exiting the station." Norman's technique illustrates the use of:
   a. reconstructive retrieval
   b. the keyword method
   c. a superimposed meaningful structure
   d. verbal mediation

•• 69. To remember the four states that come together at a single point (Colorado, Arizona, New Mexico, and Utah), Marcia remembers "CANU" (pronounced like "canoe"). Marcia's technique illustrates the use of:
   a. the keyword method
   b. a superimposed meaningful structure
   c. visual imagery
   d. verbal mediation

•• 70. To remember that the capital of the state of Washington is Olympia, Bart pictures George Washington running a race in the Olympics. Bart's technique illustrates:
   a. the keyword method
   b. verbal mediation
   c. a superimposed meaningful structure
   d. reconstructive retrieval

•• 71. If you wanted to help your students learn something by using a <u>mnemonic</u> device, which one of the following sentences would you use?
   a. "Area equals length times width" is the formula for calculating the area of a rectangle.
   b. "Do unto others as you would have them do unto you" is the Golden Rule.
   c. "My very earthy mother just sat upon new petunias" tells us the nine planets in the solar system.
   d. "Washington, Adams, Jefferson, Madison, Monroe, and Adams" are the first six presidents of the United States.

•• 72. Mnemonics probably facilitate learning and memory in a number of ways. Which one of the following is not a potential advantage of mnemonics?
   a. They relate new information to what a person already knows.
   b. They expand the capacity of working memory.
   c. They help organize information.
   d. They provide retrieval cues to aid recall.

• 73. Successful retrieval of information from long-term memory depends on three of the following factors. On which one does retrieval not depend?
   a. The part of long-term memory being searched
   b. How the information was stored in the first place
   c. The duration of working memory
   d. The presence of relevant retrieval cues

• 74. Three of the following strategies should help students remember academic material over the long run. Considering guidelines presented in the textbook, which one will not help them?
   a. Reviewing the material periodically over the course of several days or weeks.
   b. Engaging in meaningful learning by relating the material to a situation in which they are likely to use it.
   c. Preventing interference by learning each piece of information at a different time.
   d. Elaborating by drawing inferences from the things they study.

•• 75. Ms. Iwata has a long-term goal for her science students—to consider what they have learned about science as they deal with issues and problems in their daily lives. What teaching strategy will best help her students retrieve relevant scientific principles when they need them the most?
   a. Make sure that students study those principles in a no-anxiety situation.
   b. Associate those principles with as many real-life situations as possible.
   c. Maximize the use of concrete materials, and minimize the use of abstract ideas.
   d. Maximize the use of abstract ideas, and minimize the use of concrete materials.

•• 76. Sarah needs to know her division facts for a quiz tomorrow. She wants to do as well as she possibly can on the quiz. Based on findings regarding automaticity, which one of the following would be the best advice to give Sarah?
   a. "Repeat each fact at least five times silently."
   b. "Repeat each fact at least five times out loud."
   c. "Study the facts until you know each one and then do something entirely different until morning."
   d. "Study the facts until you know them all perfectly, and then continue to practice them even after that."

•• 77. Mr. Martinez wants his first grade students to be able to identify 200 reading words at the level of automaticity. Which one of the following techniques will best help his students achieve that goal?
   a. Tell them how important it is for them to know the words.
   b. Explain how the letters of the words are related to their pronunciation.
   c. Explain how some of the letters in the words are "silent letters."
   d. Give them lots of practice reading the words.

• 78. An advantage of knowing some skills to a level of automaticity is that skills learned to automaticity:
   a. require less working memory capacity
   b. promote the development of retrieval cues
   c. make meaningful learning of those skills unnecessary
   d. enhance the reconstructive nature of retrieval

•• 79. A language arts teacher teaches her students the parts of speech—noun, verb, adjective, and so on—and wants her students to continue to remember them as they study English and foreign languages in the years to come. Considering the factors affecting retrieval of information from long-term memory, which one of the following strategies should maximize the likelihood that students will remember the different parts of speech over the long run?
   a. Have students study them early in the fall and periodically review them in various contexts throughout the school year.
   b. Have students study them intensely for a month, then stay away from any discussion of them for the rest of the school year.
   c. Have students study each part of speech separately, perhaps a different one each month.
   d. Have students memorize definitions of each part of speech until they can recite the definitions word for word.

•• 80. Lucy sees a boy who looks very familiar to her, but she can't remember who he is. Then the boy says something with a thick French accent, and Lucy suddenly realizes that he is the foreign exchange student from France. In this situation, the boy's French accent helps Lucy remember by:
   a. inhibiting interference
   b. helping her elaborate on stored information
   c. facilitating a reorganization of her long-term memory
   d. providing a retrieval cue

•• 81. To remind her first-grade son Kevin to bring home his umbrella from school, his mother pins a piece of paper with a picture of an umbrella to Kevin's jacket collar. Kevin's mother is helping him remember the umbrella through the use of:
   a. a superimposed meaningful structure
   b. a retrieval cue
   c. the keyword method
   d. verbal mediation

• 82. From the perspective of cognitive psychology, recognition memory tasks are easier than recall tasks because recognition tasks:
   a. Can be answered by using less working memory capacity
   b. Don't need to be learned in a meaningful fashion
   c. Provide more retrieval cues
   d. Can usually be answered by using skills that have been learned to automaticity

•• 83. Given what we know about the effects of retrieval cues on retrieval, in which one of the following situations are students most likely to remember how the word people is spelled?

a. Have students use the word people in a meaningful sentence.
b. Give students four choices to pick from: peepal, peapul, pepull, and people.
c. Have students close their eyes and try recall what the word people looks like when they read.
d. Have students concentrate very hard on how the word sounds as it is pronounced.

• 84. Which one of the following statements is consistent with the textbook's recommendations for promoting retrieval?

a. Teach students how to create and use their own retrieval cues.
b. Show students how to use the keyword method to help them remember lists of ten items or more.
c. Spend approximately two-thirds of each class day reviewing things that students already know.
d. At the secondary school level, always use essay tests rather than multiple choice tests.

• 85. Three of the following are commonly accepted explanations of forgetting. Which one is not?

a. Information slowly fades away over time if it isn't used.
b. Information is still in memory but cannot be found when it is needed.
c. Gaps in recalled information are filled in incorrectly.
d. Strong memories overpower unrelated, but weaker, ones.

•• 86. Nora was thinking about something else the day her teacher explained the difference between the words between and among, so she has trouble using these two prepositions correctly. Nora's difficulty "remembering" the difference between the two words can probably best be explained as:

a. failure to store in long-term memory
b. failure to retrieve from long-term memory
c. decay in long-term memory over time
d. reconstruction error during retrieval

•• 87. Jenny is taking a quiz that asks for the chemical symbols of 20 elements. She remembers 19 of them but cannot remember the symbol for mercury. As she walks home from school, she suddenly remembers that the symbol for mercury is Hg. Jenny's memory problem during the quiz can best be explained in terms of:

a. interference
b. reconstruction error
c. decay
d. failure to retrieve

•• 88. Richard is studying both French and Spanish. In the same week, he learns that the French word for "mother" is mère and that the Spanish word for "mother" is madre. One day his French teacher asks Richard, "Who is married to your father?" and Richard erroneously answers, "Madre." Richard's memory error can best be explained in terms of:

   a. decay
   b. interference
   c. reconstruction error
   d. failure to store

• 89. Which one of the following statements best describes wait time and its effects?

   a. When teachers give students about five minutes of "thinking time" at the beginning of class, students are more likely to learn class information meaningfully.
   b. When teachers allow students more time to learn something, students are more likely to learn effectively.
   c. When teachers wait until students are ready to pay attention, students are more likely to learn effectively.
   d. When teachers allow students more time to respond to a question, students are more likely to answer the question.

• 90. When we increase the wait time after teacher questions from one second to three seconds, we can expect students' answers to those questions to:

   a. be more dependent on retrieval cues present in the immediate situation
   b. be longer and more complex
   c. reflect more automaticity in responding
   d. reflect a decline in interest for the subject matter

• 91. When teachers increase their wait time from one second to three seconds, other teacher behaviors are likely to change as well. Which one of the following is not a typical outcome of increasing wait time?

   a. Teachers' expectations for student performance increase.
   b. Teachers ask more complex questions.
   c. Teachers often lose the momentum of classroom activities.
   d. Teachers pursue some topics in greater depth.

• 92. Three of the following statements are accurate about students with special needs. Which one is not accurate?

   a. Students with general delays in cognitive and social functioning (e.g., those with mental retardation) may have less working memory capacity than their classmates.
   b. Students with advanced cognitive development don't need to process information as thoroughly as other students.
   c. Students with physical disabilities may have less prior knowledge to which they can relate classroom subject matter.
   d. Students with social or behavioral problems may have difficulty paying attention.

**Essay Questions**

• 93. Many cognitive psychologists believe that human memory has three components. Describe each of these components, including both its capacity and its duration. Explain how students must process information so that it arrives at the third and final component.

• 94. Describe what psychologists mean when they say that attention and working memory have a limited capacity. Discuss an implication of this limited capacity for student learning.

• 95. Students' <u>prior knowledge</u> about a topic often influences their ability to learn something new about that topic. Explain how students' prior knowledge is involved in each of the following long-term memory storage processes:

a. Meaningful learning
b. Organization
c. Elaboration
d. Visual imagery

•• 96. Choose a topic on which you might give a short explanation or lecture (perhaps ten minutes in length) to your students. With effective memory storage processes in mind, describe three different strategies you might use to help students store the information in their long-term memories easily and effectively. Using information processing theory, give a theoretical rationale for each of the strategies you propose.

•• 97. The German word for "rabbit" is <u>Kaninchen</u>. Develop two different mnemonics for remembering this vocabulary word, one using each of these two techniques:

a. Verbal mediation
b. Keyword method

•• 98. George does not know the days of the week. You want him to be able to recite all seven days in order, beginning with Sunday. Devise a <u>superimposed meaningful structure</u> you might use to help George remember them.

# ANSWER KEY

## Multiple-Choice Questions

1. b
2. a
3. c
4. a
5. d
6. d
7. b
8. c
9. b
10. a
11. a
12. d
13. c
14. b
15. c
16. d
17. a
18. a
19. b
20. d
21. a
22. b
23. c
24. a
25. d
26. b
27. b
28. d
29. a
30. c
31. b
32. b
33. c
34. b
35. b
36. b
37. c
38. a
39. b
40. d
41. a
42. c
43. c
44. d
45. d
46. a
47. c
48. c
49. d
50. a
51. d
52. b
53. c
54. b
55. d
56. a
57. c
58. a
59. b
60. b
61. d
62. b
63. d
64. a
65. c
66. d
67. a
68. d
69. b
70. a
71. c
72. b
73. c
74. c
75. b
76. d
77. d
78. a
79. a
80. d
81. b
82. c
83. b
84. a
85. d
86. a
87. d
88. b
89. d
90. b
91. c
92. b

## Essay Questions

93. The sensory register holds virtually all the information we sense (hence has a very large capacity) in a relatively unencoded form for a second or two (actually, less than a second for visual input and about 2-3 seconds for auditory input). Working memory is the component that actively processes information. It holds a small amount of information (hence has a limited capacity) for perhaps 5-20 seconds, although information can be kept there longer through the use of maintenance rehearsal. Long-term memory has a seemingly unlimited capacity and an indefinitely long duration (it may remain there quite a while, although not necessarily forever). People move information from sensory register to working memory by paying attention to it. They most effectively move it from working memory to long-term memory by connecting it to the things already stored in LTM.

94. People can only attend to and process a small amount of information, and thus can only deal with one complex task, at any one time. This limited processing capacity has several possible implications (the response needs to mention only one of these):
    - Keep students' attention focused on the task at hand.
    - Capture students' attention by making subject matter interesting, exciting, puzzling, etc.
    - Minimize distractions that take students' attention away from their schoolwork.
    - Pace instruction so that students receive only so much new information at once—so that their working memory capacity's are not exceeded.
    - Don't ask students to solve complex problems entirely in their heads.
    - Promote automaticity of basic skills that students will use in more complex activities.

95. Responses to various parts of the question are as follows:
    a. Meaningful learning is a process of relating new information to things already known.
    b. Students can only organize material when they have general organizational schemes that they can impose on the material.
    c. Elaboration involves expanding on new information (e.g., drawing inferences from it) based on information that is already stored in long-term memory.
    d. Visual imagery requires knowledge of how things typically appear.

96. Effective strategies include these:
    - Capturing and/or maintaining attention
    - Accommodating the limited capacity of working memory
    - Promoting meaningful learning
    - Facilitating organization
    - Encouraging students to elaborate
    - Facilitating visual imagery

    The response should describe three concrete strategies that reflect one or more of the above. It should also relate each strategy to the specific process(es) it promotes.

97. Responses to the two parts of the question are as follows:
    a. Verbal mediation involves connecting two things via a phrase or sentence. One possibility is "The rabbit has a can on its chin."
    b. The keyword method involves identifying one or more key words that sound similar to, or otherwise represent, the things to be remembered, and then forming a visual image. One possibility is forming a visual image of a rabbit that has a can on its chin.

98. In this case, an appropriate superimposed meaningful structure would be a word, acronym, sentence, story, or poem that represents the seven days in their correct order. An example is Susie Mae Thompson watched three fancy satellites.

## Chapter 7

# KNOWLEDGE CONSTRUCTION

| CHAPTER OUTLINE | RELEVANT TEST BANK ITEMS |
|---|---|
| CONSTRUCTIVE PROCESSES IN LEARNING AND MEMORY<br>Construction in Storage<br>Construction in Retrieval | Multiple-Choice 1–8<br>Essay 69 |
| KNOWLEDGE CONSTRUCTION AS A SOCIAL PROCESS<br>Benefits of Group Meaning-Making in the Classroom | Multiple-Choice 9–15<br>Essay 70 |
| ORGANIZING KNOWLEDGE<br>Concepts<br>Schemas and Scripts<br>Personal Theories | Multiple-Choice 16–45<br>Essay 71–72 |
| WHEN KNOWLEDGE CONSTRUCTION GOES AWRY: ORIGINS AND EFFECTS OF MISCONCEPTIONS | Multiple-Choice 46–48 |
| PROMOTING EFFECTIVE KNOWLEDGE CONSTRUCTION<br>Providing Opportunities for Experimentation<br>Presenting the Ideas of Others<br>Emphasizing Conceptual Understanding<br>Using Authentic Activities<br>Promoting Dialogue<br>Creating a Community of Learners | Multiple-Choice 49–60 |
| PROMOTING CONCEPTUAL CHANGE | Multiple-Choice 61–66<br>Essay 73 |
| CONSIDERING DIVERSITY IN CONSTRUCTIVE PROCESSES<br>Accommodating Students with Special Needs | Multiple-Choice 67–68 |
| The items in the "Integrative Questions" chapter of this Test Bank integrate the content of two or more textbook chapters. Within that chapter, the items listed to the right are relevant to Chapter 7. | Essay 25, 39 |

## Multiple-Choice Questions

•• 1. Many cognitive psychologists believe that learning and understanding are often constructive in nature. Three of the following scenarios illustrate such construction. Which scenario does not necessarily involve construction in learning?

a. Although no one has ever told her so, Peggy thinks that the night sky is a big black blanket covering the earth and that the blanket has tiny holes through which the stars shine.

b. Mr. McFarland asks his third graders to practice their multiplication tables every day. After a month of such practice, Misty can retrieve all the basic multiplication facts quickly and easily.

c. When George reads about the Vietnam War in his history book, he comes to the conclusion that the United States should never have gotten involved in Southeast Asia.

d. Because the word photosynthesis begins with photo, Jeremy guesses that it must have something to do with making pictures in photography.

• 2. Three of the following statements reflect cognitive psychologists' beliefs about the process of knowledge construction. Which statement is not consistent with their beliefs?

a. The internal "realities" that people construct are not always consistent with the "reality" of the external world.

b. Different people will often construct different meanings from the same situation.

c. The meanings that people construct from a situation depend on the knowledge that they bring to bear on that situation.

d. People can construct meaning from a situation even when they have no prior knowledge that they can relate to the situation.

•• 3. Mr. Janus tells his class, "For tomorrow's class, read pages 23 to 49 in your geography book." Three of the following students are demonstrating the process of construction in their perceptions of what their teacher has said. Which student is not?

a. Anthony doesn't hear what the teacher says because he's thinking about something else.

b. Bonita thinks the teacher is saying "history book."

c. Christopher "hears" the teacher say "pages 33 to 39" because the student next to him is coughing loudly.

d. Dena understands the teacher even though the teacher speaks with a slight accent and mispronounces "geography."

•• 4. Maria moved to this country several months ago. She has been studying English as a second language but still has much to learn about the language of her new homeland. One day her teacher tells the class, "Bring an empty coffee can to school tomorrow for a project we're going to do." Maria hears only two familiar words—"coffee" and "school"—and guesses that her teacher is saying that students should not drink coffee at school. Maria's misinterpretation illustrates which of the following?

a. Conceptual change

b. Use of a script

c. Construction in retrieval

d. Construction in storage

•• 5. Michael has just written a short research paper that describes the events surrounding the first transatlantic telegraph cable. As he rereads his paper before turning it in to his teacher, he doesn't notice that he's misspelled Atlantic as "Altantic" on one occasion, even though he knows perfectly well how the word should be spelled. Michael's proofreading error can best be explained by considering the role of _____ in the construction of meaning.
   a. a script
   b. ambiguity
   c. expectations
   d. assessment

• 6. When people are trying to understand and interpret a new event, their interpretation is most likely to be influenced by their own expectations about what "should" be happening if the event is:
   a. presented in a predominantly visual manner, rather than verbally
   b. concrete
   c. abstract
   d. ambiguous

•• 7. Morris is trying to remember how to spell the word broccoli. He retrieves the first three letters (B R O) and the last three (O L I), then assumes that the "kuh" sound in the middle of the word must be a K. He writes "brokoli" on his paper. Morris' process of remembering how to spell the word (in this case, incorrectly) illustrates the use of:
   a. a script
   b. a retrieval cue
   c. construction in retrieval
   d. verbal mediation

•• 8. Which one of the following scenarios best reflects the basic idea of individual constructivism?
   a. A student practices playing the F major scale on his violin until he can play it perfectly.
   b. Four students in a study group divide the day's reading assignment into four sections. Each student reads a section and then teaches the material to the other group members.
   c. A student tries to make sense of a poorly written and confusing magazine article.
   d. Two students discuss possible interpretations of the proverb, "We only know the worth of water when the well is dry."

•• 9. Which one of the following scenarios best reflects the basic idea of social constructivism?
   a. Two students discuss possible interpretations of the proverb, "We only know the worth of water when the well is dry."
   b. A teacher assigns a laboratory activity using cumbersome equipment that students can only use successfully by working in pairs.
   c. When a student borrows a classmate's marker without asking and then leaves the cap off overnight, making it dried out and useless by the following morning, her teacher reminds her of one of the class rules—to respect other people's property.
   d. Four students in a study group divide the day's reading assignment into four sections. Each student reads a section and then teaches the material to the other group members.

• 10. Over the course of history, science has continued to evolve as new data emerge and scientists present new ideas to explain those data. This continuing process of change in scientific thinking over the years best reflects the idea of _______.
   a. individual constructivism
   b. social constructivism
   c. conceptual change
   d. cognitive apprenticeship

• 11. Three of the following are benefits of classroom discussions. Which one is not a typical benefit of discussing information in class?
   a. Class discussions may promote more thorough understanding of a topic.
   b. Class discussions encourage students to organize their thoughts about a topic.
   c. Discussions about controversial topics encourage students to reevaluate their views.
   d. Class discussions promote more rapid learning of classroom subject matter.

• 12. From the perspective of knowledge construction, three of the following are possible reasons why classroom dialogues help students better understand classroom subject matter. Which one is not necessarily a benefit of classroom dialogues?
   a. Students are exposed to the views of other people—views that may be more accurate than their own.
   b. Students must clarify their ideas sufficiently to explain them to their classmates.
   c. Students may discover flaws in their own ideas and thoughts about a topic.
   d. Students are more likely to form visual images related to their ideas when they describe those ideas to others.

• 13. Distributed cognition can best be described as:
   a. A student choosing one problem solving strategy over other possible strategies
   b. A student trying to accomplish several different tasks simultaneously
   c. A group of students dividing up the various parts of a task that need to be done
   d. A group of students thinking about a task or problem together

• 14. Which one of the following best reflects the idea of distributed cognition?
   a. "A stitch in time saves nine."
   b. "Two heads are better than one."
   c. "Look before you leap."
   d. "Do unto others as you would have them do unto you."

•• 15. Which one of the following examples best illustrates the concept of distributed cognition?
   a. Edie, Linda, and DeWayne discuss various ways they might solve a physics problem.
   b. Mark, Jason, and Leanne each solve one-third of their homework problems and then share their results with the other two.
   c. Rhonda watches her favorite situation comedy while simultaneously eating an apple and doing her homework.
   d. Reginald thinks about the various plots he might use in the short story he is writing and then eventually chooses one of them.

• 16. Which one of the following statements best describes a concept?
   a. A definition that is learned verbatim.
   b. A vague, intuitive idea about an area of knowledge.
   c. A category of similar objects or events.
   d. A concrete example of an abstract idea.

•• 17. Which one of these is an example of undergeneralization? The concept in question is underlined.
   a. Fred thinks that spiders are insects.
   b. Ivan thinks that birds are not animals.
   c. Lenny thinks that "you" is a noun.
   d. Oscar thinks that "you" is not a noun.

•• 18. Which one of the following situations illustrates the phenomenon of overgeneralization in concept learning? In each case, the concept in question is underlined.
   a. Alvin calls a tall sunflower a tree.
   b. Brady doesn't understand why he can't build an igloo in the summer.
   c. Calvin thinks that all igloos are made out of Styrofoam.
   d. Daniel denies that a palm tree is a tree.

•• 19. Which one of these is an example of overgeneralization?
   a. Russ takes his teddy bear out for a walk because he has heard that pets need exercise.
   b. Uri times himself when he swims laps because he wants to improve his speed.
   c. Yolanda thinks she should not go to medical school because she wants to have children and, "You can't be a mom and a doctor, too."
   d. Bernita wants to take four science classes her first semester in college because she intends to major in science.

•• 20. Florida is a ________ of the concept peninsula.
   a. correlational feature
   b. defining feature
   c. positive instance
   d. negative instance

•• 21. A triangle is a _______ of the concept square.
  a. correlational feature
  b. defining feature
  c. positive instance
  d. negative instance

• 22. The surest sign that your students have mastered a concept is that they can:
  a. List all of its correlational features.
  b. List all of its defining features.
  c. Accurately identify at least one positive and one negative instance of the concept.
  d. Consistently distinguish between positive and negative instances of the concept.

• 23. Which one of the following is a defining feature of the concept island?
  a. Inaccessible by automobile
  b. Completely surrounded by water
  c. At least 100 feet wide in any direction
  d. Having a name (e.g., "Bear Island")

•• 24. Which one of the following is the best example of a correlational feature? In each case, the feature in question is underlined.
  a. Most teachers are patient.
  b. Some circles are red.
  c. All circles are round.
  d. Some animals are smaller than others.

•• 25. For the concept nurse, "female" can best be classified as:
  a. a defining feature.
  b. a correlational feature.
  c. an irrelevant feature.
  d. a rule.

•• 26. "A man is a teacher. He knows how to teach children to read and write. He can make children feel better when they are sad. However, he goes into debt and owes a great deal of money, so he robs a bank and is a thief. Is he still a teacher? Does he still know how to teach children to read and write?" A student who answers "no" to these questions is confusing:
  a. Assimilation and accommodation
  b. The abstract and the concrete
  c. Schemas and scripts
  d. Defining and correlational features

•• 27. Salience of features affects the ease with which students are likely to learn a concept. Which one of the following best illustrates a salient defining feature?
  a. "Photosynthesis" is a feature of the concept plant.
  b. "Round" is a feature of the concept circle.
  c. "Unequal sides" is a feature of the concept rectangle.
  d. A "backbone" is a feature of the concept vertebrate.

- 28. When learning a new concept, students are <u>most</u> likely to be confused when:
    a. There are too many negative instances.
    b. There are very few positive instances.
    c. Correlational features are more salient than defining features.
    d. Defining features are more salient than correlational features.

- 29. Which one of the following conditions may make a concept especially difficult to learn?
    a. An abundance of positive instances
    b. An abundance of negative instances
    c. An abundance of defining features
    d. Abstractness of defining features

•• 30. Ms. McNamara is teaching her students the concept of <u>reptile</u>. Which one of the following should Ms. McNamara <u>not</u> do?
    a. Tell her students the defining features of a reptile.
    b. Encourage her students to undergeneralize at first.
    c. Show her students examples of reptiles.
    d. Show her students things that are <u>not</u> reptiles.

- 31. If you were teaching your students a new concept, which strategy would be <u>most</u> effective?
    a. Presenting only positive instances, so students don't get confused.
    b. Presenting only negative instances, so students aren't overwhelmed.
    c. Describing the concept's correlational features.
    d. Presenting a definition that identifies defining features.

•• 32. After seeing many different examples of a <u>cow</u>, Joy begins to form an idea of what a "typical" cow looks like. This process best illustrates which one of the following views of concept learning?
    a. Metacognitive
    b. Prototype
    c. Sequential
    d. Feature lists

- 33. Which one of the following statements best describes a <u>prototype</u> of a concept?
    a. An example that typifies many positive instances
    b. A definition that emphasizes concrete defining features
    c. A definition that emphasizes abstract defining features
    d. A list of both defining and correlational features

•• 34. Ramon forms his concept of house after seeing numerous houses in his small, middle-class town in Illinois. He is then shown pictures of an igloo in northern Canada, a mansion in Illinois, a middle-class house in Mississippi, and a high-rise apartment building in New York City. Based on a prototype theory of concepts, which one is he most likely to identify as being a house?

a. The igloo.
b. The mansion.
c. The suburban house.
d. The high-rise apartment building.

•• 35. A teacher who wants to teach students the concept bird would be wise to show which one of the following as a prototype?

a. A sparrow
b. An ostrich
c. A penguin
d. A pelican

•• 36. When Mary thinks about what a dog is, several very different-looking animals come to mind, including greyhounds, German shepherds, cocker spaniels, and Chihuahuas. Which one of the following views of concept learning best characterizes Mary's knowledge of the concept dog?

a. Mental theory
b. Prototype
c. Exemplars
d. Feature list

•• 37. Three of the following teachers are following recommended practices for teaching concepts. Which one is not?

a. Mr. Adams teaches the concept fruit by showing examples of many different fruits and many different nonfruits.
b. Mr. Benito teaches the concept reptile by limiting class discussion to dinosaurs—animals that students find especially interesting.
c. Mr. Carlson teaches the concept vertebrate by giving a definition of the concept.
d. After a lesson on the concept carbohydrate, Mr. Danielson asks students to give their own examples of the concept.

• 38. Which one of the following statements best reflects how a concept learning theorist might explain the progression from single classification to multiple classification as Piaget defined these terms?

a. Children develop increasingly elaborate scripts to explain everyday events.
b. Children develop increasing knowledge about how particular concepts are interrelated.
c. Children's knowledge becomes less dependent on constructive processes over time.
d. Children's exemplars for a particular concept eventually become consolidated into a single prototype.

• 39. From the perspective of cognitive psychology, a <u>schema</u> can best be described as:
   a. An organized body of information about a particular topic
   b. A plan of action regarding how to learn something
   c. A set of reasons why a student would want to learn something
   d. A basic piece of information upon which most other knowledge must build

•• 40. Wendy sees a picture of a beach and then later tries to draw the picture from memory. She draws shells on the beach even though the beach in the picture had no shells. Using cognitive psychologists' concept of <u>schema</u>, how could we explain Wendy's error?
   a. Wendy has a schema for shells but does not have one for beaches.
   b. Wendy has a schema for beaches but does not have one for shells.
   c. Wendy's schema of how a typical beach looks includes shells.
   d. Wendy's schemas of beaches and shells are interfering with each other.

• 41. In cognitive psychology, a <u>script</u> can best be described as:
   a. A particular way of talking oneself through a difficult situation
   b. Knowledge about the typical sequence of events in an activity
   c. The things (e.g., "small talk") that someone typically says when initiating a conversation with someone else
   d. The strategy that a teacher suggests a student use to remember classroom material

•• 42. Four boys read this line from a story: "The two men entered the restaurant and ordered hamburgers." Which one of the boys is clearly using a <u>script</u> while reading the story?
   a. Alex assumes that the men probably looked at a menu before ordering.
   b. Bob is guessing that the men probably have evil motives.
   c. Colin wonders what the men look like.
   d. Devon thinks that the men should be more careful about their cholesterol intake.

• 43. The textbook describes a study by Bartlett in which college students in England read a Native American ghost story entitled "The War of the Ghosts." From Bartlett's results, we can conclude that students who read a story written from the perspective of a culture different from their own are likely to:
   a. Reject the story as being ridiculous or far-fetched
   b. Form unwarranted and prejudicial attitudes about people from that other culture
   c. Interpret the story in a way that's more consistent with their own culture
   d. Construct a more multicultural perspective of the world

• 44. Which one of the following statements best describes a <u>personal theories</u> view of knowledge construction?
   a. The ways in which children categorize their experiences usually have little relevance to physical reality.
   b. Children form hypotheses about the defining features and correlational features of a concept and then test those hypotheses against specific examples of the concept that they encounter.
   c. In the early years, children develop concrete understandings of events; these understandings become increasingly more abstract as they reach adolescence.
   d. Children develop general belief systems about how the world operates.

•• 45. Which one of the following examples best illustrates the use of a personal theory as a child learns the concept spider?

a. Julian assumes that spiders must give birth to baby spiders, just as people give birth to baby people.

b. Ian learns that spiders have eight legs, whereas insects have only six.

c. Rudy learns that spiders, along with scorpions and ticks, are members of the arachnid class.

d. Duc remembers what happened when his cousin was bitten by a black widow spider.

• 46. Generally speaking, elaboration helps students learn new information. An exception to this rule is when students elaborate on this information:

a. using misconceptions they have previously acquired

b. after having already organized it as a hierarchy

c. using information they stored many years before

d. very quickly

• 47. Three of the following are common misconceptions that elementary or secondary students are likely to have. Which one is not commonly found?

a. Any moving object has a force acting on it.

b. Most animals can survive for months without food.

c. Rivers run from north to south, but not vice versa.

d. The earth is shaped like a disk.

• 48. Students' misconceptions about the world may come from a variety of sources. Which one of the following is not a likely source that theorists have identified?

a. Students form personal theories based on how the world appears to be.

b. Teachers and textbooks sometimes provide misinformation.

c. Students believe the stories that younger children make up.

d. Common expressions in language (e.g., the sun "sets" in the west) misrepresent reality.

•• 49. Ms. Rushing, a middle school science teacher, wants her students to develop a good understanding of principles related to the concepts of force and velocity. Three of the following strategies should help her students construct such an understanding. Which strategy would educational psychologists be least likely to advocate for promoting effective knowledge construction related to force and velocity?

a. Have students experiment with objects to observe the effects that force has on velocity.

b. Perform classroom demonstrations that illustrate the concepts of force and velocity, and have students discuss alternative interpretations of the phenomena they observe.

c. Have students apply principles of force and velocity to a task in which they must move a heavy object across the room.

d. Make sure that students can recite definitions of both force and velocity, and that they can state basic principles regarding how the two are interrelated.

• 50. Many educational psychologists suggest that, rather than always prescribe the procedures that students should follow in performing certain tasks, teachers should sometimes give students the opportunity to develop such procedures on their own by experimenting with various ways of doing things. From the perspective of cognitive psychology, the advantage of letting students develop their own procedures through experimentation is that students:

a. Develop a better understanding of the subject matter in question
b. Learn how to avoid making costly mistakes
c. Learn correct procedures more quickly than they would if they simply followed their teacher's instructions about what to do
d. Acquire formal operational thinking skills much earlier than they would otherwise

•• 51. From the perspective of promoting knowledge construction, one advantage of having students read classic works of fiction is that:

a. The books serve as a form of "cognitive apprenticeship" between the authors and the students.
b. Students can see how others—in particular, the authors of the books they read—have tried to make sense of the human experience.
c. Students are more likely to undergo conceptual change when they read fiction than when they read nonfiction.
d. Challenging works of literature promote language development, which in turn leads almost immediately to a better understanding of the ideas presented in class.

• 52. Which one of the following statements best describes the notion of <u>conceptual understanding</u>?

a. Students learn all the facts that a teacher or textbook presents related to a topic.
b. Students come to the realization that a particular belief they have is incorrect.
c. Students can describe two opposing perspectives about a controversial issue.
d. Students learn ideas related to a topic in a meaningful and integrated fashion.

• 53. Three of the following teaching strategies are likely to help students acquire a conceptual understanding of classroom subject matter. Which statement, though possibly beneficial for other reasons, is <u>least</u> likely to promote conceptual understanding?

a. Exploring a topic in depth
b. Asking students to teach a topic to a classmate
c. Developing automaticity of basic skills
d. Relating new ideas to students' personal experiences

• 54. Which one of the following teaching strategies best illustrates many educational psychologists' belief that, in some situations, <u>less is more</u>?

a. Provide a general overview of a topic before discussing it in depth.
b. Present general ideas about a topic but minimize the use of supporting details.
c. Teach fewer topics, but teach each one more thoroughly.
d. Teach classroom material in short intervals of time, with lessons typically lasting 30 minutes at the most.

• 55. Three of the following are examples of authentic activities. Which one is least authentic?
  a. Collecting samples of local vegetation in a botany class
  b. Writing an editorial for the local newspaper
  c. Playing shortstop in a baseball game
  d. Taking an essay test in a history class

•• 56. Three of the following are authentic activities related to using a computer. Which one is, in and of itself, not an authentic activity?
  a. Learning how to save files on a hard drive
  b. Writing a letter to a friend using a word processing program
  c. Sending an e-mail message to a government official
  d. Analyzing data collected in a science experiment

•• 57. Ms. Villanueva has her students engage in a variety of activities in her middle school geography class. Three of the activities described below are authentic activities. Which one is not an authentic activity as educational psychologists define the term?
  a. Describing the difference between latitude and longitude clearly and concretely
  b. Constructing a map of the neighborhood around the school
  c. Finding the most direct route to Chicago on a road map
  d. Using library resources to identify a good place to take a vacation

•• 58. The textbook advocates the use of classroom dialogues for promoting knowledge construction. Which one of the following student interactions is most likely to be effective in this regard?
  a. Two students work together on a crossword puzzle that includes the week's new spelling words.
  b. The students in a cooperative learning group discuss different ways of solving a certain math problem.
  c. When a French teacher begins class by saying, "Comment allez vous?" the students reply in unison, "Trés bien."
  d. Two students help each other prepare for a quiz by giving each other practice test questions.

• 59. A community of learners can best be described as:
  a. A classroom in which a cooperative spirit of helping one another learn prevails
  b. A small group of students that chooses a special topic that it wants to pursue independently
  c. A classroom in which most activities are relatively structured discovery learning activities
  d. A classroom in which students learn almost exclusively through individual and group experimentation

• 60. If you wanted to give your students a sense of how adult scholars often interact with one another to gain new understandings of a topic, you would be most likely to:
  a. Have students create a class home page on the Internet
  b. Teach students how to read textbooks effectively
  c. Create a community of learners
  d. Teach students how to give an organized lecture

• 61. Students often hold on stubbornly to their misconceptions about the world. Three of the following are possible explanations as to why this might be so. Which statement is <u>not</u> a likely explanation for the resilience of misconceptions?
   a. All information has a natural tendency to become distorted over time.
   b. Some misconceptions are central elements of students' personal theories about the world.
   c. Students learn school material without relating it to the things they know and believe.
   d. Students elaborate on new information using their current misconceptions.

• 62. Which one of the following best describes the process of <u>conceptual change</u> as cognitive psychologists use the term?
   a. Acquiring a more sophisticated vocabulary with which to describe the events in one's life
   b. Revising one's beliefs after receiving information that contradicts those beliefs
   c. Achieving the instructional objectives that a teacher has established for a lesson or unit
   d. Developing new categories to classify objects and events

•• 63. Which one of the following examples illustrates <u>conceptual change</u>?
   a. As a Boy Scout, Andy has learned how to cook a wide variety of foods over an open fire.
   b. Brad misinterprets the scientific explanation of fire to fit what he believes—that fire is an object with substance and weight.
   c. Charlotte used to think that fire was an actual substance, but now she knows it's a chemical change.
   d. Danielle wasn't aware of how much damage fire could really do until the house next door burned down.

• 64. Three of the following strategies should help promote conceptual change. Which one probably will <u>not</u>?
   a. Pique students' interest in classroom subject matter.
   b. Have students learn definitions of important concepts to a level of automaticity.
   c. Explore a few topics in depth rather than cover many topics quickly.
   d. Identify students' misconceptions about a topic and address them during instruction.

• 65. Which one of the following strategies is <u>most</u> likely to encourage students to correct their existing misconceptions?
   a. Give students as much information about a topic as possible.
   b. Use essay questions rather than multiple choice questions when assessing what students have learned.
   c. Show students how new information contradicts what they presently believe.
   d. Encourage students to take extensive notes on their reading assignments.

•• 66. Each of the teachers below has students with misconceptions about the material they are studying. Three of the teachers are using strategies that should help their students correct these misconceptions. Which teacher is not using an effective strategy for changing misconceptions?

a. Ms. Andersen gives corrective feedback when students make statements that reflect misconceptions.
b. Mr. Bissette presents a situation that students cannot adequately explain using their current beliefs about the topic.
c. Ms. Caro reminds her students that she will be testing them on the material they are studying.
d. Mr. Darren shows students how the true explanation of something is different from, and more plausible than, their existing beliefs.

•• 67. Which one of the following examples best illustrates the idea of promoting multiple constructions of the same situation?

a. A science teacher makes it clear to students that the terms velocity and acceleration mean two different things.
b. A mathematics teacher encourages students to do their calculations first by hand and then, as a double-check, by calculator.
c. A foreign language teacher teaches students how to say, "Where is the train station?" in German.
d. A history teacher describes the Mexican-American War from the perspectives of both the United States and Mexico.

• 68. Three of the following statements are true with regard to students with special needs. Which statement is false?

a. Students with social or behavioral problems often misinterpret social situations and so respond inappropriately to them.
b. Students with advanced cognitive development typically have the same amount of knowledge that their classmates have but are able to retrieve it more quickly.
c. Students with general delays in cognitive and social functioning have a difficult time making sense of a message when the message is ambiguous or incomplete.
d. Students with general delays in cognitive development tend to have a more limited knowledge base than their classmates.

## Essay Questions

• 69. Some learning theorists propose that learning is a process of constructing knowledge. Explain the role that construction plays in each of these, illustrating your discussion of each with a concrete example:

a. Long-term memory storage
b. Long-term memory retrieval

• 70. Explain the difference between individual constructivism and social constructivism. Describe two teaching strategies consistent with each perspective.

•• 71. Identify a particular concept that you might someday teach your students. Then:
   a. Give two positive instances and two negative instances of the concept.
   b. Identify one or more defining features and one or more correlational features of the concept.
   c. With at least three of the factors affecting concept learning in mind, describe three specific strategies you would use to help your students learn the concept.

• 72. Describe what psychologists mean by the terms schema and script, and illustrate each of these concepts with a concrete example. Then explain how schemas and scripts sometimes play a role in knowledge construction.

• 73. Research tells us that students' misconceptions about a topic are often quite resistant to change, yet sometimes misconceptions must change if students are to acquire an accurate understanding of the world around them.
   a. Describe three different reasons that psychologists have offered as to why students' misconceptions are sometimes resistant to change.
   b. Describe at least three teaching strategies that theorists believe should help students change their misconceptions about the world.

## ANSWER KEY

### Multiple-Choice Questions

1. b
2. d
3. a
4. d
5. c
6. d
7. c
8. c
9. a
10. b
11. d
12. d
13. d
14. b
15. a
16. c
17. b
18. a
19. a
20. c
21. d
22. d
23. b
24. a
25. b
26. d
27. b
28. c
29. d
30. b
31. d
32. b
33. a
34. c
35. a
36. c
37. b
38. b
39. a
40. c
41. b
42. a
43. c
44. d
45. a
46. a
47. b
48. c
49. d
50. a
51. b
52. d
53. c
54. c
55. d
56. a
57. a
58. b
59. a
60. c
61. a
62. b
63. c
64. b
65. c
66. c
67. d
68. b

### Essay Questions

69. Responses to various parts of the question are as follows:
    a. Learners may construct a meaningful interpretation from the information they receive, a process that involves combining new information with things already known. A concrete example should clearly reflect pulling both old information and new information together in a constructive manner during storage.
    b. Sometimes only part of the needed information can be retrieved. In this case, general knowledge of how the world typically operates is used to fill in missing pieces. A concrete example should illustrate how retrieved information and general knowledge are pulled together during retrieval.

70. Individual constructivism is a perspective that focuses on constructive learning processes within a single person. Teaching strategies consistent with this approach include the following (what follow are examples rather than an exhaustive list; credit should be given for other appropriate strategies as well):
    - Having students experiment with objects and/or events.
    - Allowing students to develop their own procedures through a process of experimentation and trial-and-error.
    - Encouraging students to learn ideas in a meaningful, interrelated fashion (i.e., to develop conceptual understanding), rather than to learn isolated facts at a rote level.
    - Relating new material to students' prior knowledge and experiences.
    - Giving students the message (e.g., through questions in class and through classroom assessment practices) that conceptual understanding is valued.
    - Asking students to teach what they have learned to others.
    - Assigning authentic activities.

    Social constructivism is a perspective that focuses on how groups of people work together to make sense of their environment. In doing so, people may either work together at one point in time (e.g., as might be the case in a class discussion or cooperative learning group) or build on one another's ideas over a long period of time (e.g., as is the case when scientists build on and revise one another's ideas). Teaching strategies consistent with this approach include these (what follow are examples rather than an exhaustive list; credit should be given for other appropriate strategies as well):
    - Conducting class discussions.
    - Assigning cooperative learning activities.
    - Having students study the ideas of others.
    - Having students read classic literature that portrays rich interpretations of the human experience.
    - Sharing the cognitive processes involved in performing complex tasks (e.g., through a cognitive apprenticeship).
    - Creating a community of learners.

72. A schema is an organized body of knowledge about a specific topic. A script is a schema that involves a predictable sequence of events related to some activity. (The student should describe a concrete example of each of these.) Schemas and scripts promote knowledge construction by enabling learners to "fill in" missing information in a manner consistent with how objects typically are and/or events typically transpire.

73. Responses to the two parts of the question are as follows:
    a. The response should include at least three of the following ideas:
    - Learners may distort new information (via meaningful learning and/or elaboration) to be consistent with misconceptions they already hold.
    - Students tend to look for information that confirms their existing beliefs and to ignore information that contradicts their beliefs.
    - Students' existing beliefs are often more consistent with their everyday experiences; scientific explanations may be fairly abstract and difficult to relate to everyday reality.
    - Some beliefs may be integrated into cohesive personal theories; therefore, change may require changing an entire organized body of knowledge rather than a single belief.
    - Students may learn contradictory information in a rote manner and so don't relate it to their existing misconceptions.
    - Students may not retrieve an existing misconception when learning new information; therefore, the new information and the misconception co-exist in long-term memory.

    b. Strategies for promoting conceptual change include the following (the response should include at least three of these):
    - Identifying misconceptions before instruction begins so that instruction can deal specifically with them
    - Challenging students' existing beliefs
    - Describing or demonstrating a phenomenon that students cannot adequately explain using their current understanding of the world
    - Explaining why particular phenomena occur
    - Showing how the correct explanation is more plausible (i.e., makes more sense) than students' existing beliefs
    - Motivating students to learn correct explanations
    - Checking students' understanding frequently, monitoring for persistent misconceptions

## Chapter 8

# HIGHER-LEVEL THINKING SKILLS

| CHAPTER OUTLINE | RELEVANT TEST BANK ITEMS |
|---|---|
| THE NATURE OF HIGHER-LEVEL THINKING | Multiple-Choice 1–4 |
| METACOGNITION AND STUDY STRATEGIES<br>Effective Study Strategies<br>Factors Affecting Strategy Use | Multiple-Choice 5–26<br>Essay 78–79 |
| TRANSFER<br>Basic Concepts in Transfer<br>Factors Affecting Transfer<br>Importance of Retrieval in Transfer | Multiple-Choice 27–47<br>Essay 80–82 |
| PROBLEM SOLVING<br>Basic Concepts in Problem Solving<br>Cognitive Factors Affecting Problem Solving<br>Using Computer Technology to Promote Effective Problem Solving | Multiple-Choice 48–70<br>Essay 83 |
| CRITICAL THINKING | Multiple-Choice 71–74 |
| THE ROLE OF DISPOSITIONS IN HIGHER-LEVEL THINKING | Multiple-Choice 75 |
| CONSIDERING DIVERSITY IN HIGHER-LEVEL THINKING PROCESSES<br>Accommodating Students with Special Needs | Multiple-Choice 76–77 |
| THE BIG PICTURE<br>General Strategies for Promoting Higher-Level Thinking Skills | Essay 84 |
| The items in the "Integrative Questions" chapter of this Test Bank integrate the content of two or more textbook chapters. Within that chapter, the items listed to the right are relevant to Chapter 8. | Multiple-Choice 9, 11<br>Essay 26–28, 39 |

## Multiple-Choice Questions

• 1. Which one of the following best describes a lower-level question?
  a. It requires a simple response, as in a multiple choice or true-false format.
  b. It asks students to retrieve information actually given to them during instruction.
  c. It requires a nonverbal response, such as pointing to an object.
  d. It asks students to think about and integrate information that they learned at an earlier age.

• 2. A higher-level question asks students to respond in which one of the following ways?
  a. To develop an answer not specifically provided in class
  b. To recall information from more advanced classes
  c. To recall information learned several years ago
  d. To engage in both positive and negative transfer

•• 3. Which one of the following is a higher-level question?
  a. "Can you remember the three categories of rocks that we studied yesterday?"
  b. "Now that I have done one multiplication problem on the board, can you do the next two multiplication problems?"
  c. "Can you use what we learned about snakes and what we know about climate in North America to guess where this snake might live?"
  d. "Here are the same rocks that we studied yesterday. Can you sort them into three piles—sedimentary, igneous, and metamorphic—the way we did yesterday?"

•• 4. In a science lesson on heat, Ms. Jones explains that heat is the result of molecules moving back and forth very quickly and that gases are heated more quickly than liquids. The following day, she asks her class the following four questions. Which one is a higher-level question?
  a. "Who can remember yesterday's discussion about heat?"
  b. "What is heat?"
  c. "Which one is heated more quickly—a gas or a liquid?"
  d. "Why is it cooler near the ocean on a hot summer day?"

•• 5. Jeffrey needs to study for an upcoming exam. He does a number of things to prepare for the exam, four of which are listed below. Three of these illustrate metacognition. Which one reflects little if any metacognitive activity?
  a. He allows himself adequate study time for the exam.
  b. He directs his eyes to the first page of his textbook.
  c. He identifies a suitable mnemonic technique that will help him remember a difficult piece of information.
  d. He tests himself to see if he is sufficiently prepared for the exam.

•• 6. Which one of the following is the best illustration of metacognition?
   a. Andrea is studying for a spelling test. She writes each spelling word five times in her nicest handwriting.
   b. Betsy stays up late studying for a geography test. The following morning in school, she is too tired to think straight during the test.
   c. Connie is studying for a history test. She knows that she has trouble with dates, so she checks herself by giving herself a short quiz after each chapter.
   d. Dolly is preparing to take the Scholastic Assessment Test (SAT), so she checks out an SAT preparation book from the local library and reads it from cover to cover.

• 7. Three of the following statements are accurate with regard to metacognition. Which one is not accurate?
   a. By high school, most students have developed an effective way to study.
   b. Students in the early elementary grades have little understanding of how they can best learn.
   c. Metacognitive skills become more important as students study more challenging material.
   d. Students with greater awareness about how best to learn achieve at higher levels in the classroom.

• 8. Your students are reading a textbook chapter that you've assigned. Given what we know about how students identify "important" information when they read, which one of the following things in the chapter are they least likely to focus on?
   a. A formula
   b. Sentences in italics
   c. The last sentence of each paragraph
   d. An interesting detail

• 9. Judging from the textbook's discussion of students' ability to identify important information, when will students be most likely to identify something in a lesson as being important?
   a. When their teacher writes it on the chalkboard.
   b. When it is an abstract theme that underlies a lesson.
   c. When it is presented at the beginning of a lesson.
   d. When it is presented at the end of a lesson.

• 10. How does note taking affect students' recall of lecture information?
   a. It interferes with recall, because students are less likely to pay attention when they're taking notes.
   b. It increases recall by helping students encode the information.
   c. It increases recall for details but not for main ideas.
   d. It increases recall only if the notes are quite brief.

•• 11. Which one of the following best illustrates concept mapping?

a. Alexandra puts the words force, gravity, velocity, acceleration, and time on a piece of paper; she then draws lines between pairs of related words and describes the relationships.

b. Bob draws a chart listing the sequence of events leading up to World War II in chronological order.

c. Calvin makes a chart showing the hierarchy that biologists use to classify animals; his chart includes such concepts as vertebrates, invertebrates, mammals, fish, birds, mollusks, crustaceans, and so on.

d. Donna lists the defining and correlational features of the concept canine.

• 12. Which one of the following statements best describes the usefulness of concept mapping?

a. It allows students to record all the information about a subject in essay form so that they can succeed on essay tests.

b. It allows students to record distinct ideas from a lecture individually so they don't get similar ideas mixed up.

c. It provides a good "filler" activity at the end of the day, when students are tired and ready to go home.

d. It helps teachers organize lessons and gives students a way to understand interrelationships among concepts.

•• 13. Which one of the following students is elaborating as he takes notes in class?

a. While his math teacher demonstrates a mathematical procedure on the chalkboard, Ed writes "Meet Pat after school" in the margin of his notebook.

b. Jason writes down every word his science teacher says, hoping that it will all make sense when he reads it later.

c. In his Spanish class, Hugh writes each new vocabulary word in his notebook five times to help him remember it.

d. In science, Frank is taking notes about how water expands when it freezes and adds, "That's why our fish tank broke when I left it outside last winter."

•• 14. Which one of the following situations best illustrates the process of elaborative interrogation?

a. As Lynette, Martin, and Fred study for a science quiz one evening, they go over the questions on the study guide their teacher handed out in class that day; they know that if they can answer all the questions successfully, they will do well on the quiz.

b. As she reads Douglas Adams' science fiction novel, The Hitchhiker's Guide to the Galaxy, Suzette develops a list of questions that she would ask the author about why he wrote the story the way he did.

c. As LaWanda and Megan study their history book together, they take turns making up and asking each other questions about why various historical events may have happened the way they did.

d. Vance makes notations in his notes regarding things he doesn't understand and needs to ask his teacher about.

•• 15. When students summarize material they are studying, they learn it more thoroughly. Which one of these students is most effectively summarizing?

a. Jerry writes down the important ideas and identifies relationships among them.
b. Laura writes down everything she can remember from the lesson.
c. Nora writes each main point on a separate index card and then jots down all the details she can remember about each one.
d. Phyllis lists the general themes of a lesson in single words and short phrases.

• 16. The textbook recommends three of the following strategies for helping students learn to summarize class material. Which strategy does it not recommend?

a. Begin by asking students to summarize large chunks of material.
b. Have them practice first on well-organized material.
c. Have them work in cooperative groups to develop summaries.
d. Ask students to summarize reading assignments on a regular basis.

• 17. Which one of the following statements accurately describes the relationship between comprehension monitoring and academic achievement?

a. High achievers automatically know whether they understand something, so they do not have to monitor their comprehension.
b. High achievers are more likely to monitor their comprehension of class material than low achievers.
c. Low achievers are more likely to ask their teacher for assistance when they don't understand something.
d. Low achievers are more likely to be worried about their grades, so they monitor their comprehension frequently.

•• 18. Three of the following are examples of comprehension monitoring. Which one is not?

a. After reading a chapter in a textbook, Annette makes sure she has accomplished the objectives listed on the chapter's first page.
b. Bruce asks himself questions about the material he is reading and tries to answer them.
c. Cara stops at the end of each section to see if she can summarize what she's just read.
d. Dwayne looks at all the headings and subheadings in a chapter before he begins to read the chapter itself.

•• 19. Which one of the following students illustrates an illusion of knowing?

a. Anthony doesn't understand the concept of entropy.
b. Belinda doesn't know how to swim.
c. Corissa thinks she understands the concept of inertia, but she really doesn't.
d. Daryl doesn't think he is a very good tennis player, even though he is the best player on the school tennis team.

•• 20. A student who has an illusion of knowing is most likely to:

a. Elaborate on difficult-to-learn material.
b. Express surprise about a low test score.
c. Know the general meaning of material but be unable to repeat it verbatim.
d. Summarize what he or she has just read.

• 21. As a teacher, you are concerned that many of your students are learning less than they think they are learning as they read their textbooks. Your best strategy would be to:
   a. Have them underline or highlight at least 50% of what they read.
   b. Instruct them to read the book two or three times instead of just once.
   c. Suggest questions that they can ask themselves as they read.
   d. Copy difficult-to-understand sentences in their notebooks.

• 22. Given research on effective study skills, which one of the following techniques should you <u>not</u> recommend to a struggling student?
   a. Take notes on a lecture only after it is over.
   b. Elaborate on information.
   c. Find main ideas.
   d. Summarize information.

• 23. Three of the following factors influence students' ability to use effective study strategies. Which one is largely <u>irrelevant</u> to students' use of effective strategies?
   a. Whether they've been taught effective strategies
   b. Whether they are "morning people" or "night owls"
   c. How much they already know about the topic they are studying
   d. How well they have monitored their comprehension during previous study sessions

• 24. Students' <u>epistemological beliefs</u> can best be described as students' views about:
   a. What instructional techniques are most likely to help them learn classroom material
   b. How researchers develop theories from the data they collect
   c. How long they are likely to remember the things that they learn in school
   d. The nature of knowledge and how it is acquired

•• 25. Which one of the following pairs of students best illustrates a difference with respect to students' <u>epistemological beliefs</u>?
   a. Irene thinks that doing well in high school is important for getting into a good college, but Isabelle thinks that she can get into college with mediocre grades as long as she has high SAT scores.
   b. Julie likes going to school because that's where she sees her friends every day, but Janette likes going to school because of all the new things she learns there.
   c. Keith thinks that learning geography means memorizing place names, but Kareem thinks that learning geography means understanding migration and settlement patterns.
   d. Loren is well aware of the criteria that his teacher is using to evaluate his classroom performance, but Luke is clueless about why he is doing poorly in the same teacher's class.

•• 26. Imagine that you are a high school principal who wants students to develop effective study strategies before they graduate. With research about effective study skills programs in mind, which of the following approaches would be the best one to take?

a. Purchase textbooks that are about two years below students' present reading level.
b. Have teachers incorporate study skills training into the specific academic courses they teach.
c. Have a one-semester study skills course that all students take in their freshman year of high school.
d. Have a one-semester study skills course that all students take in their senior year of high school.

•• 27. Which one of the following illustrates positive transfer?

a. Robert is trying to learn the spelling of the word "shepherd," so he remembers how he learned to spell "tomcat" by putting two words together and spells it "sheepherd."
b. Vince notices that rules of grammar are not always the same in English and Japanese.
c. Zelda uses the formula for calculating the area of a circle when she wants to know how much bigger a 10" pizza is than a 7" pizza.
d. David is trying to learn to program a computer. He reads his programming manual but is confused by some of its instructions.

•• 28. Which one of the following situations illustrates negative transfer?

a. Alexis knows a great deal about World War I but very little about World War II.
b. Beth learns that spiders are different from insects.
c. After learning about verb conjugations in her Latin class, Christine easily learns to conjugate verbs in her French class.
d. Forgetting that she is no longer at school, Darlene raises her hand to speak at the family dinner table.

•• 29. Which one of the following is the best example of negative transfer?

a. Nellie sees five squared ("$5^2$") in her math book and reads it as "fifty-two."
b. Fred knows he can get Bs in his classes without having to study at all.
c. José is trying to remember when the Civil War started, so he recalls all he can about American history and decides the war must have taken place in the 1860s.
d. Eleanor wants to tie a string securely to her pencil so she can hang it from her notebook, but she has forgotten how to tie a square knot.

•• 30. People who learn a second language typically apply patterns of speech production used in their native tongue and thereby speak the second language with an accent. This phenomenon is an example of:

a. General transfer
b. Situated cognition
c. Positive transfer
d. Negative transfer

•• 31. Nathan has been playing golf with his parents for many years. When he goes out for the school baseball team, he has trouble hitting the ball because he keeps confusing the swing of the bat with how he swings a golf club. Nathan's difficulty reflects:

a. Negative transfer
b. General transfer
c. Mental set in problem solving
d. Rote learning

•• 32. Which one of the following alternatives most clearly illustrates general, as opposed to specific, transfer?

a. The skills Arnold has developed as a marathon runner helps him later in life when he jogs for exercise.
b. Brian has learned study skills in his sociology class that he also finds useful in his nutrition class.
c. Conway's knowledge of addition and subtraction helps him balance his checkbook.
d. David's knowledge of the human digestive system helps him understand the digestive system of an earthworm.

•• 33. Which one of the following is the best example of general transfer?

a. Iris is trying to learn how to ride a bicycle, and she uses the pedaling motion she learned while riding a tricycle.
b. Melinda is trying to learn the 26 amendments to the Constitution, so she makes up a memory trick similar to one she used when she had to learn the 12 cranial nerves in biology.
c. Polly is trying to learn division facts and suddenly realizes that these facts are simply the reverse of facts she learned when she studied multiplication.
d. Thomas is learning how to play a new computer game in his homeroom class and uses the same "jump and shoot" strategy he learned playing video games at home.

•• 34. Weston is working on a science project and wants to make his papier-mâché volcano "erupt." He remembers that when his mother combined vinegar and baking soda while following a recipe, the batter foamed up as she added the vinegar. So he tries mixing vinegar and baking soda in his volcano, and the mixture bubbles. Weston is showing:

a. General transfer
b. Intuitive transfer
c. Specific transfer
d. Negative transfer

•• 35. Mary is majoring in drama. Mary's parents want her to study advanced mathematics as a way of strengthening her mind; with a stronger mind, they argue, she will be able to learn her lines more easily when she is rehearsing for a play. Based on their reasoning, which one of the following perspectives of transfer do Mary's parents hold?

a. Information processing
b. Situated cognition
c. Formal discipline
d. Specific transfer

• 36. Which one of the following statements best describes a situated cognition perspective of transfer?
  a. Prior knowledge is more likely to be transferred when it is consciously retrieved from long-term memory.
  b. Knowledge and skills acquired in one context are unlikely to be used in a very different context.
  c. Studying principles of deductive and inductive reasoning leads to more logical thought processes in a variety of contexts.
  d. Students are more likely to transfer new knowledge when their teacher describes the situations in which they might use it.

•• 37. Which one of the following examples best illustrates the notion of situated cognition as it relates to transfer?
  a. When Rachel learns the concept inertia, she immediately recalls a variety of phenomena that the concept can explain.
  b. Lucinda doesn't enjoy her history class because her teacher expects students to memorize a lot of names, dates, and places.
  c. It doesn't occur to Jennie that she can use algebra to solve a problem in her physics class.
  d. Eleanor enjoys physical education class because she always feels more energized afterward.

•• 38. Which one of the following teachers is obviously keeping the notion of situated cognition in mind as he or she helps students transfer what they are learning in school?
  a. Ms. Sporer asks her students to speculate about what might have happened if the Europeans had not "discovered" the New World until the 1800s.
  b. Mr. Mendoza makes sure that each one of the students in his instrumental music class knows the difference between the treble and bass clefs.
  c. Ms. Sabih gives each of her elementary art students a hunk of clay and then says, "I'd like you to mold your clay into a mythical creature of some kind—into an animal that no one has ever seen before."
  d. Mr. Gerberg takes his middle school math students to the grocery store so that they can use their math skills to do some comparison shopping.

•• 39. Considering contemporary theorists' views on general transfer, which one of the following skills is most likely to transfer across very different situations?
  a. The ability to be creative
  b. The ability to take good notes on a lecture
  c. The ability to remember complex ideas
  d. The ability to memorize a poem

•• 40. Considering what we know about transfer, in which of the following situations is transfer least likely to happen?
  a. Students who have studied rules of formal logic are now studying geography.
  b. Students who know the basic addition facts are now studying the basic subtraction facts.
  c. Students who have learned to play softball are now learning baseball.
  d. Students who know Spanish are now learning French.

•• 41. Which one of the following recommendations is consistent with current beliefs about transfer?
   a. "Take computer programming to help you develop your analytical thinking skills."
   b. "Study German so you will have an easier time learning Japanese next year."
   c. "Studying calculus will help you think more abstractly about the various subjects you will study in college."
   d. "Use your knowledge of algebra to solve this chemistry equation."

• 42. Three of the following are accurate statements about factors that affect transfer. Which statement is inaccurate?
   a. Students are more likely to transfer what they have learned when they have learned it in a meaningful, rather than rote, fashion.
   b. Students are more likely to transfer what they have learned when they have studied it for a lengthy period of time.
   c. Students are more likely to transfer what they have learned when they have learned general principles rather than specific facts.
   d. Students are more likely to transfer what they have learned when they see it as "belonging" to a particular academic subject area.

•• 43. Considering factors that affect transfer, identify the group of students most likely to transfer what they are learning.
   a. Students in Mr. Allen's geography class are studying several countries this week, memorizing the locations of their rivers and major cities.
   b. Students in Ms. Elbert's music class are practicing major chords in different keys this semester, practicing each one over and over again in different songs.
   c. Students in Mr. Ivy's science class are studying the characteristics of mammals and reptiles this week.
   d. Students in Ms. Martin's social studies class are studying major events in the history of Mexico this month, beginning with the Aztec empire and continuing until the present time.

•• 44. In which one of the following situations are we most likely to find transfer?
   a. Alice learns how to add 2-digit numbers and then studies how to add 3-digit numbers.
   b. Brianne learns how to plant corn and then learns how to prune a hedge.
   c. Cathy learns early British history and then learns early Japanese history.
   d. Devlin learns how to play softball and then learns how to play a card game.

•• 45. Ms. Sharp wants her students to use what they learn in psychology class to interact with other people more effectively. Given what we know about factors that promote transfer, which approach is most likely to accomplish this objective?
   a. Ask questions that encourage students to review the basic principles they have learned about human interaction.
   b. Have students describe strategies that might be effective in human interaction.
   c. Present a prototype of how effective interaction occurs.
   d. Have students apply effective interaction skills in role-playing situations.

•• 46. Having learned how to conjugate the past tense of the verb walk by adding ed (I walked, you walked, he walked, etc.), a foreign student studying English should be able to conjugate which verb most easily?
   a. see
   b. do
   c. eat
   d. play

•• 47. Leo has recently studied the principle of reinforcement in his psychology class. He is now trying to teach his daughter good table manners. From a cognitive psychology perspective of transfer, is Leo likely to use the principle of reinforcement in helping his daughter learn manners?
   a. Definitely yes.
   b. Definitely no.
   c. Only if he has previously learned the principle of reinforcement to a level of automaticity.
   d. Only if he retrieves the principle of reinforcement at the time he is teaching his daughter.

• 48. Which one of the following characterizes a well-defined problem?
   a. A clear goal
   b. Solvable only by a heuristic
   c. Several possible correct solutions
   d. Missing information

•• 49. Which one of the following problems is the best example of an ill-defined problem?
   a. Determining the average of a group of test scores
   b. Helping a friend whose feelings have been hurt
   c. Clearing a driveway after a snowstorm
   d. Staying dry in a rainstorm

• 50. Which one of the following are students least likely to get in a typical classroom?
   a. Instruction in how to use a particular algorithm
   b. The knowledge they need to solve a problem
   c. Lots of practice solving well-defined problems
   d. Lots of practice solving ill-defined problems

• 51. Which one of the following describes how we can best teach students to solve ill-defined problems?
   a. Give them a lot of practice in solving well-defined problems, and the ability to solve ill-defined problems will follow naturally.
   b. Give them answers to problems, and then have them figure out how those answers were obtained.
   c. Teach them strategies for better defining ill-defined problems.
   d. Teach them an algorithm for solving each type of ill-defined problem.

•• 52. Which one of the following problems is most likely to be solved with a heuristic rather than an algorithm?

a. Calculating the volume of a cylinder.
b. Resolving an argument.
c. Finding the word "antonym" in the dictionary.
d. Locating books about spiders in the school library.

•• 53. Which is the best example of someone using a heuristic in problem solving?

a. Susan wants to know how long it will take her to drive from Phoenix to Los Angeles. She knows that the distance is 400 miles, and she figures she will average 50 miles an hour with stops, so she predicts the trip will take 8 hours.
b. Vinnie has a round hot tub that is six feet in diameter; he wants to build a top to cover it. He remembers the formula for calculating the area of a circle and works out how many feet of lumber he needs.
c. John wants to buy a computer. He compares prices at different computer stores and buys whatever is least expensive.
d. Marion can't think of a plot for the short story she needs to write. She breaks her task into smaller pieces: First she will decide who or what her main character will be, then she will think of a conflict for that character to experience, and finally she will identify a reasonable resolution of that conflict.

• 54. Three of the following strategies should help your students solve ill-defined problems more effectively. Which strategy is least likely to be useful to them?

a. Teach them to break a problem into several smaller and better-defined problems.
b. Help them identify which pieces of information they need and which they don't.
c. Teach them how to use the library or Internet to find any information they may need to solve the problem.
d. If they get overly frustrated with the problem, give them the correct answer and explain the algorithm you used to find it.

•• 55. Three of the following teachers should help their students solve problems more effectively? Which teacher probably will not?

a. When students struggle with arithmetic word problems, Mr. Azari gives them subtle hints about how to proceed.
b. Mr. Bennington presents many ill-defined problems in biology and asks students to make each one more specific and clear-cut.
c. Ms. Costas has students work on difficult problems in small, cooperative groups.
d. Ms. Driver teaches students abstract principles of logic (e.g., "If all As are Bs and all Bs are Cs, then...").

• 56. Many cognitive factors affect a student's ability to solve a problem. Which of the following is not one of these factors?

a. The depth of the student's knowledge relevant to the problem
b. The size of the student's sensory register
c. The student's working memory capacity
d. How the student encodes the problem in memory

•• 57. William is trying to calculate the price of his groceries in his head. He has four apples for 35¢ each, five potatoes for 15¢ each, and three cake mixes for $2.25 each. He begins by thinking to himself, "Let's see, four times 35¢ is what? Two times 35¢ is 70¢, and then two times 70¢ is $1.40. And then what do I do next? Oh, yes, I need to know what five times fifteen equals. I can't remember, but let's see if I can figure it out...." From the perspective of cognitive psychology, William may have trouble solving the problem because:

a. His working memory capacity may be insufficient to hold and process all the information.
b. He is encoding the problem incorrectly.
c. He is demonstrating functional fixedness with regard to his knowledge of multiplication facts.
d. He is using an inappropriate heuristic.

• 58. From the perspective of cognitive psychology, why should we <u>not</u> expect students to solve complex problems <u>in their heads</u>?

a. The capacity for complex problem solving does not emerge until late adolescence.
b. Asking students to solve complex problems promotes rote memorization rather than meaningful learning.
c. Students' working memories can hold only a few pieces of information at a time.
d. By trying to solve complex problems in their heads, students are likely to "unlearn" some of the information stored in their long-term memories.

•• 59. Missy is given this problem:

Mt. Washington is lower than Mt. Jefferson.
Mt. Washington is higher than Mt. Adams.
Which mountain is highest?

Missy reads the fourth word incorrectly—she thinks the word is <u>higher</u> rather than <u>lower</u>—and consequently answers the problem incorrectly. From the perspective of cognitive psychology, Missy's difficulty is due to:

a. Her limited working memory capacity
b. Functional fixedness
c. The way she encodes the problem
d. The fact that she is retrieving information that she has learned in a rote rather than meaningful fashion

•• 60. Perry is trying to solve the following riddle: "What creature walks first on four legs, then two, then three?" He tries repeatedly to think of an animal that might walk on three legs, but he can only think of animals that walk on either two or four legs. Finally, he is told the correct answer—a human being, who crawls, then walks, then walks with a cane. Which one of the following is the most likely explanation of Perry's difficulty?

a. He has encoded the problem with too narrow a definition of "legs."
b. He doesn't have enough working memory capacity.
c. He doesn't have a sufficient knowledge base.
d. He is suffering from functional fixedness.

•• 61. Which one of the following examples most clearly illustrates the effect of <u>mental set</u> on problem solving?
   a. Albert is trying to solve a physics problem on a class exam. He is so anxious that he can't remember how to do the problem.
   b. Bradley can't find the right size of test tube to complete a chemistry lab.
   c. Charlie is doing a series of addition problems. He overlooks the subtraction sign on the last problem, so he adds when he should subtract.
   d. Doug is angry that another boy stole his bicycle, and so he steals a bicycle from someone else.

•• 62. Which one of the following examples most clearly illustrates how <u>mental set</u> can interfere with problem solving?
   a. Abigail wants to make amends with a boyfriend she recently fought with. However, the boy tells her that he is now dating someone else.
   b. Bernadette needs to calculate the volume of a pyramid. She knows she learned the correct formula in class, but she can't seem to remember it now.
   c. Corinne is working on a jigsaw puzzle. One of the pieces to the puzzle is missing.
   d. Danielle's car won't start. It doesn't occur to her that she can take the bus to work because she has always driven her car to work.

• 63. Three of the following strategies should help students learn to encode problems correctly in memory. Which one is <u>unlikely</u> to do so?
   a. Make problems concrete for students.
   b. Point out features of a problem that give clues about how to solve it.
   c. Have students draw a picture of the problem.
   d. Have students work exclusively on one kind of problem at a time.

• 64. Research indicates that students are more likely to be successful problem solvers in a given subject area when they:
   a. Demonstrate problem solving expertise in other, very different subject areas.
   b. Know the subject matter well.
   c. Have had extensive training in logical thinking.
   d. Pay considerable attention to details.

• 65. When educators use the expression "less is more" in their discussions of transfer and problem solving, they mean that:
   a. Students are more likely to apply what they learn when they focus on learning a few things very well.
   b. Students are more likely to transfer what they learn to new problems when they spend less time per day in direct instruction.
   c. Students will more successfully transfer what they've learned to new problems when those problems are simple rather than complex.
   d. Students can only store so much in working memory at any one time.

•• 66. Which one of the four teachers below is most likely to facilitate problem solving in the classroom?

   a. Ms. Axelrod wants her students to develop a single "best" strategy for encoding problems.
   b. Ms. Blakely wants her students to have an in-depth knowledge of the topics they study.
   c. Ms. Corning wants her students to learn why algorithms are almost always better than heuristics for solving problems.
   d. Ms. Darwin wants her students to learn why heuristics are almost always better than algorithms for solving problems.

•• 67. Which one of the following examples most clearly illustrates the role of <u>retrieval</u> in problem solving?

   a. Arnie is trying to solve a physics problem on a class exam. He is so anxious that he can't remember how to do the problem.
   b. Bradley is trying to solve a problem on his physics test, but he was absent the day his teacher talked about such problems.
   c. Charlie is doing a series of addition problems. He overlooks the subtraction sign on the last problem, so he adds when he should subtract.
   d. Doug is angry that another boy stole his bicycle, and so he steals a bicycle from someone else.

• 68. Three of the following strategies illustrate the use of <u>metacognitive processes</u> in problem solving. Which strategy is <u>least</u> metacognitive in nature?

   a. Breaking a complex problem into smaller, easier subproblems
   b. Continually monitoring progress toward problem solution
   c. Identifying a logical approach to solving a problem
   d. Looking up the correct answer at the back of the textbook

• 69. If we want to enhance students' metacognitive processes during problem solving, we would be <u>most</u> likely to:

   a. Ask students to use algorithms rather than heuristics to solve problems
   b. Ask students to use heuristics rather than algorithms to solve problems
   c. Suggest questions that students might ask themselves as they work on problems
   d. Encourage students to encode problems visually rather than verbally whenever possible

• 70. Ideally we should engage students in authentic problem-solving activities as often as possible. When such activities are logistically impossible or impractical, the most "authentic" alternative is probably

   a. Telling colorful anecdotes about how people have solved problems in the local community
   b. Presenting computer simulations of real-world problems
   c. Giving verbal descriptions of problems (e.g., mathematical "word problems")
   d. Assigning readings about how experts have solved real-world problems

• 71. Critical thinking can best be described as involving:
   a. Knowing the best course of action to take in complex situations
   b. Using heuristics to solve problems
   c. Keeping an open mind
   d. Judging the value of information or arguments

•• 72. Which one of the following is the best example of critical thinking as the textbook defines the term?
   a. Lorenzo complains to his teacher, "When the textbook author talks about the importance of recycling, he doesn't explain how the advantages outweigh the disadvantages."
   b. Justin says to his friend Victor, "I think I can guess why you're feeling sad today."
   c. Muriel asks her teacher, "Why do we have to start school so early in the morning? I have trouble thinking clearly before ten o'clock in the morning."
   d. Rachel mumbles to herself as she reads her history book, "Why does the year 1929 sound so familiar? Oh, yes, now I know. That's the year the stock market crashed."

•• 73. Only one of the following students is definitely engaging in critical thinking. Which one?
   a. Louise has a puzzled look as she reads her textbook. "I don't understand what the author is trying to say," she thinks.
   b. Sam reads over his responses to the essay questions on an astronomy test. "I think I've done my best," he tells himself. "I'm pretty sure I answered the first two questions correctly. I'm not so sure how well I did on the last question, however."
   c. As Morgan watches her lab partner experiment with a pendulum, she says, "You just changed the length of the string at the same time you added more weight. That won't tell us anything."
   d. Raul jumps at the chance to learn how to use desktop publishing software. "I'm particularly interested in learning how to integrate text and graphics," he tell his teacher.

• 74. Three of the following teaching strategies should promote critical thinking. Which one, although beneficial in other ways, will not necessarily promote critical thinking skills?
   a. Ask students to evaluate the quality of a variety of scientific research studies.
   b. Have students relate new material to things that they have already learned.
   c. Have students debate a controversial issue by taking a perspective in direct opposition to what they actually believe.
   d. Ask students to read a persuasive essay and look for possible flaws in the author's line of reasoning.

• 75. Three of the following are dispositions associated with the use of higher-level thinking skills. Which one is not necessarily associated with higher-level skills?
   a. Acceptance of mistakes as inevitable and potentially helpful
   b. Desire to get the correct answer as quickly as possible
   c. Eagerness to make sense of surprising events
   d. Willingness to try harder in the face of failure

• 76. We are likely to find three of the following characteristics in students with advanced cognitive development. Which one are we not likely to find?
   a. More effective learning strategies
   b. Greater tendency to apply classroom material to new situations
   c. More advanced problem-solving strategies
   d. More frequent use of mental sets in solving problems

•• 77. Which one of the following strategies best describes the concept of metacognitive scaffolding?
   a. Providing support mechanisms that can help students use newly acquired learning strategies
   b. Teaching students the importance of thinking carefully about the things they are learning
   c. Guiding students step-by-step through problem-solving algorithms
   d. Teaching students that successful learning often does not occur in a rapid all-or-none fashion, but instead may take considerable time and effort on their part

**Essay Questions**

• 78. You are hired to teach a struggling student (Joy) more effective study skills. Describe five different strategies that you will teach Joy so that she can study and learn more effectively. Include at least one strategy that will enable Joy to transfer the things she learns to new situations.

•• 79. Luke approaches you before class and expresses his frustration about having done so poorly on yesterday's exam. "I studied for hours and hours," he tells you. "I guess I'm just not a very good test-taker." You know that your test was a good measure of what you taught your students. You also know that students seldom do poorly on your tests simply because they are poor test-takers. Considering the textbook's discussion of study strategies, what other possible explanation might you give Luke as to why he thought he knew the material well yet earned a low test score. And with your explanation in mind, describe a strategy you might teach him for improving his performance next time.

• 80. Distinguish between positive and negative transfer, and give a concrete example of each to illustrate your discussion.

•• 81. Identify something you will be teaching your students that you will want them to be able to use in the "real world." With the factors affecting transfer in mind, describe four different strategies you can use to help students transfer what they learn to situations outside the classroom. For each strategy, be specific and concrete as to what you would do.

•• 82. Imagine that you are teaching a course in educational psychology to future teachers. You want your students to transfer what they learn in your course to how they teach their students. Describe three strategies you might use to help your students apply what they learn in your class to their own teaching practices.

- 83. Describe the role that each of the factors below plays in students' ability to solve problems. Illustrate the role of each with a concrete example.
  a. Working memory capacity
  b. Encoding
  c. Retrieval from long-term memory

•• 84. Identify a particular grade level at which you hope to teach some day. If appropriate, also identify the particular subject area in which you plan to specialize (science, social studies, language arts, physical education, etc.). Then describe three different strategies you might use to promote higher-level thinking skills in your students. Illustrate each strategy with a specific, concrete example of what you might do.

## ANSWER KEY

### Multiple-Choice Questions

| | | | | |
|---|---|---|---|---|
| 1. b | 17. b | 33. b | 49. b | 65. a |
| 2. a | 18. d | 34. c | 50. d | 66. b |
| 3. c | 19. c | 35. c | 51. c | 67. a |
| 4. d | 20. b | 36. b | 52. b | 68. d |
| 5. b | 21. c | 37. c | 53. d | 69. c |
| 6. c | 22. a | 38. d | 54. d | 70. b |
| 7. a | 23. b | 39. b | 55. d | 71. d |
| 8. c | 24. d | 40. a | 56. b | 72. a |
| 9. a | 25. c | 41. d | 57. a | 73. c |
| 10. b | 26. b | 42. d | 58. c | 74. b |
| 11. a | 27. c | 43. b | 59. c | 75. b |
| 12. d | 28. d | 44. a | 60. a | 76. d |
| 13. d | 29. a | 45. d | 61. c | 77. a |
| 14. c | 30. d | 46. d | 62. d | |
| 15. a | 31. a | 47. d | 63. d | |
| 16. a | 32. b | 48. a | 64. b | |

### Essay Questions

78. Strategies for teaching Joy effective study skills are these (the response should describe five strategies, including one that will promote transfer of classroom material—preferably at least one of the first two bulleted items or a reasonable facsimile):
    - Show her how to connect new material to the things she already knows (i.e., to learn meaningfully).
    - Show her how to elaborate on the material (e.g., by using elaborative interrogation).
    - Encourage her to identify important information.
    - Teach her good note-taking strategies.
    - Show her ways that she might organize material (e.g., outlining, concept mapping).
    - Give her questions that she can attempt to answer as she reads.
    - Teach her to summarize what she is studying.
    - Teach her to monitor her comprehension (e.g., by asking herself questions).

79. Luke may have had an illusion of knowing the material: He used ineffective study strategies (e.g., rote memorization) and failed to monitor his comprehension, so he thought he knew the material better than he really did. Luke needs to develop a strategy for monitoring his comprehension (e.g., self-questioning).

80. In positive transfer, something learned at one time facilitates learning or performance at a later time. In negative transfer, something learned at one time interferes with learning or performance at a later time. The response should illustrate each of these concepts with a concrete example.

81. Possible strategies to be derived from the factors affecting transfer include these (the response should apply at least four of the strategies below as it describes in concrete terms how to facilitate the transfer of a specific idea or skill to real world settings):
    - Examine a few topics in depth rather than many topics superficially.
    - Make sure students master classroom material.
    - Promote meaningful learning.
    - Teach general principles.
    - Provide many and different examples and opportunities for practice.
    - Develop school tasks that resemble real world situations.
    - Present material close in time to the occasions on which students will need to use it.
    - Relate classroom material to the outside world.
    - Promote multiple associations between classroom material and real world situations.

82. Here are several strategies one might use to promote the transfer of educational psychology to classroom teaching (the response should describe at least three of these strategies or reasonable facsimiles):
    - Examine a few topics in depth rather than many topics superficially.
    - Promote meaningful learning.
    - Teach general psychological principles rather than specific facts.
    - Relate concepts, principles, and theories to classroom practices.
    - Provide many and different classroom examples.
    - Provide opportunities to practice applying the material.
    - Make sure students master the material.
    - Teach the material just before, or at the same time as, students are teaching in the classroom.

83. Responses to various parts of the question are as follows:
    a. Because working memory capacity is limited, students can only consider so many aspects of a problem at once. When a problem is complex and multifaceted, students may have difficulty keeping all its components in mind at once. The response should illustrate the effects of working memory capacity with a concrete example.
    b. How students encode a problem in memory (e.g., the interpretations they impose on the problem) affects the strategies they bring to bear on the problem and the possible solutions they consider. The response should illustrate the effects of encoding with a concrete example.
    c. Problem solving success depends on whether students retrieve essential information from long-term memory. The response should illustrate the effects of retrieval with a concrete example.

84. The student should identify a particular grade level and, at least for the secondary grades, a particular content domain as well. The student should then describe three strategies for promoting higher-level thinking skills. Following are the strategies listed in the final "Big Picture" section of Chapter 8:
    - Emphasize meaningful learning and conceptual understanding over rote memorization.
    - Teach higher-level thinking skills within the context of specific topics.
    - Communicate that knowledge is subject to change as new evidence comes in.
    - Encourage higher-level thinking through group discussions and projects.
    - Use authentic activities to promote transfer of thinking skills to real-life settings.
    - Foster dispositions as well as skills.
    - Incorporate higher-level thinking into assessment activities.

    Alternatively, the student might describe one or more strategies that the textbook suggests for promoting metacognition, transfer, problem solving, or critical thinking in particular. Each strategy should be illustrated with a specific example.

## Chapter 9

# BEHAVIORIST VIEWS OF LEARNING

| CHAPTER OUTLINE | RELEVANT TEST BANK ITEMS |
|---|---|
| BASIC ASSUMPTIONS OF BEHAVIORISM | Multiple-Choice 1–3<br>Essay 93 |
| CLASSICAL CONDITIONING<br>Classical Conditioning of Emotional Responses<br>Generalization<br>Extinction | Multiple-Choice 4–15<br>Essay 94 |
| OPERANT CONDITIONING<br>Contrasting Classical and Operant Conditioning<br>Reinforcement in the Classroom<br>Using Reinforcement Effectively | Multiple-Choice 16–49<br>Essay 95–96 |
| SHAPING NEW BEHAVIORS | Multiple-Choice 50–52<br>Essay 97–99 |
| EFFECTS OF ANTECEDENT STIMULI AND RESPONSES<br>Cueing<br>Setting Events<br>Generalization<br>Discrimination<br>Behavioral Momentum | Multiple-Choice 53–58 |
| REDUCING AND ELIMINATING UNDESIRABLE BEHAVIORS<br>Extinction<br>Cueing Inappropriate Behaviors<br>Reinforcing Incompatible Behaviors<br>Punishment | Multiple-Choice 59–79<br>Essay 100–102 |
| MAINTAINING DESIRABLE BEHAVIORS OVER THE LONG RUN | Multiple-Choice 80–84 |

| | |
|---|---|
| ADDRESSING ESPECIALLY DIFFICULT CLASSROOM BEHAVIORS<br>Applied Behavior Analysis<br>Functional Analysis and Positive Behavioral Support | Multiple-Choice 85–89 |
| CONSIDERING DIVERSITY IN STUDENT BEHAVIORS<br>Accommodating Students with Special Needs | Multiple-Choice 90–91 |
| STRENGTHS AND POTENTIAL LIMITATIONS OF BEHAVIORAL APPROACHES | Multiple-Choice 92 |
| The items in the "Integrative Questions" chapter of this Test Bank integrate the content of two or more textbook chapters. Within that chapter, the items listed to the right are relevant to Chapter 9. | Multiple-Choice 8, 10–12, 14<br>Essay 23, 27, 29, 32–39 |

## Multiple-Choice Questions

• 1. One characteristic common to all behaviorist learning theories is an emphasis on:
  a. The effect of the environment on learning
  b. The importance of rewards
  c. The importance of each and every event in a person's life
  d. How one learns by observing the behavior of others

• 2. When behaviorists describe the learner as a "black box," they mean that:
  a. Many stimuli have no noticeable effect on the learner.
  b. Events occurring within the learner cannot be studied scientifically.
  c. Nothing occurs inside the learner.
  d. A learner makes many responses in the absence of any observed external stimulus.

•• 3. Which one of the following examples best illustrates the effect of contiguity on learning?
  a. Because you studied hard Thursday night, you do well on an exam Friday morning.
  b. Because you did well on Friday's exam, you get a good grade at the end of the semester.
  c. As you step onto a tennis court for the first time, you recall how you saw tennis players at Wimbledon serve the ball.
  d. Because a classmate embarrasses you in front of your friends, you associate that classmate with bad feelings.

• 4. Ivan Pavlov conducted a series of studies that led him to propose his theory of classical conditioning. In these studies Pavlov observed how a dog learned to:
  a. Bark when meat was presented.
  b. Bark when meat was taken away.
  c. Wake up when a bright visual stimulus (such as a light) was presented.
  d. Salivate to a simple stimulus such as a light.

• 5. Classical conditioning typically occurs when:
  a. A response is followed by two stimuli.
  b. A response is followed by an unpleasant stimulus.
  c. Two stimuli are presented at about the same time.
  d. A response is followed by a single reinforcing stimulus.

• 6. Which one of the following describes a <u>conditioned stimulus</u> in classical conditioning?
  a. A stimulus that elicits a response without any prior learning being necessary.
  b. A stimulus that begins to elicit a response it has not previously elicited.
  c. A stimulus that follows the conditioned response.
  d. A stimulus that follows the unconditioned response.

•• 7. Edward is severely beaten by his alcoholic father on several occasions. Before long, Edward begins to shake whenever his father approaches. In this situation, Edward's father is:
  a. An unconditioned stimulus
  b. A conditioned stimulus
  c. An unconditioned response
  d. A conditioned response

•• 8. Matthew once had a teacher who punished him severely whenever he did poorly on a mathematics test. Now he refuses to open a math book, saying that he is "too scared" to do so. He has learned to associate mathematics with the pain of punishment. Here, the painful punishment is:
  a. An unconditioned stimulus
  b. An unconditioned response
  c. A conditioned stimulus
  d. A conditioned response

•• 9. Which one of the following responses is most likely to be learned through classical conditioning?
  a. Feeling anxious around horses
  b. Taking a walk on a nice day
  c. Doing homework
  d. Waving to a friend

• 10. Which one of the following statements best describes the phenomenon of <u>generalization</u> in behaviorist learning theories?
  a. Learning a complex skill is much easier once students have learned other, simpler skills.
  b. Students sometimes make an inappropriate response in a particular situation even when they have responded correctly in that situation on numerous other occasions.
  c. Students think that because their classmates are allowed to behave in a particular way, such behavior is acceptable for themselves as well.
  d. When students learn to respond to a certain stimulus in a particular way, they are likely to respond to similar stimuli in the same way.

•• 11. A boy who is beaten severely by his alcoholic father begins to show signs of fearing not only his father, but other men as well. His fear of men who have <u>not</u> beaten him is an example of:

a. Discrimination
b. Extinction
c. Negative reinforcement
d. Generalization

• 12. When are classically conditioned responses most likely to decrease (i.e., undergo extinction)?

a. When the unconditioned stimulus is continually experienced in the absence of the conditioned stimulus.
b. When the conditioned stimulus is continually experienced in the absence of the unconditioned stimulus.
c. When the conditioned response is continually exhibited in the absence of the unconditioned response.
d. When, and only when, the conditioned response is not generalized to a new situation.

•• 13. Which one of the following situations illustrates extinction of a classically conditioned response?

a. Alfonso thinks school is a waste of time because he doesn't learn anything he can really use.
b. Brian experiences more and more anxiety about mathematics as his math problems become increasingly challenging.
c. Carla becomes less afraid of tests over time when she finds that she can succeed at them.
d. Deirdre doesn't like keeping her desk clean because she has too much stuff to arrange it all neatly inside.

•• 14. Nick is extremely anxious whenever he takes a test. From a classical conditioning perspective, we should:

a. Give him a few extremely difficult tests at first, and then gradually give him easier ones.
b. Give him a few easy tests while he is feeling relaxed.
c. Reinforce him for each test question he answers correctly.
d. Reassure him that he can do well if he tries hard.

• 15. If we want to apply a classical conditioning view of learning to our teaching behaviors, we should:

a. Make sure students know which stimuli they should respond to.
b. Reinforce acceptable behaviors and ignore unacceptable ones.
c. Reinforce acceptable behaviors and punish unacceptable ones.
d. Plan classroom activities that students find enjoyable.

• 16. The basic idea underlying operant conditioning is that:

a. Responses are learned primarily through repetition.
b. Responses are affected by the consequences that follow them.
c. Learners are more motivated to acquire some behaviors than others.
d. Stimulus-response associations, once learned, are permanent.

•• 17. Three of the following are examples of operant conditioning. Which one is not?

a. Andrew gives his dog Maggie a scrap of food from his plate whenever Maggie begs at the dinner table. Before long, Maggie is by Andrew's side begging at every meal.

b. Bart uses obscene words when he speaks in class. His teacher scolds him for such language in front of his classmates. Much to the teacher's dismay, Bart's use of obscene words increases.

c. Carol's room has been a disaster area for more than a month, with toys and clothes lying about everywhere. Carol's mother has told Carol that, once the room has been cleaned, they will spend a day at the zoo. There is no noticeable improvement in Carol's housekeeping habits.

d. Daniel once went to visit the elderly woman next door, and she gave him a couple of homemade cookies. Now Daniel goes to see the woman almost every day after school and comes home a half an hour later still licking crumbs off his lips.

•• 18. Mr. Smart tells his students that they can do whatever they want for the first ten minutes of class, but then must turn their attention to the day's assignment. The students are delighted with their ten minutes of "free time" but then do not attend to the assignment when it is time for them to do so. From an operant conditioning perspective, what mistake has Mr. Smart made?

a. Reinforcement is not immediate.

b. He has used negative reinforcement instead of positive reinforcement.

c. Free time is not an effective reinforcer for most students.

d. The "reinforcer" is not contingent on the response.

• 19. Classical conditioning and operant conditioning are two types of learning described by behaviorists. A major difference between them is that:

a. Classical conditioning deals almost exclusively with stimuli, whereas operant conditioning deals almost exclusively with responses.

b. Classical conditioning deals almost exclusively with responses, whereas operant conditioning deals almost exclusively with stimuli.

c. Classically conditioned responses are voluntary, whereas responses learned through operant conditioning are involuntary.

d. Classically conditioned responses are involuntary, whereas responses learned through operant conditioning are voluntary.

• 20. Operant conditioning theorists use the term reinforcement rather than "reward" because:

a. One type of reinforcement (negative reinforcement) is actually a form of punishment.

b. The term "reward" implies a consequence that others would judge to be desirable.

c. The term "reward" can refer only to a material reinforcer.

d. The term "reward" can refer only to a social reinforcer.

• 21. Primary reinforcers are stimuli that:

a. Satisfy physiological needs

b. Are the most effective of all reinforcers

c. Work only with students in the lower elementary grades

d. Are effective even when presented before the desired response

•• 22. Which one of the following is a primary reinforcer?
   a. A penny
   b. A hundred dollars
   c. A glass of water
   d. Praise

•• 23. Good grades are reinforcing to some students, but not to others. Someone explaining this fact from an operant conditioning perspective would say that good grades are <u>most</u> likely to be reinforcers to students who:
   a. Come from middle class backgrounds
   b. Have been told that good grades can help them get a scholarship
   c. Have previously associated grades with other reinforcers
   d. Have never received a grade above C

•• 24. Jerome is a student in your classroom for whom the only effective reinforcer is something to eat, such as candy. You would like Jerome to find your praise reinforcing as well. From an operant conditioning perspective, your best strategy would be which one of the following?
   a. Whenever you give Jerome something to eat, give him praise as well.
   b. Explain to Jerome how important it is that he not be so reliant on concrete reinforcers.
   c. Explain to Jerome that praise gives him feedback about the things he is doing well.
   d. Show Jerome that all his classmates respond positively to praise.

• 25. Which one of the following statements best describes <u>positive reinforcement</u>?
   a. Reinforcement consists of getting something one finds desirable.
   b. Reinforcement consists of getting rid of something one finds <u>un</u>desirable.
   c. A desirable classroom behavior is reinforced.
   d. An <u>un</u>desirable classroom behavior is reinforced.

•• 26. In three of the following situations, positive reinforcement is occurring. In which situation is positive reinforcement <u>not</u> occurring?
   a. Samantha begins behaving better in class when Ms. James allows her to spend extra time with her friends for exhibiting appropriate behavior.
   b. Mr. Lewis consistently praises Mark for completing his independent seatwork on time, and Mark's work habits improve.
   c. Ms. Villareal scolds Jeremy every time he speaks out of turn, but Jeremy's speaking out is increasing rather than decreasing.
   d. Mr. Salazar smiles at Ellen every time she acts appropriately toward her classmates, but Ellen's social behaviors don't improve.

•• 27. Bill's behaviors in Ms. Kennedy's class are really distracting to other students. For example, he whispers to the boy beside him when Ms. Kennedy is giving directions on how to do any assignment. He flings paper clips at a girl across the room. He makes strange grunting noises that a few classmates find amusing. Ms. Kennedy glares at him or admonishes him whenever he behaves in a distracting way, yet his inappropriate behaviors are <u>increasing</u> rather than decreasing. Which one of the following interpretations best explains why Bill's behaviors are increasing?

a. Ms. Kennedy is positively reinforcing him for the distracting behaviors.
b. Ms. Kennedy is negatively reinforcing him for the distracting behaviors.
c. Ms. Kennedy is vicariously reinforcing him for the distracting behaviors.
d. Ms. Kennedy is punishing him for the distracting behaviors.

•• 28. Which one of the following is the best example of a <u>social reinforcer</u>?

a. Getting a new outfit that you think is "cool."
b. Being allowed to play basketball at a friend's house after you finish your homework.
c. Being told that you did a good job.
d. Feeling good about your own generosity toward a less fortunate classmate.

•• 29. Which one of the following is the best example of the use of the <u>Premack principle</u>?

a. Getting a new outfit that you think is "cool."
b. Being allowed to play basketball at a friend's house after you finish your homework.
c. Being told that you did a good job.
d. Feeling good about your own generosity toward a less fortunate classmate.

•• 30. Ms. Aguilar's third-grade students enjoy art and spend much of their free time drawing and painting. If she tells them, "You can paint as soon as you finish your arithmetic problems," she is providing:

a. Negative reinforcement
b. An activity reinforcer
c. An intrinsic reinforcer
d. Intermittent reinforcement

•• 31. One common educational practice is to chart students' progress over time so that students can see their own improvement. These progress charts often lead to higher student achievement in the absence of other observable forms of reinforcement. The effectiveness of such charts in changing behavior illustrates the role of reinforcement:

a. As feedback
b. As an immediate, rather than delayed, consequence
c. As a delayed, rather than immediate, consequence
d. In standardized achievement testing

•• 32. Which one of the following is the best example of <u>intrinsic reinforcement</u>?

a. Getting a new outfit that you think is "cool."
b. Being allowed to play basketball at a friend's house after you finish your homework.
c. Being told that you did a good job.
d. Feeling good about your own generosity toward a less fortunate classmate.

• 33. The term negative reinforcement can best be described as a situation in which:
  a. Something the student wants is presented after a response
  b. Something the student wants is taken away after a response
  c. Something the student doesn't want is presented after a response
  d. Something the student doesn't want is taken away after a response

•• 34. Which one of the following is an example of negative reinforcement?
  a. A teacher praises Kevin profusely, to the point that it embarrasses him, when he does his homework.
  b. When Kathleen insults another student while waiting in line for lunch, her teacher moves her to the end of the line.
  c. When Edward complains about a classmate who is picking on him, his teacher allows him to come in from recess on bitterly cold days.
  d. When Priscilla answers a teacher's question incorrectly, Mike teases her unmercifully.

•• 35. In the middle of a difficult exam, Robert tells his teacher that his stomach hurts, and the teacher immediately sends him to the school nurse. On several later occasions when he has a difficult test or assignment, Robert again tells his teacher that he doesn't feel well. Each time he is sent to the school nurse without completing his work. From an operant conditioning perspective, we can say that Robert is:
  a. Being punished for complaining about his stomach.
  b. Being negatively reinforced for complaining about his stomach.
  c. Being intermittently reinforced for complaining about his stomach.
  d. Developing an unconditioned response to complain.

•• 36. Stacey dislikes physical education class because her classmates tease her about her lack of strength and coordination. One day Stacey unintentionally hits one of her classmates, and the teacher sends her to the principal's office for the remainder of the class time. Stacey becomes increasingly aggressive in class and so spends more and more time in the principal's office. From an operant conditioning perspective, we can explain this situation by saying that Stacey is:
  a. Receiving a social reinforcer.
  b. Being reinforced through the Premack Principle.
  c. Being negatively reinforced for her aggression.
  d. Generalizing her response to the principal's office.

•• 37. When Mr. Thompson yells at his students, they stop being so noisy. Mr. Thompson is receiving ________ for his yelling behavior.
  a. intermittent reinforcement
  b. negative reinforcement
  c. intrinsic reinforcement
  d. punishment

•• 38. Six-year-old Jack has recently learned to appreciate the value of money, so his father assigns him some simple housekeeping chores to be performed throughout the week. He tells Jack that completion of these chores will earn him an allowance of one dollar every Saturday. Jack rarely completes his chores. From an operant conditioning perspective, which one of the following is <u>most</u> likely to be the reason why Jack is not doing his chores?

a. Reinforcement is not immediate.
b. Reinforcement is not contingent on the desired response.
c. Money is not an effective reinforcer for most six-year-olds.
d. The reinforcer is presented before the response.

• 39. If you wanted to encourage kindergartners to <u>delay gratification</u>, you would be most likely to:

a. Tell them that how well they behave at the end of the day is really what counts
b. Ask them to focus on how good it feels to do something nice for a classmate
c. Talk about how their learning efforts today will pay off in the years to come
d. Occasionally remind them that they will get a bigger reward by waiting a couple of hours

• 40. If you were to apply the concept of <u>terminal behavior</u> in teaching a lesson, which one of these things would you do?

a. Identify the things students should be able to do at the end of the lesson.
b. Identify the sequence in which you should teach various parts of the lesson.
c. Reward students who successfully complete the lesson.
d. Make sure all students have mastered the prerequisite skills on which the lesson depends.

• 41. Three of the following statements are consistent with the textbook's recommendations regarding the effective use of reinforcement. Which statement is <u>in</u>consistent with the textbook's recommendations?

a. Use the same reinforcer for all students.
b. Be explicit about what behaviors lead to what consequences.
c. Describe desired behaviors concretely.
d. Monitor students' progress when using reinforcement to improve behavior.

•• 42. In Mr. Medeiros's classroom, students are given play money each time they turn in an assignment; they receive additional amounts of money if the assignment is turned in on time and if it is done correctly. At the end of each week, students can use their "money" to purchase special privileges (free time, special privileges, etc.). Mr. Medeiros' approach can best be characterized as:

a. Intermittent reinforcement
b. A group contingency
c. A token economy
d. A contingency contract

•• 43. Mr. Richards gives his class fifteen minutes of free time whenever at least 95% of the class gets a passing grade on a test. Mr. Richards is using:
   a. A social reinforcer
   b. Intrinsic reinforcement
   c. A group contingency
   d. A continuous reinforcement schedule

•• 44. Ms. Martin has several students who are chronic misbehavers. She meets individually with each student, and together she and the student agree to a plan for improving the student's behavior and a suitable reinforcement for appropriate behavior change. Ms. Martin is using:
   a. Reinforcement of an incompatible behavior
   b. A contingency contract
   c. Self-reinforcement
   d. Self-monitoring

• 45. An essential element of a contingency contract is that:
   a. Every student have a contract concerning the same behavior.
   b. Behaviors are reinforced in a concrete fashion at least once a day.
   c. Teacher and student agree on the desired behavior and its consequence.
   d. All students receive the same reinforcers.

•• 46. Which one of the following illustrates all the necessary elements of a contingency contract?
   a. Mr. Osaka wants to reduce Penny's aggressive behaviors toward her classmates. He and Penny meet and discuss the problem, agreeing on the specific behaviors she should demonstrate and the reinforcers she will receive when she does so. They both sign a contract that describes the desired behaviors and the reinforcement.
   b. Ms. Quineras wants Ramon to learn to stay in his seat and complete his assignments during independent seatwork time. She makes up a contract for Ramon that describes the consequence he can expect if he does not behave appropriately. They both sign it, and she follows through with the consequence when he misbehaves.
   c. Mr. Sellers wants to help Trina learn to complete her homework in a more timely fashion. He has Trina write up a contract stating that she will complete her homework on time and specifying the reinforcer she would like to receive each time she does so. Both teacher and student sign the contract, and Mr. Sellers reinforces Trina as she has requested.
   d. Mr. Enright develops a contract for her fifth graders that lists several classroom rules the students must agree to abide by. Each student signs the contract, thereby agreeing to follow the rules and acknowledging that there will be consequences when they disobey those rules.

•• 47. Ms. Hernandez is concerned about Brian, a student in her high school chemistry class who rarely interacts with other students. Ms. Hernandez decides to smile at Brian on those occasions when she happens to notice him talking with another student. Yet after three weeks she sees little change in his behavior. Based on this information, which one of the following is definitely wrong with Ms. Hernandez's approach?

a. Brian has little to gain by changing his behavior.
b. Brian is receiving intermittent rather than continuous reinforcement.
c. Social interaction is not an intrinsically reinforcing activity.
d. A smile is not an effective reinforcer.

•• 48. Which one of the following examples best illustrates the concept of baseline as behaviorists use the term?

a. Dimitri is afraid of the school swimming pool after he almost drowns in it one day.
b. Louisa likes the attention she gets from boys when she wears tight sweaters.
c. Marsha starts copying her best friend's homework assignments regularly after she finds out that she gets better grades if she does so.
d. Justin talks in class all the time, even though his teacher and classmates do nothing to encourage him.

•• 49. Leonard rarely says nice things to anyone else. Using operant conditioning terminology, we can say that:

a. Leonard's baseline for this behavior is very low.
b. Leonard will benefit only from intrinsic reinforcement for such behavior.
c. Leonard has little tolerance for such behavior.
d. Leonard's social skills are generalizing to a different situation.

• 50. Which one of the following best describes shaping?

a. Reinforcement becomes increasingly stronger over time.
b. Reinforcement is weaned away over time, until a student is doing something without being reinforced.
c. The behavior being reinforced changes over time so that it increasingly resembles the desired terminal behavior.
d. Praise is the only reinforcer used, and the specific things that are said to a student change as the student improves.

•• 51. Mr. Johnson wants a hyperactive boy to be able to sit quietly for at least 15 minutes at a time. To do this, he begins praising the boy for sitting still for one minute, then for two minutes, and only for four minutes, and so on. Mr. Johnson's strategy reflects which one of the following concepts?

a. Shaping
b. Generalization
c. Intermittent reinforcement
d. Discrimination learning

•• 52. Warren has earned himself a reputation for being the class clown. His teacher, Ms. Washington, used to laugh at Warren's funny remarks, but is now trying to discourage Warren's disruptive behavior by ignoring his jokes. In spite of Ms. Washington's attempts to ignore Warren, Warren sometimes tells a joke so funny that Ms. Washington laughs in spite of herself. Rather than decreasing his joke-telling, Warren begins telling even more outrageous jokes. Inadvertently, Ms. Washington is modifying Warren's joke-telling behavior through:

   a. Punishment
   b. Extinction
   c. Shaping
   d. Negative reinforcement

•• 53. Lori has learned that when she wants to say something in class, she must raise her hand before doing so. At home, however, she speaks without ever raising her hand ahead of time. We can say that the classroom has become a(n) ____ for Lori's hand-raising behavior.

   a. generalized stimulus
   b. antecedent stimulus
   c. positive stimulus
   d. negative reinforcer

•• 54. Which one of the following statements best illustrates the process of <u>cueing</u> acceptable behaviors?

   a. "Does anyone know why Henry isn't in school today?"
   b. "Thank you, everyone, for following the format I asked you to use on your math papers. It makes them easier for me to grade."
   c. "Students who are sitting quietly will be the first ones to be dismissed."
   d. "Who is planning to try out for the school play after school today?"

•• 55. A teacher wants to encourage her students to work cooperatively with one another as they study classroom subject matter. If she wants to use the concept of a <u>setting event</u> to encourage such cooperative behavior, she might:

   a. Praise her students when they cooperate with one another
   b. First give students a task in which they can<u>not</u> work with one another
   c. Say, "I like how Sally and John are helping one another today," loudly enough that other students can hear
   d. Provide instructional materials that students can only use by working together

•• 56. Oliver tells a tasteless joke at a party and gets a big laugh. The next day, he tells the same joke in class, thinking people will laugh. Instead, his teacher takes him aside after class and gives him a stern lecture about why he should not say such things about a particular ethnic group. In operant conditioning terminology, we could say that Oliver:

   a. Has generalized from one situation to another inappropriately
   b. Is being shaped to tell tasteless jokes
   c. Is receiving negative reinforcement for his joke-telling behavior
   d. Experiences a group contingency at the party, but not in class

•• 57. Sharon has learned that her language arts teacher answers her questions willingly, but that her biology teacher discourages questions. Sharon therefore asks questions in language arts, but not in biology. In operant conditioning terminology, Sharon is:

a. On a continuous reinforcement schedule
b. Being shaped
c. Showing generalization
d. Showing discrimination

•• 58. A physics teacher wants her students to work on several difficult physics problems that involve calculating velocity, acceleration, or time using the formula v = a x t. The teacher first has her students work on a few easy problems involving the formula. She then presents the more difficult problems; when she does so, she finds that her students are reasonably persistent in working at the problems, and most of her students eventually solve them correctly. By using the easy problems to promote persistence in her students during the more difficult ones, the teacher is, in behaviorist terminology, using the concept of:

a. cueing
b. behavioral momentum
c. discrimination
d. intermittent reinforcement

•• 59. Caleb continually blurts out the answers to Mr. Karowski's questions, to the point where other students rarely have a chance to respond. Mr. Karowski decides to ignore Caleb's behavior, hoping that it will decrease if he doesn't pay attention to it. Mr. Karowski is applying the behaviorist principle of _________ in his treatment of Caleb.

a. intermittent reinforcement
b. extinction
c. punishment
d. incompatible behavior

•• 60. Sean is a high school student who seems angry most of the time. He often vents his anger by swearing at his teacher. One day his teacher decides to extinguish Sean's swearing by ignoring him whenever he swears. Yet over the next few weeks, Sean continues to swear as frequently as he always has. Three of the following are possible explanations as to why Sean's swearing is not decreasing. From an operant conditioning perspective, which one is not a likely explanation based on this information?

a. Sean's swearing has previously been reinforced on an intermittent basis.
b. Sean is being reinforced for swearing by means of the Premack Principle.
c. Other students are reinforcing Sean's swearing.
d. Swearing allows Sean to release pent-up anger, so he is being negatively reinforced.

• 61. Three of the following teacher behaviors illustrate cueing as a way of dealing with inappropriate behavior. Which one does not illustrate cueing?

a. Moving closer to a student who may be cheating on an exam.
b. Putting one's finger on one's lips when the class gets too noisy.
c. Glaring at a student who is reading a comic book instead of getting to work on an assignment.
d. Putting a student in time-out after she's insulted a classmate.

• 62. Your class has just returned from lunch. Although all your students are in their seats, they are busily chattering and having difficulty focusing their attention on the next lesson. Which one of the following strategies is most consistent with the textbook's recommendations regarding effective strategies for reducing undesirable behaviors?

a. Ignore the behavior and proceed with the lesson, figuring that your students will settle down within a few minutes.
b. Ridicule those students who are talking the loudest.
c. Let students know that their behavior is unacceptable by flicking the light switch.
d. Tell your students that if they don't settle down, you'll give them a difficult homework assignment.

• 63. Which one of the following statements best characterizes how <u>reinforcement of incompatible behavior</u> helps reduce inappropriate behavior in the classroom?

a. When we reinforce different students for different behaviors, they begin to discover which behaviors are appropriate and which are not.
b. Negative reinforcement of an incompatible behavior can ultimately reduce the frequency of that behavior.
c. An undesirable behavior will decrease when the student is reinforced for behaving in an opposite manner.
d. We can reduce serious behavior problems by allowing students to engage in less serious misbehaviors.

•• 64. Which one of the following is an example of reinforcing an incompatible behavior as a way of eliminating an undesirable behavior?

a. Samantha is very shy and socially withdrawn. Her teacher reinforces her with a smile whenever she interacts with her classmates.
b. Johnny's wisecracks have become so annoying that his teacher keeps him in from recess whenever he speaks inappropriately.
c. Mary has learned to reinforce herself whenever she gets all her spelling words correct.
d. Jerry must stay after school on days when he arrives late.

•• 65. Loretta has been painting graffiti on the school walls after school hours. The school principal and the school counselor discuss this problem and finally agree that they will try to eliminate Loretta's graffiti-painting by asking her to chair a Clean-Up-The-School ("CUTS") committee, then giving her school-wide recognition for her efforts. The counselor is suggesting:

a. Cueing
b. Reinforcement of an incompatible behavior
c. Presentation punishment
d. Removal punishment

•• 66. Which one of the following is the best example of punishment as behaviorists define it?
   a. Kelly has been acting up in the classroom all year. Her teacher's frequent reprimands haven't made much of a difference in Kelly's behavior.
   b. Leonard is a real distraction to his classmates, often burping in a way that makes other students laugh. His teacher places him in a corner where others can't hear him burping.
   c. Whenever Marvin has trouble sitting still, his teacher has him run up and down the hall three times to release pent-up energy.
   d. After Norma spends a few minutes in the time-out room for hurting a classmate's feelings, she acts more compassionately toward that classmate in the future.

•• 67. Ms. Smythe keeps Eric after school whenever he swears in class. Even though Eric has been kept after school each day for the past three weeks, his swearing has increased rather than decreased. Given what we know about the effects of punishment on behavior, Ms. Smythe should probably conclude that:
   a. Her punishment is only temporarily suppressing Eric's swearing.
   b. The punishment is too severe.
   c. Eric's swearing will decrease eventually.
   d. Staying after school is reinforcing for Eric.

• 68. In which one of the following situations is punishment of a misbehavior justified?
   a. Any time a behavior interferes with other students' learning.
   b. When other disciplinary strategies have failed.
   c. When a student has exhibited the behavior at least three times.
   d. Never. Negative reinforcement of inappropriate behavior is always the method of choice.

• 69. Which one of the following accurately describes the difference between negative reinforcement and punishment?
   a. Negative reinforcement is essentially the same as punishment, but without the negative connotations that punishment has.
   b. Negative reinforcement increases the frequency of behavior, whereas punishment decreases it.
   c. Negative reinforcement always decreases the frequency of behavior, whereas punishment often increases it.
   d. Both consequences decrease behavior, but punishment is more likely to make students angry and defiant.

•• 70. Tammy is scolded for submitting a messy math homework paper, so she tries to do her math problems more neatly after that. The scolding Tammy received is an example of:
   a. Positive reinforcement
   b. Negative reinforcement
   c. Presentation punishment
   d. Removal punishment

•• 71. Alex loses his best friend Tyler when he tattles on Tyler at recess. Alex learns that tattling on friends is not a good idea. The loss of Tyler's friendship is an example of:
   a. Positive reinforcement
   b. Negative reinforcement
   c. Presentation punishment
   d. Removal punishment

•• 72. George enjoys being on the debating team, but he is taken off the team when he inadvertently utters an obscene word during a debate. George's removal from the team is an example of:
   a. Reinforcement of an incompatible behavior
   b. Negative reinforcement
   c. Presentation punishment
   d. Removal punishment

•• 73. Linda wears bell-bottom pants to school, and her classmates tease her about them. As soon as she gets home, Linda throws the pants in the trash. Linda's being teased is an example of:
   a. Reinforcement of an incompatible behavior
   b. Negative reinforcement
   c. Presentation punishment
   d. Removal punishment

• 74. Only one of the following consequences has been shown to be an effective and appropriate punishment for most students. Which one?
   a. Suspension from school
   b. Scolding
   c. Embarrassment in front of classmates
   d. Extra homework

•• 75. When Judy becomes verbally aggressive toward her peers, she is placed in a quiet and boring room for five minutes. The procedure being used here is most commonly known as:
   a. Time-out
   b. A logical consequence
   c. Response cost
   d. In-school suspension

•• 76. In Mr. Marshall's classroom, students who acquire 20 points in one day can have a half hour of free time at the end of the day. Mr. Marshall awards points to his students for good behavior and deducts points when they misbehave. The deduction of points for misbehavior is known as:
   a. Time-out
   b. A logical consequence
   c. Response cost
   d. In-school suspension

• 77. Which one of the following is the major advantage of in-school suspension over out-of-school suspension as a consequence for serious and chronic misbehavior?
   a. In-school suspension is more convenient and less expensive for the school district.
   b. In-school suspension enables a student to keep up with schoolwork.
   c. In-school suspension gives teachers and administrators a better chance to explain why the punished behavior is unacceptable.
   d. In-school suspension eliminates the need for parents to become involved in school affairs.

• 78. Which one of the following is the major reason why assigning extra schoolwork is <u>not</u> an appropriate punishment for classroom misbehavior?
   a. It gives students the message that classwork is an unpleasant task.
   b. It decreases the likelihood that students will do their assignments appropriately.
   c. It asks students to perform tasks without the scaffolding they need for completing those tasks successfully.
   d. It is negative reinforcement rather than punishment.

• 79. Three of the following are recommended practices when using punishment to reduce an inappropriate behavior. Which one is <u>not</u> recommended?
   a. Punish the behavior each time it occurs.
   b. Tell students ahead of time what behaviors are unacceptable and will be punished.
   c. Explain why a punished behavior is unacceptable.
   d. Administer a student's punishment in front of classmates so they learn by example.

• 80. Which one of the following is most likely to maintain desirable classroom behavior over the long run?
   a. A desire to please one's teacher
   b. A desire to please one's classmates
   c. Enjoyment of classroom topics and activities
   d. Positive feedback

• 81. Which one of the following statements most accurately describes <u>intermittent reinforcement</u>?
   a. The reinforcement a student receives becomes stronger over time.
   b. A primary reinforcer is used at first, but it is gradually replaced by a secondary reinforcer.
   c. A particular response is reinforced on some occasions but not others.
   d. One response is reinforced for a while, then another response is reinforced, then another, and so on, over a period of several weeks or months.

•• 82. Ms. O'Connor reinforces James every time she sees him reading independently. Once he is reading on a regular basis, she begins to reinforce him only every second time, then only every third time, and so on, gradually reinforcing him less and less often. From an operant conditioning perspective, we can predict that Jimmy will:
   a. Continue to read independently.
   b. Read less and less often.
   c. Read only when he is coerced to do so.
   d. Stop reading altogether.

•• 83. At the beginning of the school year, Mr. Webber is concerned that Frances rarely does her independent seatwork. He begins praising Frances for each seatwork assignment she completes, and by January she is completing her assignments regularly. To make sure that the behavior continues in the years to come, what would operant conditioning theorists tell Mr. Webber to do now?

a. Praise her more often than before.
b. Praise her for only some of her completed assignments.
c. Punish Frances when she doesn't complete an assignment.
d. Switch from a social reinforcer to the Premack Principle.

•• 84. John and Bill have both learned that when they whine and complain, their teacher will hurry over to see what's wrong. John's teacher gives him attention every time he complains. However, Bill's teacher gives him attention only on some of the occasions he complains. Both teachers eventually realize that they are reinforcing the boys for inappropriate behavior, and so they both stop attending to them when they whine and complain. From an operant conditioning perspective, we can predict that:

a. Both boys will whine and complain even more than before.
b. Both boys will stop their whining and complaining almost immediately.
c. Bill's complaining will decrease more rapidly than John's.
d. John's complaining will decrease more rapidly than Bill's.

• 85. Applied behavior analysis can best be described as a group of techniques that can change a student's behavior by changing the student's:

a. Self-concept
b. Environment
c. Curriculum
d. Attitude

• 86. Research studies indicate that applied behavior analysis techniques:

a. Leads to significant improvements in both academic achievement and social skills.
b. Promotes improvement in academic achievement but not in social skills.
c. Promotes improvement in social skills but not in academic achievement.
d. Has little long-term effect on students' classroom performance.

• 87. Three of the following are often found in applied behavior analysis programs, but only one is also found in functional analysis and positive behavioral support. Which one distinguishes functional analysis and positive behavioral support from applied behavioral analysis?

a. Identifying an effective reinforcer
b. Following desirable behavior with reinforcement
c. Telling students which behaviors lead to which consequences
d. Exploring underlying purposes that a student's behavior may serve

•• 88. Vanessa frequently complains of getting terrible headaches and so ends up at the nurse's office several times a week. Yet two different physicians have been unable to find a cause for Vanessa's headaches, and Vanessa's parents report that their daughter rarely has headaches at home. Vanessa is falling further and further behind in her schoolwork, so Vanessa's teacher and parents meet with the nurse and school psychologist to brainstorms possible solutions to Vanessa's problem. The school psychologist suggests that the teacher keep track of the occasions when Vanessa complains about a headache. Two weeks later, the teacher reports that all of Vanessa's complaints occur just before a test or difficult assignment. Suddenly the teacher and parents begin to suspect that perhaps Vanessa complains of headaches as a way of getting out of difficult schoolwork. Here we see the initial steps in a process known as:

a. The use of incompatible behaviors
b. Functional analysis
c. Behavioral momentum
d. Extinction of inappropriate behavior

• 89. Three of the following are typical components of positive behavioral support. Which one is <u>not</u>?

a. Reinforcing new behaviors on an intermittent basis
b. Providing numerous opportunities for the student to make choices
c. Teaching appropriate behaviors that can substitute for inappropriate ones
d. Changing the classroom environment to make inappropriate behaviors less likely

• 90. From a behaviorist perspective, we are likely to see diversity in our students with respect to three of the following. Which one is <u>not</u> a major source of diversity in students?

a. The extent to which various secondary reinforcers are effective
b. The ways in which students respond to various stimuli
c. The importance of the environment for learning
d. The kinds of behaviors that have been reinforced in the past

• 91. Three of the following statements are true with respect to students who have special educational needs. Which statement is <u>false</u>?

a. Extrinsic reinforcers are rarely effective for students with mental retardation.
b. Students with social or behavioral problems have difficulty identifying situations when particular behaviors are appropriate.
c. Students with specific cognitive difficulties may have trouble discriminating among similar stimuli.
d. Students with mental retardation have trouble generalizing what they've learned to new situations.

• 92. Which one of the following has been shown to be a potential drawback of using behaviorist techniques in the classroom?

a. They may be useless when students have little motivation to change their behavior.
b. They are often ineffective with students who have special educational needs, such as students with social or behavioral problems.
c. Improvements last only as long as the behaviorist intervention continues.
d. Extrinsic reinforcement may undermine any intrinsic motivation a student has for behaving appropriately.

**<u>Essay Questions</u>**

• 93. Behaviorist theories share a number of common underlying assumptions. Describe <u>three</u> assumptions that behaviorists make and the implication of each one for classroom practice.

•• 94. Edward was accidentally hurt in his physical education class last week when a large boy ran into him and knocked the breath out of him. Edward is now afraid to go to physical education. Explain this situation in terms of classical conditioning, identifying the UCS, UCR, CS, and CR.

•• 95. In each of the following situations, a student either is learning or has learned something. (1) Classify each of the situations as involving either classical or operant conditioning. (2) Defend your answer by analyzing the situation within the context of the learning paradigm you have chosen.
   a. When James begins running down the hall toward the cafeteria, his teacher asks him to walk instead. James begins walking, and the teacher gives him a smile. After that, James always makes sure that he walks rather than runs to the cafeteria.
   b. Ralph's friend offers him an illegal drug. Ralph takes the drug and finds that it makes him feel great. Ralph begins to buy the drug himself and takes it more and more frequently.
   c. Linda is a bright, academically capable girl. Once when she was sick, she failed an important test. Now she is very anxious whenever she takes a test.

• 96. Distinguish among positive reinforcement, negative reinforcement, presentation punishment, and removal punishment. Give a concrete example of each.

•• 97. Greg has terrible study habits: whenever he is given an assignment to be done either in class or at home, he doesn't begin the assignment until he has been repeatedly nagged by either you (his teacher) or by his parents. Furthermore, Greg seems unable to complete assignments without constant prodding to stay on task. Explain how you might use <u>operant conditioning</u> to help Greg develop better study habits. Be concrete and specific in your explanation of what you would do, and be sure to include each of the following in your description:
   a. The baseline
   b. The terminal behavior
   c. A secondary reinforcer you might use
   d. Shaping
   e. Some means of preventing extinction

•• 98. A girl in your classroom rarely interacts with her classmates. She is obviously quite lonely but apparently has no confidence in her ability to make friends. <u>Using an operant conditioning perspective</u>, describe how you might help the girl develop social skills through <u>shaping</u>. In your discussion, be sure to include:
   a. The specific behavior(s) you would shape
   b. A specific reinforcer you might use, and why you make the choice you do
   c. The sequence of steps you might take as you shape the desired behavior

•• 99. You are giving tennis lessons to a beginning tennis player. Describe how you would teach the proper tennis swing through <u>shaping</u>. Specify:
   a. An appropriate terminal behavior
   b. A reinforcer you might use
   c. The specific steps you would take during shaping
   d. When you would use continuous reinforcement
   e. When you would use intermittent reinforcement

•• 100. Ursula is always getting out of her seat at inappropriate times. You scold her every time she does this, but her behavior seems to be getting worse rather than better.
   a. From an operant conditioning perspective, why is Ursula's getting-out-of-seat behavior increasing rather than decreasing?
   b. How might you decrease her behavior by <u>reinforcing an incompatible behavior</u>? Describe your procedure in detail, specifying the reinforcer and the behavior you will reinforce.

•• 101. In each of the following situations, a person is learning through either reinforcement or punishment. Classify each situation as involving one of these four consequences: positive reinforcement, negative reinforcement, presentation punishment, or removal punishment. Then explain why you chose the answer you did.
   a. Because Danielle fails her math class, she is taken off the school dance squad.
   b. Joe always does his homework assignments as soon as he gets them so he won't have to worry about them anymore.
   c. Lisa and Fran are giggling together in the back of the classroom. Their teacher scowls at them. They are embarrassed and shut up.
   d. A teacher finds that by yelling at her students when they get too rowdy, they will settle down and be quiet for a while. (Focus on what is happening to the <u>teacher</u>.)

•• 102. David is continually fighting with other children. Devise a plan to eliminate the fighting by using a combination of both reinforcement of incompatible behavior and punishment. In your discussion, be sure to explain:
   a. What incompatible behavior(s) you will reinforce
   b. What reinforcer you will use, and why
   c. What punishment you will use, and why

# ANSWER KEY

## Multiple-Choice Questions

1. a
2. b
3. d
4. d
5. c
6. b
7. b
8. a
9. a
10. d
11. d
12. b
13. c
14. b
15. d
16. b
17. c
18. d
19. d
20. b
21. a
22. c
23. c
24. a
25. a
26. d
27. a
28. c
29. b
30. b
31. a
32. d
33. d
34. c
35. b
36. c
37. b
38. a
39. d
40. a
41. a
42. c
43. c
44. b
45. c
46. a
47. b
48. d
49. a
50. c
51. a
52. c
53. b
54. c
55. d
56. a
57. d
58. b
59. b
60. b
61. d
62. c
63. c
64. a
65. b
66. d
67. d
68. b
69. b
70. c
71. d
72. d
73. c
74. b
75. a
76. c
77. b
78. a
79. d
80. c
81. c
82. a
83. b
84. d
85. b
86. a
87. d
88. b
89. a
90. c
91. a
92. d

## Essay Questions

93. Assumptions underlying behaviorism are these (the student's response should describe at least three of them):
    - People's behaviors are the result of their experiences with the environment.
    - Learning can be described in terms of stimulus-response relationships.
    - Learning involves a change in behavior.
    - Learning is more likely to occur when there is contiguity between two stimuli and/or responses.
    - Many species, including humans, learn in similar ways.

    Each assumption that the student identifies should be accompanied by an appropriate implication.

94. Edward associated physical education class with losing his breath—something that frightened him. Losing his breath was the UCS; being afraid as a result was the UCR. Physical education class and the boy who ran into him were associated with losing his breath; hence they were CSs. Fearing physical education class and fearing the boy became CRs. It is sufficient to identify one CS and one CR.

95. Responses to various parts of the question are as follows:
    a. This is operant conditioning (walking is a voluntary response). Walking is reinforced by the teacher's smile and increases in frequency as a result.
    b. This is operant conditioning (taking a drug is a voluntary response). Taking the drug is reinforced by the feeling it produces, so the behavior increases in frequency.
    c. This is classical conditioning (anxiety is an involuntary response). Failure is the UCS; the anxiety that results from failure is the UCR. A test is associated with failure, so it is the CS; the anxiety caused by a test alone is the CR.

96. Positive reinforcement is a consequence whereby a presumably desirable stimulus is presented; negative reinforcement is a consequence whereby a presumably unpleasant stimulus is removed. Presentation punishment involves the presentation of an aversive stimulus; removal punishment involves the removal of a presumably desirable stimulus. Both positive and negative reinforcement lead to an increase in the behavior they follow. Both presentation punishment and removal punishment lead to a decrease in the behavior they follow. Each of these four concepts should be illustrated with a concrete example.

97. Responses to various parts of the question are as follows:
    a. Greg's baseline for completing his assignments without reinforcement is essentially zero—he doesn't do them.
    b. The desired terminal behavior is doing his homework on a regular basis without being prodded.
    c. Possible secondary reinforcers include praise, feedback, favorite activities, checkmarks or other tokens that can be traded in for something special, etc. (Any reasonable secondary reinforcer is acceptable here.)
    d. Descriptions of a shaping procedure will vary; the response should describe reinforcing a series of steps that become increasingly more similar to the desired terminal behavior.
    e. Extinction can be prevented by continuing to reinforce Greg on an intermittent basis after the terminal behavior has been reached. It can also be prevented by continuing to provide an extrinsic reinforcer until such time as Greg finds studying behavior intrinsically reinforcing. (One of these strategies, or a reasonable equivalent, is sufficient.)

98. Responses to various parts of the question are as follows:
    a. One or more social behaviors (e.g., carrying on a conversation, smiling at others, initiating interaction with a classmate, etc.) should be shaped.
    b. Because the girl appears to be lonely, some form of social reinforcer (praise, attention, etc.) may be appropriate. Or perhaps, if the girl really wants to make friends, positive feedback regarding appropriate social behavior might be sufficient. (One of these or any other well-justified reinforcer is acceptable here.)
    c. Any series of steps that resemble closer and closer approximations to effective interaction with peers is acceptable here. A complete response should probably have three steps at a minimum.

99. Responses to various parts of the question are as follows:
    a. The terminal behavior is an effective tennis swing defined in some concrete, observable fashion—for example, swinging the racket in such a way that it gets the ball over the net and into the opponent's court at least 80% of the time.
    b. Assuming that the student is taking tennis lessons voluntarily, an appropriate reinforcer might be praise, feedback, or some other simple stimulus that conveys a job well done. (Any justifiable reinforcer is acceptable here.)
    c. Any series of steps that resemble closer and closer approximations to an effective tennis swing is acceptable here. A complete response should probably have three steps at a minimum.
    d. The teacher should use continuous reinforcement until the terminal behavior has been reached (i.e., until the end of the shaping process).
    e. The teacher should switch to intermittent reinforcement once the student is using an effective swing regularly.

100. Responses to the two parts of the question are as follows:
    a. Scolding is apparently reinforcing to Ursula, because the behavior is increasing rather than decreasing.
    b. Ursula should be reinforced for sitting in her seat. The response should describe a reasonable reinforcer for Ursula (perhaps teacher attention in one form or another).

101. Responses to various parts of the question are as follows:
    a. This is removal punishment: a pleasant state of affairs (being on the dance squad) is removed after Danielle fails her math class.
    b. This is negative reinforcement: Joe is doing his homework in order to get rid of something unpleasant (his feeling of worry).
    c. This is presentation punishment: something presented (a scowl) leads to a decrease in giggling behavior.
    d. This is negative reinforcement: the teacher's yelling is reinforced by the removal of something she doesn't like (her students' rowdy behavior).

102. Responses to various parts of the question are as follows:
    a. Incompatible behavior in this situation might be either any nonaggressive behavior or specifically prosocial behavior.
    b. A specific reinforcer should be identified and a rationale given as to why this particular reinforcer was chosen.
    c. A specific punishment should be identified that is consistent with the textbook's guidelines for using punishment and a rationale given as to why this particular punishment was chosen.

    The response should describe both the reinforcement of appropriate behaviors toward other children and punishment for fighting.

# Chapter 10
# SOCIAL COGNITIVE VIEWS OF LEARNING

| CHAPTER OUTLINE | RELEVANT TEST BANK ITEMS |
|---|---|
| BASIC ASSUMPTIONS OF SOCIAL COGNITIVE THEORY | Multiple-Choice 1–4<br>Essay 64 |
| THE SOCIAL COGNITIVE VIEW OF REINFORCEMENT AND PUNISHMENT<br>Expectations<br>Vicarious Experiences<br>Cognitive Processing<br>Choice of Behavior<br>Nonoccurrence of Expected Consequences | Multiple-Choice 5–16<br>Essay 65–66 |
| MODELING<br>How Modeling Affects Behavior<br>Characteristics of Effective Models<br>Helping Students Learn from Models | Multiple-Choice 17–27<br>Essay 67 |
| SELF-EFFICACY<br>How Self-Efficacy Affects Behavior<br>Factors in the Development of Self-Efficacy | Multiple-Choice 28–36<br>Essay 68 |
| SELF-REGULATION<br>Self-Regulated Behavior<br>Self-Regulated Learning<br>Self-Regulated Problem Solving | Multiple-Choice 37–57<br>Essay 69–70 |
| RECIPROCAL CAUSATION | Multiple-Choice 58–60 |
| CONSIDERING DIVERSITY FROM A SOCIAL COGNITIVE PERSPECTIVE<br>Using Diverse Models to Promote Success and Self-Efficacy<br>Promoting Self-Regulation in Students with Special Needs | Multiple-Choice 61–62 |
| THE BIG PICTURE<br>Unifying Ideas in Social Cognitive Theory<br>Comparing the Three Perspectives of Learning | Multiple-Choice 63<br>Essay 71 |

| The items in the "Integrative Questions" chapter of this Test Bank integrate the content of two or more textbook chapters. Within that chapter, the items listed to the right are relevant to Chapter 10. | Multiple-Choice 8–10, 12<br>Essay 20–21, 23, 27–29, 32–37, 39 |
|---|---|

## Multiple-Choice Questions

• 1. Social cognitive theory can best be characterized as being concerned with learning:
   a. Communication skills
   b. Socially appropriate behaviors
   c. Through observations of others
   d. From a sociological rather than psychological perspective

•• 2. Ms. Goodsell is thinking about how she might help the students in her introductory French class learn to pronounce the word <u>bonjour</u> correctly. Which one of her thoughts below is most consistent with a <u>social cognitive</u> perspective of learning?
   a. "If I explain the parts of the word—if I tell them that <u>bon</u> means "good" and <u>jour</u> means "day"—then they will have an easier time understanding why the word is pronounced the way it is."
   b. "Maybe I should show them how I form my mouth and lips as I pronounce the word, and encourage them to imitate me."
   c. "Maybe I should explain how certain letters and letter combinations are consistently pronounced differently in French than they are in English."
   d. "I need to be patient. Correct pronunciation will come in time for those students who are really motivated to speak French."

• 3. Three of the following assumptions underlie social cognitive theory. Which one does <u>not</u>?
   a. Behavior is goal-directed in nature.
   b. Reinforcement has an indirect rather than direct effect on learning.
   c. Reinforcement has an effect not only on the individual being reinforced, but on others as well.
   d. Learning cannot occur unless a change in behavior also occurs.

•• 4. Which one of the following instances of learning can be explained more easily by social cognitive theory than by operant conditioning?
   a. Playing the role of a German soldier in the school play, Andy says his lines using a German accent similar to one he's heard in the movies a few times.
   b. Brad discovers that to get his teacher's approval he must turn in his writing assignments without a single error in grammar, spelling, or punctuation.
   c. Craig finds that he gets one "special" girl's attention when he shows off on the playground.
   d. Darren has stopped trying in school, because he seems to get low grades no matter what he does.

•• 5. A guest speaker is coming to your classroom, and you want your students to treat her with courtesy and respect. You decide to give your students 15 minutes of free time if they show appropriate behavior during the guest's visit. From the perspective of social cognitive theory, your reinforcement is only likely to work if your students:

a. Also experience intrinsic reinforcement for good behavior.
b. Expect that this consequence will follow their good behavior.
c. Have previously been directly reinforced for such behavior.
d. Have previously been vicariously reinforced for such behavior.

• 6. Which one of the following statements best describes vicarious reinforcement?

a. Anticipating future reinforcement.
b. Receiving reinforcement after behaving inappropriately.
c. Remembering reinforcement that one has previously received.
d. Watching someone else receive reinforcement for a behavior.

•• 7. Which one of the following examples illustrates vicarious reinforcement?

a. Alice notices that her friend Ellen gets extra attention from the teacher when she acts helpless. Alice begins to act helpless as well.
b. Bill knows that he will get a higher grade if he turns in a research paper that is typed rather than handwritten, but he turns in a handwritten paper anyway.
c. Connie sees her friend Maria scolded for chewing gum in class. She quickly takes her own gum out of her mouth.
d. David sees how Justin gets good grades when he works hard on his mathematics homework, but David doesn't want to work that hard.

•• 8 Which of the following is an example of vicarious punishment?

a. Alice notices that her friend Ellen gets extra attention from the teacher when she acts helpless. Alice begins to act helpless as well.
b. Bill knows that he will get a higher grade if he turns in a research paper that is typed rather than handwritten, but he turns in a handwritten paper anyway.
c. Connie sees her friend Maria scolded for chewing gum in class. She quickly takes her own gum out of her mouth.
d. David sees how Justin gets good grades when he works hard on his mathematics homework, but David doesn't want to work that hard.

• 9. According to social cognitive theorists, reinforcement affects learning because it:

a. Encourages students to pay attention
b. Reduces the likelihood of punishment
c. Strengthens stimulus-response connections
d. Makes students feel good, thereby eliminating any emotions that might interfere with the learning process

• 10. Your students will undoubtedly know a great many things, and they will not be able to show you everything they know. According to social cognitive theorists, your students will be most likely to show you:

a. Things they learned recently rather than a long time ago.
b. Things they think they will be reinforced for demonstrating.
c. Things they have learned at a concrete rather than abstract level.
d. Things they are especially excited about.

•• 11. Which one of the following is the best example of a student working for an incentive?
   a. Arnold's teacher gives him a big hug after he surprises her by bringing her a cupcake from home.
   b. Betsy decides not to talk in class because her teacher ridiculed her earlier in the day when she gave an incorrect answer.
   c. Cyril stays out late, even though he knows he will be punished when he gets home.
   d. Doris is studying so that she can pass her history test.

• 12. An incentive is likely to be an effective motivator for students only when:
   a. It is described in explicit terms.
   b. It will be available by the end of the same day.
   c. Students believe it is within their reach.
   d. Students believe that their friends will think it's a really "cool" thing to get.

•• 13. Ms. Jefferson promises her students special treats if they turn in their homework assignments the next day. But the following day Ms. Jefferson forgets to bring the treats she promised. From the perspective of social cognitive theory, what has just happened to the students who turned in their homework assignments?
   a. They have been negatively reinforced for doing so.
   b. They have been punished for doing so.
   c. They have been vicariously reinforced for doing so.
   d. Their behavior has been extinguished.

• 14. From the perspective of social cognitive theory, it is essential that we follow through with the reinforcement we have said will follow certain behaviors. Why is such follow-through important?
   a. When expected reinforcement doesn't occur, students feel punished.
   b. Vicarious reinforcement alone is a relatively ineffective means of changing behavior.
   c. Students' self-efficacy is adversely affected if they don't receive reinforcement on a regular basis.
   d. Students learn more quickly when they are reinforced intermittently rather than continuously.

•• 15. Two boys are fighting on school grounds during recess. Fighting is against school rules, and the boys know this. Even so, a teacher who sees them lets them continue to fight rather than punishing them for doing so. Judging from what social cognitive theorists say regarding what happens when expected punishments don't occur, we can predict that these boys will be:
   a. Less likely to fight in the future.
   b. More likely to fight in the future.
   c. Likely to feel guilty when they stop fighting.
   d. Likely to imitate more appropriate social behaviors in the future.

•• 16. John is caught cheating on a homework assignment. He suffers no consequences for doing so, even though cheating is in clear violation of school policy. From a social cognitive perspective, which one of the following predictions can we make about John's future behavior?

a. He will cheat less frequently.
b. He will cheat as frequently as he has in the past.
c. He will cheat more frequently.
d. He will regress to a lower stage of moral reasoning.

•• 17. Sharon knows that Kathy frequently completes her assignments long after they are due. She has noticed that their teacher willingly accepts Kathy's late assignments because Kathy always has a creative excuse for turning them in late. Sharon begins to do the same thing—she turns in assignments past the due date and makes up excuses for why she is late. Sharon's increase in excuse-making is due to:

a. Shaping and intrinsic reinforcement
b. An increase in self-reinforcement
c. A decrease in self-regulation
d. Modeling and vicarious reinforcement

• 18. Research studies indicate that three of the following can be learned through modeling. For which one has modeling <u>not</u> been shown to be a significant factor in learning?

a. Increasing one's IQ score
b. Resisting the advances of strangers
c. Prosocial behavior
d. Aggression

•• 19. Which one of the following is the best example of a <u>symbolic model</u>?

a. A detective on a television show
b. The school principal
c. An older brother or sister
d. The police officer who lives next door

• 20. "Students will exhibit a particular response less frequently if they have seen a classmate punished for that response." This statement best describes the _______ effect of modeling.

a. observational learning
b. response facilitation
c. response inhibition
d. response disinhibition

• 21. "Students are more likely to engage in a forbidden behavior if they see others behaving that way without being punished." This statement best describes the _______ effect of modeling.

a. observational learning
b. response facilitation
c. response inhibition
d. response disinhibition

•• 22. Trudy makes an obscene gesture in class, and the teacher punishes her severely. Other students in class observe both the gesture and the punishment. Based on social cognitive theory, what can we guess about what those students have learned and how they are likely to behave in the future?

a. They don't know how to make the gesture, but they do know that the teacher will punish them severely for inappropriate behavior.
b. They know how to make the gesture but are likely to forget it within a few days.
c. They know how to make the gesture and are likely to make it in class in the future.
d. They know how to make the gesture but are unlikely to make it in class.

•• 23. Considering what we know about the kinds of models people are likely to imitate, we can guess that the girls in our classes will be <u>least</u> likely to imitate:

a. Anita, a skillful auto mechanic
b. Brianne, head majorette in the school band
c. Claudia, the most popular girl in school
d. Darla, a graceful dancer

•• 24. Imagine that you are a teacher at a junior high school. Below are four behaviors you might exhibit in your classroom. Considering the textbook's discussion of modeling, choose the behavior your students are <u>least</u> likely to imitate.

a. You show them how to estimate the price of an outfit they might want to buy.
b. You show them how to fill out their class schedule form for next year.
c. You show them how much you enjoy reading professional education journals.
d. You show them how to make a tasty fruit drink for a hot day.

•• 25. These four teachers claim to be practicing principles from social cognitive theory. Based on the following information, which one is <u>not</u>?

a. Mr. Anderson makes sure students are paying attention when he shows them how to do long division problems.
b. Ms. Benson has students read biographies of people who have worked unselfishly for others (e.g., Albert Schweitzer, Clara Barton, Mahatma Gandhi).
c. Mr. Carlson tells his class he smokes cigarettes, although he wishes he'd never started.
d. Ms. Donaldson shows her new second-grade class how to spell her name by writing it in huge letters on the chalkboard.

• 26. Social cognitive theorists propose that three of the following are essential for modeling to occur. Which one is <u>not</u> essential?

a. Motivation to perform the behavior.
b. Memory of the observed behavior.
c. Reinforcement for good performance.
d. Attention to the model.

•• 27. Three of the following depict situations in which a teacher is facilitating the retention component of modeling. Which one does not depict such a situation?

  a. As he writes a capital J on the board, Mr. Anson tells his kindergartners, "To write a capital J, you make a fishhook with a line across the top."
  b. Mr. Byers suggests, "Let's play some background music while I show you how to use the dipstick to measure your oil level."
  c. Mr. Caruso says, "There are several critical steps involved in throwing a pot on the potter's wheel. Repeat these steps to yourself as you work so you don't forget them."
  d. As he demonstrates how to throw a baseball correctly, Mr. Duffy says, "Now repeat these words as you throw the ball: back, up, thrust, release."

• 28. In what way does self-efficacy differ from such terms as self-concept and self-esteem?

  a. Self-efficacy refers only to behaviors that we learn through modeling.
  b. Self-efficacy results primarily from vicarious reinforcement and punishment.
  c. Self-efficacy varies, depending on the specific task to be performed.
  d. Self-efficacy only appears after we begin to regulate our own behavior.

•• 29. Only one of the following definitely illustrates high self-efficacy. Which one?

  a. Amy knows she is a good singer.
  b. Bertha swims the fastest butterfly on the swim team.
  c. Carmen enjoys being with her friends.
  d. Danielle recently got a score of 120 on an intelligence test.

•• 30. Jim has a high sense of self-efficacy regarding his ability to work with his hands. Based on this information, we would predict three of the following from social cognitive theory. Which one of the following would we not necessarily predict?

  a. Jim will frequently choose activities that involve working with his hands.
  b. Jim will be a bit careless when he works with his hands, so he will frequently make silly little mistakes.
  c. Compared to Joe, who has low self-efficacy, Jim will do a better job at such "hands-on" tasks.
  d. If Jim has difficulty at a task requiring his handiwork, he will tend to "try, try again" until he gets it right.

• 31. Three of the following statements are true with regard to students' self-efficacy. Which statement is false?

  a. Students with low self-efficacy usually try harder at a task.
  b. Students with high self-efficacy achieve at higher levels than those with low self-efficacy, even when previous achievement has been equivalent.
  c. Students tend to choose activities at which they know they can be successful rather than those at which they think they will fail.
  d. Students' perceptions of their ability to succeed at a task are usually fairly accurate.

• 32. Listed below are four reasons why students might not want to take their schoolwork seriously or to try very hard to succeed at classroom tasks. Which one of these reasons is consistent with the concept of self-efficacy?
  a. Anthony is more interested in horsing around with his friends.
  b. Bernice is so anxious in the classroom that she can't "think straight."
  c. Carol doesn't think she has the ability to do the work successfully.
  d. Danny thinks his teacher doesn't like him.

•• 33. Three of the following experiences should promote higher self-efficacy about the task in question. Which one probably won't?
  a. Andrea discovers that she only does well on her weekly spelling tests when she wears her lucky necklace.
  b. On the first day of geometry, Bob's teacher tells the class, "The things in your textbook may look difficult to you now, but with a little effort and practice you'll have the basics down pat by December."
  c. Carmella does better in her Spanish class than she expected to.
  d. Dick's friend tells him, "You shouldn't have any problem in American Literature. I'm no smarter than you are, and I got an A."

• 34. Should students ever be allowed to fail at classroom tasks? According to social cognitive theorists, the answer is:
  a. Yes. Self-efficacy is highest when students fail at a task several times in a row before accomplishing it successfully.
  b. Yes. Occasional failures interspersed among frequent successes teach students that perseverance pays off.
  c. No. Failure gives students the message that school is not an enjoyable place to be.
  d. No. Even a single failure can seriously deflate students' self-efficacy.

•• 35. Mr. Limpitlaw wants to increase his female students' self-efficacy for mastering simple car maintenance procedures. He can best do this by:
  a. Presenting a film that shows an experienced auto mechanic at work.
  b. Describing how easily he learned these things when he was their age.
  c. Having the students read a book with clear, step-by-step instructions for changing the oil and the air filter.
  d. Having the students watch other girls successfully change the oil and the air filter.

• 36. Which one of the following statements best reflects the concept of collective self-efficacy?
  a. Over time, students develop a general sense of self-efficacy that influences their performance in a wide variety of content domains.
  b. As students get older, their self-confidence about performing certain tasks becomes fairly stable and so is less influenced by any single success or failure experience.
  c. Students may have greater confidence about accomplishing a task when they work with others rather than alone.
  d. Some students have greater self-confidence when they have technological resources (spreadsheet software, access to the Internet, etc.) to help them in their efforts.

• 37. Three of the following are aspects of <u>self-regulation</u> as social cognitive theorists define the term. Which one is <u>not</u> necessarily an aspect of self-regulation?
a. Reading an assigned textbook chapter
b. Feeling guilty or ashamed after failing
c. Deciding whether one's own behavior is within an acceptable range
d. Setting standards regarding acceptable behavior for oneself

• 38. Three of the following are aspects of self-regulation as social cognitive theorists describe it. Which one is <u>not</u> necessarily an example of self-regulation?
a. Setting standards regarding what is acceptable behavior for oneself
b. Asking a classmate for help on an assignment
c. Reinforcing oneself for appropriate behavior
d. Punishing oneself for inappropriate behavior

• 39. Maria is what social cognitive theorists would describe as a <u>self-regulating</u> person when it comes to her moral behavior. Given this information, which one of the following descriptions best describes Maria's moral behavior?
a. She works for social incentives; for example, she contributes to charity if she thinks that other people will like her better for doing so.
b. She behaves in morally appropriate ways only when she thinks other people are watching her.
c. She has an internal set of standards regarding right and wrong behavior, and she feels guilty when she violates those standards.
d. She has an internal set of standards regarding right and wrong, but those standards seldom influence the way she actually behaves.

•• 40. From a social cognitive theory perspective, which one of the following children most clearly reflects a key ingredient of <u>self-regulation</u> as social cognitive theorists define it?
a. Anne remembers to do her chores so that she will get her weekly allowance.
b. Bob is proud of the fact that he always keeps a promise.
c. Carol hopes she can stay awake during class because she knows she will be tested on the information being presented.
d. Donald refrains from punching a classmate because he thinks his teacher might be watching.

• 41. Social cognitive theorists tell us that students are most likely to work for goals that:
a. Their parents have set for them.
b. Their teachers have set for them.
c. Peer pressure imposes on them.
d. They have chosen for themselves.

•• 42. Several students in Mr. Samber's class have trouble keeping themselves on task during independent seatwork assignments. Mr. Samber gives each of these students a piece of paper on which they are to make a check mark every time they find themselves doing something <u>other</u> than their assignment during seatwork time. Mr. Samber is using which one of the following techniques for changing behavior?
a. A contingency contract
b. Reinforcement of an incompatible behavior
c. Removal punishment
d. Self-monitoring

• 43. When students keep a written record of their own desirable and undesirable behaviors, then:
   a. Desirable behaviors increase in frequency, but undesirable behaviors remain the same.
   b. Undesirable behaviors decrease in frequency, but desirable behaviors remain the same.
   c. Desirable behaviors increase and undesirable behaviors decrease.
   d. Such record-keeping has little effect on behavior.

• 44. Which strategy for promoting self-regulation is most consistent with Vygotsky's concept of self-talk?
   a. Self-reinforcement—praising oneself for appropriate behavior.
   b. Self-instructions—reminding oneself about appropriate actions.
   c. Self-monitoring—keeping track of how one is behaving.
   d. Self-punishment—reprimanding oneself for inappropriate behavior.

•• 45. Natalie is sometimes too impulsive when she answers multiple choice questions on standardized achievement tests: She picks an answer before she has even read all the alternatives. Natalie knows she has a problem and would really like to change her behavior. The best strategy we can use to help Natalie is:
   a. Self-instructions
   b. Intermittent reinforcement
   c. Cueing
   d. Punishment

• 46. Three of the following strategies are consistent with the textbook's recommendations for helping students learn to engage in self-evaluation. Which strategy, although possibly beneficial for other reasons, is least likely to promote self-evaluation?
   a. Giving students detailed feedback about their biology lab reports.
   b. Having students reflect on the strengths and weakness of their performance in a daily journal.
   c. Having students compile portfolios of their best work.
   d. Give students a checklist of things to look for as they read the first draft of their research papers.

•• 47. Which one of the following illustrates the self-imposed contingencies aspect of self-regulation?
   a. Adele feels terrible when she inadvertently hurts a classmate's feelings.
   b. Bonnie knows how happy her parents will be if she brings home a good report card.
   c. Clint doesn't like striking out when it's his turn at bat because his teammates will think he's a bad baseball player.
   d. Daryl checks his watch frequently as he takes a standardized test to be sure he can finish the test in the allotted time.

•• 48. Mark often comes to school wearing sandals instead of sneakers on days that he has physical education. He is getting angry with himself regarding his chronic forgetfulness about appropriate footwear. His teacher suggests that he treat himself to an hour of television only on days when he has remembered to wear sneakers. Mark's teacher is suggesting that Mark use:

a. Vicarious reinforcement
b. Intermittent reinforcement
c. A self-imposed contingency
d. Self-monitoring

•• 49. Which one of the following strategies is most likely to promote <u>self-regulation</u> in students?

a. Mr. Adams knows that many students have trouble learning algebra. He spends the first few weeks of class having students engage in activities that will make algebraic concepts concrete and understandable.
b. When assigning a lengthy research project, Mr. Barnett advises his students to break the project down into a number of smaller tasks and then to reinforce themselves after they complete each one.
c. To build endurance, Mr. Carruthers asks his physical education students to run progressively longer distances each week.
d. Mr. D'Amato asks his students to look in a mirror and write a poem about what they see.

•• 50. Three of the following strategies should help students become more <u>self-regulated</u>. Which one will <u>not</u>?

a. Ms. Alexander encourages Andy to set a target for himself regarding the number of sit-ups he will be able to do by the end of the month.
b. Mr. Bottenberg teaches Beth to reinforce herself whenever she gets her homework done on time.
c. Ms. Carlson asks Craig to make a check mark on a piece of paper whenever he finds himself talking out of turn.
d. Mr. D'Angelo asks a teacher aide to keep a close eye on Darlene and, when necessary, to remind her to stay on task.

• 51. Three of the following are characteristics of <u>self-regulated learning</u>. Which one is <u>not</u> necessarily a characteristic associated with self-regulated learning?

a. Trying to focus one's attention on the task at hand
b. Figuring out how best to use the time one has to accomplish a particular learning task
c. Deciding what one wants to learn while studying assigned reading materials
d. Working as hard as possible to achieve the teacher's instructional objectives

•• 52. Three of the following students are showing signs of self-regulated learning. Which student does not show any evidence of self-regulated learning?

a. As Adam studies his German vocabulary words, he occasionally stops to check himself to see which words he needs to study further.

b. Blake knows that, for purposes of college admission, his performance in math class is more important than his performance in drama class, so he works harder in the first class than in the second.

c. Craig beams with pleasure when his teacher praises his English essay, because her opinion of his work is very important to him.

d. Drew thinks to himself, "Tonight I'll skim the reading assignment in history just to get a general idea of what the chapter's all about. Tomorrow I'll read it again in more depth."

• 53. On average, self-regulated learners tend to:

a. Perform better on a continuous reinforcement schedule than on an intermittent reinforcement schedule

b. Achieve at higher levels in the classroom

c. Be less interested in extracurricular activities than their classmates

d. Require more of a teacher's time and attention than do other students, but this time and attention is a good investment over the long run

•• 54. Three of the following teachers are using strategies that should promote self-regulated learning. Which teacher, while almost certainly helping students learn more effectively, is probably not promoting self-regulated learning?

a. Ms. Henry recruits several parents to provide one-on-one tutoring for students who are having difficulty in a particular subject area.

b. Mr. Isaacs gives his students several criteria they should use to evaluate their own research papers.

c. Mr. Jankowski has his students work in small groups to learn about various endangered species.

d. Ms. Lin requires all her students to do projects for the school science fair, but she lets them make their own decisions about the nature of their projects.

•• 55. Nora has a quick temper, overreacting in anger every time one of her classmates does something she doesn't like. Her teacher suggests that whenever another student annoys her, she should: (1) stop to decide what behavior in particular is bothering her, (2) think about several possible ways of responding to the behavior, and (3) choose the response that is most likely to be both productive and prosocial. In self-regulation terminology, the teacher is trying to promote ________ in Nora.

a. Self-imposed contingencies

b. Self-regulated learning

c. Self-regulated problem solving

d. Self-monitoring

•• 56. Which one of the following examples best illustrates a student who has had mediation training?
   a. Saul makes a check mark on an index card every time he speaks out in class without permission. At the end of each hour, he counts the number of check marks he has recorded.
   b. Melinda works diligently at her math homework, thinking carefully about how to do each problem and then taking it one step at a time.
   c. When Sally studies her textbook, she stops to think about the things she already knows about the topic and tries to relate what she reads to her prior knowledge.
   d. When he sees two of his classmates arguing at lunch, Abbott joins them and encourages each of them to view the conflict from the other's perspective.

•• 57. Gang-related activity is increasing at the high school at which you teach. At a faculty meeting, the school principal voices her concern that hostile interactions among members of rival gangs are escalating. You think about the research described in the textbook's discussion of self-regulation, and then you suggest that the school:
   a. Encourage students to determine their own goals for academic achievement
   b. Provide mediation training for its students
   c. Develop strategies for enhancing students' self-efficacy with regard to interpersonal relationships
   d. Teach its students how to use self-imposed contingencies

• 58. Which one of the following statements best illustrates social cognitive theorists' notion of reciprocal causation?
   a. Students are more likely to model a behavior for which they have seen others reinforced.
   b. Modeling can only occur when students are capable of performing the behavior they observe.
   c. Students are unlikely to exhibit a behavior for which they think they will be punished.
   d. The environment affects students' behavior, but their behavior also affects the environment they experience.

•• 59. In social cognitive theorists' conceptualization of reciprocal causation, which one of the following is a person factor?
   a. Alma expects to do well in science this year.
   b. Bree got an A in science last year.
   c. Curt's friend Doug will be in his science class this year.
   d. Doug has already read the first two chapters of his science textbook.

•• 60. If we consider the concept of reciprocal causation, we must conclude that students' classroom experience is influenced:
   a. Primarily by what teachers do in the classroom
   b. Primarily by how students think about classroom material
   c. Both by classroom events and by what students themselves do
   d. Largely by things that have happened to students in the past

•• 61. From the perspective of social cognitive theory, why might inner-city African American students learn more from an African American model who grew up in a ghetto than from a model of a different race or background?
   a. Because this model is more likely to behave in a gender-appropriate manner.
   b. Because the students are more likely to perceive this model as being competent.
   c. Because the students are more likely to realize that this model has prestige.
   d. Because the students will view this model's behavior as being applicable to their own situation.

• 62. Three of the following statements are accurate about students with special needs. Which statement is <u>not</u> necessarily accurate?
   a. Students with specific cognitive difficulties often have low self-efficacy for academic tasks.
   b. Students with general delays in cognitive and social functioning (e.g., students with mental retardation) are unable to develop self-regulatory skills even with training.
   c. Students with advanced cognitive development (e.g., gifted students) sometimes have little experience in dealing with failure.
   d. Students with social or behavioral problems often have friends who model inappropriate social behavior.

• 63. Which one of the following statements describes an accurate comparison between behaviorist and social cognitive theories of learning?
   a. Both perspectives ignore the role that thought processes play in learning.
   b. Only social cognitive theorists propose that reinforcement affects observers as well as the individuals actually being reinforced.
   c. Both behaviorists and social cognitive theorists propose that punishment has little or no effect on behavior.
   d. Both behaviorists and social cognitive theorists use the concept of extinction to explain what happens when a response is no longer reinforced.

## <u>Essay Questions</u>

• 64. A number of assumptions underlie social cognitive theory. Describe <u>three</u> of these, and derive an implication of each one for classroom practice.

• 65. Define the concept of <u>vicarious reinforcement</u> and give a concrete classroom example to illustrate its effects on students' behavior.

• 66. What happens when students do not get the reinforcement they think they will get for behaving in a certain way? What happens when they expect to be punished for something but are not? From the perspective of social cognitive theory, describe the effects that the nonoccurrence of expected reinforcement and expected punishment are likely to have on students' later behavior.

•• 67. Modeling can be a very effective teaching strategy. Choose a specific behavior you might teach your students through modeling. Then describe how you would take into account the four essential processes necessary for student modeling to occur.

•• 68. You are teaching your students how to do something—perhaps how to solve a math problem, write a research paper, or do a side dismount from the parallel bars—and you find that your students have low self-efficacy for doing the task.

   a. Describe a specific task that you might eventually be teaching.
   b. Considering the factors affecting self-efficacy that the textbook describes, develop two strategies you might use to enhance your students' self-efficacy for performing the task. For each one, describe what you would do in specific and concrete terms.

•• 69. Social cognitive theorists propose that people often become increasingly self-regulating over time.

   a. Explain what social cognitive theorists mean by the term self-regulation.
   b. Identify a response you would like to see your students make in an increasingly self-regulated fashion. Then describe two specific strategies you might use to promote their self-regulation. Your strategies should be based on concepts and/or principles that social cognitive theorists provide.

•• 70. Imagine that you are a compulsive overeater. Describe two different strategies based on the concept of self-regulation through which you might cut down on eating. Be specific as to how you might implement each method.

• 71. Compare and contrast cognitive psychology, behaviorism, and social cognitive theory with respect to each of the following:

   a. How learning is defined
   b. The role that consequences of behavior play in learning
   c. The role that mental processes play in learning

# ANSWER KEY

## Multiple-Choice Questions

| | | | | |
|---|---|---|---|---|
| 1. c | 14. a | 27. b | 40. b | 53. b |
| 2. b | 15. b | 28. c | 41. d | 54. a |
| 3. d | 16. c | 29. a | 42. d | 55. c |
| 4. a | 17. d | 30. b | 43. c | 56. d |
| 5. b | 18. a | 31. a | 44. b | 57. b |
| 6. d | 19. a | 32. c | 45. a | 58. d |
| 7. a | 20. c | 33. a | 46. a | 59. a |
| 8. c | 21. d | 34. b | 47. a | 60. c |
| 9. a | 22. d | 35. d | 48. c | 61. d |
| 10. b | 23. a | 36. c | 49. b | 62. b |
| 11. d | 24. c | 37. a | 50. d | 63. b |
| 12. c | 25. c | 38. b | 51. d | |
| 13. b | 26. c | 39. c | 52. c | |

## Essay Questions

64. The textbook lists five assumptions underlying social cognitive theory:
    - People can learn by observing others.
    - Learning is an internal process that may or may not result in a behavior change.
    - Behavior is directed toward particular goals.
    - Behavior eventually becomes self-regulated.
    - Reinforcement and punishment have several indirect effects (rather than a direct effect) on learning and behavior.

    The response should include at least three of these assumptions; each one should be accompanied by an appropriate implication.

65. Vicarious reinforcement is a phenomenon whereby an individual's behavior increases after he or she observes someone else being reinforced for that behavior. The response should include a concrete example to illustrate.

66. The nonoccurrence of expected reinforcement for a behavior is punishing, and the behavior should decrease in frequency. The nonoccurrence of expected punishment for a behavior is reinforcing, and the behavior should increase in frequency.

67. The response should identify a classroom behavior that can realistically be taught through modeling. It should also include an explanation of how these four processes are taken into account:
    - Attention—The response should include some means of capturing students' attention.
    - Retention—The response should include some way of helping students remember what they observe.
    - Motor reproduction—Students must be physically capable of executing the behavior.
    - Motivation—Students must have some reason why they want to demonstrate the behavior.

68. Responses to the two parts of the question are as follows:
    a. The response should describe a specific classroom task or objective.
    b. Four factors affecting self-efficacy are these (the response should present two strategies for enhancing students' self-efficacy for performing the task; the strategies should be based on two of the factors listed below and described in concrete terms):
       - Previous successes and failures: Students have higher self-efficacy when they are usually successful at a task (however, an occasional failure interspersed among successes teaches students that success comes only through effort and perseverance).
       - Messages from others: Students have higher self-efficacy, at least over the short run, when their teachers communicate the belief, through either words or actions, that the students can be successful.
       - Successes and failures of others: Students have higher self-efficacy when they observe others, especially their peers, be successful.
       - Successes and failures of the group as a whole: Students may have greater self-efficacy when they work with others rather than alone.

69. Responses to various parts of the question are as follows:
    a. Self-regulation is a process of setting standards and goals for oneself and engaging in behaviors that enable one to meet those standards and goals. (Any description that reflects this general idea is acceptable.)
    b. A student behavior that is appropriately self-regulated (study skills, independent seatwork, interpersonal conflict resolution, etc.) should be identified. Then, two concrete strategies should be described that reflect two or more of these general recommendations:
       - Provide opportunities for students to set their own goals (ideally, these goals should be challenging yet achievable).
       - Have students observe and record their own behavior.
       - Have students talk themselves through a task.
       - Have students evaluate their own performance; possibly compare their self-evaluations to their teacher's evaluations.
       - Teach students to reinforce themselves for successful performance.
       - Give students opportunities to learn without teacher assistance (through assignments that students accomplish either individually or in small groups).
       - Occasionally assign activities in which students have considerable leeway regarding goals, use of time, and so on.
       - Provide any scaffolding that students might initially need to help them use self-regulating strategies.
       - Model self-regulating cognitive processes by "thinking aloud" about these processes.
       - Teach students steps to follow when they encounter a difficult problem.
       - Teach students to mediate one another's interpersonal conflicts.

70. The response should describe two strategies consistent with the textbook's discussion of self-regulation. Below are some possibilities:
    - Set a goal regarding how much weight you want to lose.
    - Keep a record of what you are eating.
    - Weigh yourself regularly and record your findings.
    - Give yourself instructions as to what to do when you're hungry or when you encounter food.
    - Reinforce yourself for eating appropriately and/or losing weight.

71. Responses to various parts of the question are as follows:
    a. Cognitive psychology and social cognitive theory both define learning as an internal mental phenomenon. Behaviorism defines it as a behavior change.
    b. Cognitive psychology does not focus on the consequences of behavior. Social cognitive theory considers consequences experienced either directly or vicariously. Behaviorists focus on reinforcement and punishment experienced personally; a strict operant conditioning perspective (e.g., that of B. F. Skinner) focuses exclusively on reinforcement.
    c. Cognitive psychology focuses on mental processes. Social cognitive theory considers them, although not in as much detail. Mental processes play little role in behaviorism.

## Chapter 11

# MOTIVATION AND AFFECT

| CHAPTER OUTLINE | RELEVANT TEST BANK ITEMS |
|---|---|
| THE NATURE OF MOTIVATION<br>How Motivation Affects Learning and Behavior<br>Intrinsic Versus Extrinsic Motivation | Multiple-Choice 1–7 |
| THEORETICAL PERSPECTIVES OF MOTIVATION<br>The Trait Perspective<br>The Behaviorist Perspective<br>The Social Cognitive Perspective<br>The Cognitive Perspective | Multiple-Choice 8–11 |
| WHAT BASIC NEEDS DO PEOPLE HAVE?<br>Self-Worth<br>Relatedness | Multiple-Choice 12–21<br>Essay 40–41 |
| AFFECT AND ITS EFFECTS<br>Hot Cognition<br>Anxiety | Multiple-Choice 22–36<br>Essay 42 |
| ADDRESSING DIVERSITY IN MOTIVATION AND AFFECT<br>Accommodating Students with Special Needs | Multiple-Choice 37–38 |
| THE BIG PICTURE<br>Guiding Principles | Multiple-Choice 39 |
| The items in the "Integrative Questions" chapter of this Test Bank integrate the content of two or more textbook chapters. Within that chapter, the items listed to the right are relevant to Chapter 11. | Multiple-Choice 12–13<br>Essay 37 |

## Multiple-Choice Questions

•• 1. Which one of the following examples best illustrates the concept of situated motivation?
   a. Nathan gets extremely upset when he gets anything less than a perfect score on a test paper, probably because his parents have always expected him to be perfect at everything he does.
   b. Last year Ophelia was bored to tears in history class, but this year she loves history because her teacher seems to make the subject come alive.
   c. Polly is afraid of water because once, when she was a little girl, she almost drowned.
   d. Quinton would really like to play on his high school basketball team but, because he's quite short, he has settled for what he considers to be second-best: being on the wrestling team.

• 2. The four statements below describe effects that motivation may have on learning and/or behavior. Three of the statements are accurate. Which one is not accurate?
   a. Motivation influences how students process information.
   b. Motivation enhances students' memory for irrelevant information.
   c. Motivation increases students' persistence at tasks.
   d. Motivation influences the choices that students make.

• 3. Three of the following statements are true about human motivation. Which one is false?
   a. It directs a student's behavior toward a particular goal.
   b. It is essential before learning can occur.
   c. It determines what things will be reinforcing to a student at a particular time.
   d. It increases the effort that students put forth.

•• 4. Which one of the following is the best example of extrinsic motivation?
   a. Enjoying scary movies
   b. Finding a good book impossible to put down
   c. Thinking that aerobic exercise is a healthy way to spend your time
   d. Wanting a good grade in your history class

•• 5. Which one of the following students is displaying extrinsic motivation?
   a. Carin wants to be an accountant because she likes working with numbers.
   b. Brad wants to be a veterinarian because he loves animals and wants to help them.
   c. Albert wants to become a professional football player so others will admire him.
   d. Donnetta wants to become an actress because she thinks acting is fun.

•• 6. Which one of the following students is displaying intrinsic motivation?
   a. Annette loves to play the viola and so practices for at least an hour every day.
   b. Bob works hard in his classes because his parents have promised to buy him a car if he gets at least a 3.5 grade-point-average this year.
   c. Cassie does her math homework faithfully every night because she likes her teacher and wants to please him.
   d. Dennis takes physics because he wants to become an engineer and make a lot of money.

• 7. Three of the following are true statements about intrinsic and extrinsic motivation. Which one is false?
   a. Reminding students of how important good grades are will promote extrinsic rather than intrinsic motivation.
   b. Compared to students who are extrinsically motivated, students who are intrinsically motivated are more likely to learn classroom material in meaningful and effective ways.
   c. Students' intrinsic motivation to learn school subject matter tends to decrease as they get older.
   d. Intrinsic and extrinsic motivation are mutually exclusive: Students who have one are highly unlikely to have the other.

•• 8. Which one of the following descriptions of a student best illustrates a trait perspective of motivation?
   a. "Did you see that big grin on Maurice's face when the principal announced that he was the winner of the essay contest?"
   b. "Jane is always putting herself in dangerous situations. Maybe she likes the adrenaline rush that comes with living on the edge."
   c. "Chloe seems bored with what's going on in class most of the time. I've tried everything I can think of to motivate her, but so far nothing's worked."
   d. "David is really struggling with his reading, and his spelling is atrocious. I wonder if he has an undiagnosed learning disability."

•• 9. Marc loves playing ping pong. When he plays with a friend, he concentrates intently on the game and tries very hard to win. He experiments with different shots (occasionally losing a game in the process) and eventually perfects a few shots that are extremely difficult for an opponent to return. From a trait perspective of motivation, which one of the following is most likely to be true about Marc?
   a. He has a high need for affiliation.
   b. He has a high need for approval.
   c. He has high achievement motivation.
   d. He is a sensation seeker.

•• 10. Which one of the following situations best illustrates the role of drive in motivation?
   a. After not having time for either breakfast or lunch, Adam eats three large hamburgers for dinner.
   b. Bernice is intrigued by her psychology course; it explains why she and her friends do some of the things they do.
   c. Connor works out at the gym each day; his goal is to win the title of "Mr. Fitness."
   d. Debbie writes notes to her friends whenever she gets bored in class.

•• 11. Which one of the following descriptions of a student best illustrates a cognitive perspective of motivation?
   a. "Eron loves the attention he gets from his classmates when he tells jokes in class."
   b. "I don't think Mary gets much to eat at home. She always seems to be hungry at school."
   c. "Reggie gets very upset with himself when he makes mistakes or doesn't know how to do something. It's as if he's not happy unless he's perfect."
   d. "Shelley is convinced that her poor performance in class is due to 'bad tests' and 'unfair grading.' In fact, Shelly would do a lot better if she studied more often."

• 12. From the perspective of Maslow's hierarchy of needs, how are students likely to react when they have several different needs at one time?
   a. They will attempt to meet their physiological and safety needs before attending to esteem needs.
   b. They will attempt to meet all of their needs simultaneously, and this may interfere with learning.
   c. They will attempt to meet their need for self-actualization before meeting esteem or belonging needs.
   d. They will first attempt to meet their esteem needs, with little concern for their physiological needs, so they may come to school hungry.

•• 13. If you were to incorporate Maslow's hierarchy of needs into your teaching practices, you would be most likely to:
   a. Emphasize the importance of getting good grades.
   b. Make sure your students feel safe and secure.
   c. Focus on the use of intrinsic reinforcers (such as feeling proud) rather than extrinsic reinforcers (such as praise) for all students.
   d. Remind students frequently about how their current achievements in school will affect their success as adults.

• 14. Which one of the following best describes the concept of <u>self-worth</u> as a factor in motivation?
   a. Students are always comparing their own performance to that of the adults around them.
   b. In early adolescence, students believe that they are invulnerable to the typical dangers of life.
   c. In the high school years especially, most students greatly underestimate their ability levels.
   d. Students like to believe that they are competent individuals.

•• 15. Marion puts off doing a project for the science fair until she has so little time to do it that she cannot possibly complete a good project. Such behavior is most consistent with the concept of:
   a. Self-handicapping
   b. Drive
   c. Trait anxiety
   d. Hot cognition

• 16. Three of the following statements about the <u>need for relatedness</u> are accurate. Which one is <u>not</u>?
   a. It seems to be especially high in early adolescence.
   b. In some students, it may be reflected in a desire to look "cool"; in others, it may be manifested in a desire to help those who are less fortunate.
   c. According to anthropologists, humans' need for relatedness is far greater now than it was 2000 years ago.
   d. For many students, relating to peers will be one of their highest priorities during the school day.

•• 17. When choosing a partner to work on a science fair project, James selects a close friend who isn't particularly good in science. With this information in mind, which one of the following is <u>most</u> likely to be true about James?

a. He has a high need for affiliation.
b. He has a high need for approval.
c. He has a mastery goal.
d. He has a lot of anxiety about doing well on the task.

• 18. Which one of the following statements is true regarding students' <u>need for affiliation</u>?

a. Elementary students generally have a high need for affiliation, but it usually diminishes after puberty.
b. High school students have a greater need for affiliation than junior high school students.
c. All students have a high need for affiliation throughout their school years.
d. Students vary considerably in their need for affiliation.

• 19. As a teacher, you want to satisfy your students' need for affiliation without taking too much valuable instruction time. Which one of the following is consistent with the textbook's recommendations for doing so?

a. Occasionally remind students that they can visit with their friends during recess and again at lunch.
b. Allow students to intermingle freely during class.
c. Integrate group work into classroom activities.
d. Allow students to take "talk breaks" for five minutes every hour, during which they visit with anyone they wish.

•• 20. While working on a series of math problems, Kate stops after each problem to ask her teacher, "Did I do this right?" or "Is this one okay?" With this information in mind, which one of the following is <u>most</u> likely to be true about Kate?

a. She has a high need for affiliation.
b. She has a high need for approval.
c. She has learned helplessness.
d. She has strong safety needs.

• 21. You have noticed that Tamara has a high <u>need for approval</u>. With this in mind, you know you can best help her achieve in the classroom by:

a. Giving her challenging tasks—those at which she may or may not succeed
b. Praising her frequently for what she does well
c. Letting her work independently
d. Showing her how her performance compares to that of her classmates

•• 22. Which one of the following is the best example of <u>hot cognition</u>?

a. Thinking of a new strategy for solving a difficult problem
b. Getting excited when you read about a possible cure for AIDS
c. Realizing that you finally understand Einstein's law of relativity
d. Having a mental block that interferes with your writing ability

•• 23. You go to an art museum on a Sunday afternoon. Judging from researchers' findings with respect to hot cognition, which one of the following pictures are you most likely to remember?

a. A man with a gaping chest wound
b. A pleasant farm scene, with cows grazing by a stream
c. One dog baring its teeth at another
d. Fruit in a colorful Mexican pot

•• 24. Which one of the teachers below is using a strategy consistent with the concept of hot cognition?

a. Ms. Kozloff shows her students a colorful video that depicts the lives of animals that live on the African plains.
b. Mr. Waterman encourages his students to try to find the best in each of their classmates.
c. Ms. Schuler has her students engage in fifteen minutes of vigorous exercise before they sit down to tackle some difficult math problems.
d. Mr. Ramirez portrays the Holocaust so vividly that her students become very angry at the atrocities the Nazis committed.

•• 25. Which one of the following examples characterizes anxiety rather than fear, as the textbook distinguishes between the two terms?

a. Olivia has to get up in front of her class to give an oral presentation about Central America. She has prepared well for the presentation but still feels nervous.
b. Paula doesn't want to go home because she just failed a history exam. Her parents have told her she will be grounded for two weeks if she fails a test.
c. Reanna doesn't want to give her oral presentation about sickle-cell anemia. She always stutters badly, and she knows some of her classmates will laugh at her.
d. Shannon is apprehensive about the possibility of a tornado. There have been several tornado warnings throughout the day, and she can hear the wind howling loudly outside the classroom window.

•• 26. Which one of the following is the best example of state anxiety rather than trait anxiety?

a. Thea is often nervous in math class, where she rarely participates unless her teacher specifically calls on her. She sits quietly at her desk, and she does not interact with her classmates because she finds it difficult to do so without shaking.
b. Ursula is an excellent student, but she has considerable trouble speaking to others in any of her classes. She performs very well on tests and other written work, but she gets exceptionally anxious during group work and oral reports.
c. Viola becomes nervous when she has to give a presentation in front of her English class. This is the first time she has ever had to do something like this and she doesn't know how well she will do.
d. Wendell becomes nervous whenever he has to take any kind of paper-pencil test, even when he knows what questions are going to be on the test and is thoroughly prepared.

•• 27. Which one of the following individuals clearly has <u>state anxiety</u>?

a. Ann doesn't like physical education class because she knows she's not much of an athlete.
b. Bob has always had a fear of heights.
c. Chris panics when he discovers he studied the wrong chapter for today's quiz.
d. Dana has always struggled with mathematics, so she takes only the minimum number of math courses required.

•• 28. Which one of the following is definitely an example of <u>trait anxiety</u>?

a. Jan runs faster than usual when she is chased by a pit bull across school grounds.
b. Tommy becomes nauseous every time he takes a test.
c. Zack did not pass the last math test, but he has done well on previous math tests.
d. Joe draws a blank the first time he reads an essay question.

• 29. Which one of the following statements is most accurate about how anxiety affects students' performance in the classroom?

a. A little bit of anxiety can facilitate learning and performance, and high anxiety can facilitate performance on very easy tasks.
b. The best way to deal with anxiety is to eliminate it. Totally relaxed students learn more and perform better.
c. High anxiety can facilitate performance on very difficult tasks, but it may get in the way when students try to do tasks that they have learned to do quickly and automatically.
d. A little bit of trait anxiety may facilitate learning, but state anxiety can be detrimental to performance.

•• 30. Your students have been given a challenging task—one at which they can succeed only if they work hard. Considering what we know about the effects of anxiety on performance, which one of the following students is <u>most</u> likely to complete the task successfully?

a. Adam is feeling quite "mellow" today; his attitude is <u>que sera, sera</u>—whatever happens, happens.
b. Berta is feeling really "up tight" about how she does on task because her performance is going to affect whether she passes or fails the class.
c. Cassie doesn't care; in fact, she's half asleep.
d. Damion wants to do well on the task and is a little anxious about it, but not to the point where his hands are sweaty or his stomach is in a knot.

• 31. With the textbook's discussion of anxiety in mind, identify the best approach to taking a difficult exam.

a. Worry a little bit about the exam, but not too much.
b. In your mind, imagine the worst possible thing that could happen if you fail the exam.
c. Worry about the exam as you study the night before, but be as relaxed as possible when you take it.
d. Be completely relaxed both when you study and when you take the exam.

•• 32. Which one of the following students is most likely to have facilitating anxiety?
  a. Art doesn't begin his twenty-page research report for his psychology class until the night before it is due.
  b. Bert has heard that his statistics professor is an easy grader, so he isn't the least bit worried about getting at least a B in his statistics course.
  c. Curt can't find the note cards he made for his book report, and in five minutes it will be his turn to give his report.
  d. Dave is nervous about doing well in the 100-meter dash.

•• 33. Luis suffers from extreme test anxiety. Three of the statements below probably describe Luis. Which one does not?
  a. As he takes a test, he looks closely and carefully at the wording of each test question.
  b. He has trouble thinking clearly about how to answer each question.
  c. He is more worried than his classmates about how his teacher will evaluate his performance.
  d. He gets lower test scores than his classmates, even though he knows the material as well as they do.

•• 34. Considering the textbook's definitions of threat and challenge, identify the situation below that is most likely to pose a threat rather than a challenge?
  a. You think you can probably make the basketball team, but only if you practice every day at home.
  b. You're asked to climb up a twenty-foot rope hanging from the ceiling. You've climbed ten feet before, but you've never climbed twenty feet.
  c. You've invited a professor to dinner and are trying a recipe you've never tried before.
  d. You are required to take a college course in nuclear physics, even though you failed basic physics in high school.

• 35. In fifth grade last year, Elena was a happy, easygoing student. Now that she's moved to junior high school and begun sixth grade, she's becoming increasingly anxious and uptight. Three of the following are probable reasons for her growing anxiety. Which one is least likely to be true?
  a. It's harder to get the good grades she was used to getting in elementary school.
  b. Her junior high school teachers want to know more about her than her fifth-grade teacher ever did.
  c. She's uncomfortable with the many ways that her body is changing now that she's reached puberty.
  d. She is finding that she has to compete with her peers, both for grades and for a place on the girls' basketball team.

- 36. As teachers, we can probably best help students overcome debilitating anxiety in the classroom by:
  a. Downplaying the importance of education; putting less emphasis on working hard and more on relaxing and having fun.
  b. Allowing them to work at whatever subjects they like best until they feel ready to tackle other, perhaps more difficult subjects.
  c. Communicating to them that they can succeed with effort, and that mistakes can be corrected.
  d. Reminding them how important it is that they demonstrate mastery of the school district's instructional objectives for the year.

- 37. Three of the following statements are true with regard to student diversity in motivation. Which one is false?
  a. If we compare students from various ethnic backgrounds, those from Asian American families are least likely to have debilitating test anxiety.
  b. Students from some ethnic minority groups may be particularly interested in achieving high grades so that they can make their parents proud.
  c. On average, girls have a higher need for affiliation than boys.
  d. Girls are more likely than boys to try hard in school and earn good grades.

- 38. Three of the following statements are true with regard to students who have special educational needs. Which one is false?
  a. Students who are gifted may engage in self-handicapping if they have strong friendships with low achievers.
  b. Students with general delays in cognitive functioning tend to give up easily when they encounter difficulty on a task.
  c. Students with learning disabilities and other specific cognitive disabilities are often reluctant to ask for help when they need it.
  d. Students with social or behavioral problems rarely have the debilitating anxiety that plagues some of their nondisabled classmates.

- 39. If we were to summarize what we know about student motivation, we would be most likely to say that:
  a. Students learn and perform best when strong emotions are kept at bay.
  b. Students are more likely to be motivated in the classroom when they know they can succeed at classroom tasks.
  c. Students' needs for affiliation and academic achievement are mutually incompatible; when they are striving to meet one of these needs, they will have difficulty meeting the other.
  d. Students are most likely to do well in the classroom when they know that their teacher's affection and respect depend on their level of achievement.

**Essay Questions**

- 40. In a short paragraph, describe the basic idea underlying self-worth theory. In a second paragraph, explain what self-handicapping is and the role it plays relative to self-worth. To illustrate your discussion, describe two different kinds of self-handicapping that students might exhibit in or outside of the classroom.

•• 41. Some motivation theorists believe that human beings have a basic need for relatedness.
   a. In a paragraph, explain what theorists mean by this concept, and describe three different student behaviors you might see that would indicate a high need for relatedness.
   b. In three additional paragraphs, describe three different strategies you might use to address students' need for relatedness in the classroom. Be specific as to what you might do.

• 42. Describe how your students' level of anxiety is likely to affect their classroom learning and performance. Be sure to include the concepts of facilitating anxiety and debilitating anxiety in your discussion. Then describe three strategies you can use to keep students' anxiety at a productive level.

## ANSWER KEY

### Multiple-Choice Questions

1. b
2. b
3. b
4. d
5. c
6. a
7. d
8. b
9. c
10. a
11. d
12. a
13. b
14. d
15. a
16. c
17. a
18. d
19. c
20. b
21. b
22. b
23. a
24. d
25. a
26. c
27. c
28. b
29. a
30. d
31. a
32. d
33. a
34. d
35. b
36. c
37. a
38. d
39. b

### Essay Questions

40. Some motivation theorists propose that people have a strong need to protect their general sense of competence—that is, to protect their sense of self-worth. In some cases, people engage in behaviors that actually undermine their chances of success, but such behaviors enable them to maintain their sense of self-worth even as they are failing; this phenomenon is known as self-handicapping. Examples of self-handicapping include the following (the response should include at least two of these *or* offer two plausible alternatives):
    - Setting such high goals that even the most able individual could not attain them
    - Procrastinating, putting off a task until success is virtually impossible
    - Reducing effort, to the point where success is highly unlikely
    - Using alcohol or drugs that will inevitably reduce performance

41. Responses to the two parts of the question are as follows:
    a. The need for relatedness is the need to feel socially connected and to secure others' love and respect. This need may manifest itself in a variety of student behaviors, such as the following (give credit for other reasonable examples as well):
       - Interacting with peers, perhaps at the expense of getting schoolwork done
       - Being concerned about projecting a favorable public image
       - Showing concern for others' welfare
       - Helping others
       - Showing susceptibility to peer pressure

    b. The response should describe at least three strategies for addressing students' need for relatedness. Following are examples of appropriate strategies (other strategies are possible as well):
       - Include group activities (e.g., class discussions, cooperative learning) in the weekly schedule.
       - Show students that you like and respect them and are concerned about their well-being.
       - Express approval for students' achievements and good deeds.
       - Reward students for high achievement by giving them some free time at the end of class to interact with their friends.
       - Help students maintain a good "image" in the eyes of their peers (e.g., don't single them out as being high achievers if their friends don't value academic achievement; scold them privately rather than publicly for any wrongdoings).
       - Occasionally rearrange seating assignments as a way of helping students get to know some of their classmates better.

       Each of these strategies should be described in sufficiently specific and concrete terms that you have a fairly good idea as to what the teacher would do and why it would address students' need for relatedness.

42. Generally speaking, some anxiety promotes learning and performance; this is facilitating anxiety. A great deal of anxiety often interferes with effective learning and performance; this is debilitating anxiety. Easy, automatic tasks are often facilitated by high levels of anxiety, but more difficult tasks are best executed with low or moderate levels. Possible strategies a teacher can use to keep students at a facilitative level include these (the response should list at least <u>three</u> of these or reasonable facsimiles; you may also want to accept other, well-justified strategies):
    - Communicate clear expectations for students' performance.
    - Hold realistic expectations for students' achievement.
    - Enhance students' self-efficacy for performing the task.
    - Have a somewhat predictable classroom routine.
    - Match the level of instruction to students' current knowledge and abilities.
    - Teach effective learning and study strategies so that students can be successful.
    - Provide support or scaffolding to help students master subject matter.
    - Provide specific feedback rather than global evaluations.
    - Allow students to correct errors.

## Chapter 12

# COGNITIVE FACTORS IN MOTIVATION

| CHAPTER OUTLINE | RELEVANT TEST BANK ITEMS |
|---|---|
| SELF-PERCEPTIONS AND INTRINSIC MOTIVATION<br>Self-Efficacy<br>Self-Determination | Multiple-Choice 1–12<br>Essay 75 |
| EXPECTANCIES AND VALUES<br>Internalizing the Values of Others<br>Fostering Expectancies and Values in the Classroom | Multiple-Choice 13–19 |
| INTEREST<br>Situational Versus Personal Interest<br>Promoting Interest in Classroom Subject Matter | Multiple-Choice 20–23 |
| GOALS<br>Mastery and Performance Goals<br>Work-Avoidance Goals<br>Social Goals<br>Career Goals<br>Capitalizing on Students' Goals | Multiple-Choice 24–40<br>Essay 76 |
| ATTRIBUTIONS: PERCEIVED CAUSES OF SUCCESS AND FAILURE<br>Dimensions Underlying Students' Attributions<br>How Attributions Influence Affect, Cognition, and Behavior<br>Developmental Trends in Attributions<br>Factors Influencing the Development of Attributions<br>Mastery Orientation Versus Learned Helplessness | Multiple-Choice 41–60<br>Essay 77–78 |
| TEACHER EXPECTATIONS AND ATTRIBUTIONS<br>How Expectations and Attributions Affect Classroom Performance<br>Forming Productive Expectations and Attributions for Student Performance | Multiple-Choice 61–68 |

| | |
|---|---|
| CONSIDERING DIVERSITY IN THE COGNITIVE ASPECTS OF MOTIVATION<br>Ethnic Differences<br>Gender Differences<br>Socioeconomic Differences<br>Accommodating Students with Special Needs | Multiple-Choice 69–72 |
| THE BIG PICTURE<br>General Principles of Motivation<br>Revisiting the Four Theoretical Perspectives | Multiple-Choice 73–74 |
| The items in the "Integrative Questions" chapter of this Test Bank integrate the content of two or more textbook chapters. Within that chapter, the items listed to the right are relevant to Chapter 12. | Multiple-Choice 9, 15–16<br>Essay 20, 23, 37, 39 |

## Multiple-Choice Questions

•• 1. Some theorists propose that two conditions (both involving self-perceptions) are essential for intrinsic motivation. Considering these conditions, in which one of the following situations would you be most likely to be intrinsically motivated to learn how to water-ski?

a. When you know that learning to water-ski will give you a sense of accomplishment.

b. When a skillful water-skier promises to teach you.

c. When someone who has just learned to water-ski promises to teach you.

d. When you think you can be successful and voluntarily choose to ski.

•• 2. Under some conditions, negative feedback can increase students' intrinsic motivation to perform school tasks. With these conditions in mind, choose the statement below that is most likely to promote intrinsic motivation.

a. "Yours is the lowest quiz score in the entire class, Bill. I want you to see if you can do better than at least half of your classmates next time."

b. "The German Club should be embarrassed about the mess it left in the cafeteria after school yesterday. Do you want the rest of the school to think that German Club members are slobs?"

c. "I know you have the ability to write a better essay than this, Janet. Let me give you some suggestions about what you might do differently next time."

d. "I'm not pleased with the projects that you students turned in yesterday. You should be ashamed of yourselves for not taking the assignment more seriously ."

•• 3. The textbook describes two conditions that may be essential for intrinsic motivation. With these conditions in mind, choose the teacher below who is most likely to promote intrinsic motivation in his or her students.

   a. Ms. Andre gives her students concrete suggestions about how to improve their clay sculptures.
   b. Mr. Brooks reminds his students that the deadline for their research paper is a week from Friday.
   c. Mr. Chambers praises his students for continuing to work quietly when he was called away from the classroom.
   d. Ms. Dacono reminds her students, "You should know your multiplication tables by now."

• 4. If you want to promote intrinsic motivation in your students, you should:

   a. Help them master challenging tasks
   b. Remind them of how proud their parents will be of their achievements
   c. Remind them of how important school grades are for getting into college
   d. Give them enough easy tasks to boost their sense of self-efficacy

•• 5. Which teacher is most likely to promote intrinsic motivation in his or her students?

   a. Mr. Abrams reminds students in his class on automobile repair that a good auto mechanic can always find a job.
   b. Ms. Bohlender writes in the margin of John's paper that he needs to work to improve his spelling.
   c. Ms. Chang offers a bag of popcorn to the group of students that finishes its cooperative group project first.
   d. Ms. Downey tells Tommy that his research report was excellent and that he should be very proud of the job he did.

•• 6. You're teaching the times tables to your class. Today you plan to give a timed test of the multiplication math facts. Your goal is to promote intrinsic motivation. Given what we know about intrinsic motivation, which one of the following strategies should be most effective?

   a. Tell students that you expect them to get a certain number of items correct.
   b. Promise five minutes of free time to students who get a certain number of items correct.
   c. Encourage students to see if they can do better on the test than they did last time.
   d. Put a shiny gold star on every perfect test paper.

• 7. Which one of the following strategies is most consistent with the textbook's recommendations for promoting intrinsic motivation?

   a. Give points for successful performance and deduct an equal number of points for errors.
   b. Encourage students to keep their mistakes to a minimum.
   c. Don't make a big deal of students mistakes.
   d. Use one student's errors to show another student what not to do.

•• 8. The ideal balance of success and failure in a classroom is one in which students are usually successful, but are challenged and occasionally fail. According to the textbook's discussion of motivation, why might this be so?

a. Students need to learn that an occasional mistake doesn't doom them to permanent failure.

b. People can only satisfy their need for relatedness by occasionally failing at tasks.

c. Students develop internal attributions only when they succeed more often than they fail.

d. Students need to have a generally successful classroom experience in order to develop performance goals.

• 9. Which one of the following statements best describes motivation theorists' concept of a sense of self-determination?

a. Reinforcing yourself when you do a good job

b. Believing that you have some choice about what you do

c. Deciding what kind of person you want to become

d. Knowing that you can accomplish something if you just put your mind to it

• 10. Three of the following teaching strategies should promote intrinsic motivation. Which one will not?

a. Giving students occasional choices about how to accomplish classroom objectives

b. Describing desired classroom behaviors in an informational manner rather than as what students "must" do

c. Reminding students about how important their grades will be when they apply to college

d. Showing students how a topic that they are studying, although perhaps not interesting, is something they will find useful in their lives

•• 11. Which one of the following teaching strategies is most likely to increase students' sense of self-determination?

a. Mr. Aas reminds his students that they cannot participate in the school's extracurricular sports program if their grade-point-averages fall below 2.0.

b. Ms. Brown asks her third graders to develop some class rules to ensure that all class members will have a chance to express their ideas openly.

c. Mr. Cranwell explains to his middle school students why good writing skills are important in the business world.

d. Mr. Diaz gives his students enough practice with basic arithmetic facts that they learn them to a level of automaticity.

• 12. Even in the best of schools, students will inevitably encounter "controlling" circumstances that may undermine intrinsic motivation; end-of-semester grades, academic competitions, district-mandated achievement tests, and requirements for college admission are just a few examples. As a way of helping to maintain students' intrinsic motivation under such circumstances, the textbook recommends that teachers:

a. Praise students for keeping their minds on their schoolwork.

b. Focus students' attention on challenging performance goals.

c. Tell students to close their eyes and imagine that they are working in an environment in which such external controls do not exist.

d. Remind students that the most important thing to keep in mind is the value of school tasks in and of themselves.

•• 13. Which one of the following illustrates the role of expectancy in motivation?
   a. Antonio plays for hours on end in the bathtub.
   b. Bernie's parents promise him a new bike if he can learn.
   c. Chip's older brother almost drowned last year.
   d. Drew is pretty sure he can learn if he tries.

• 14. A student's expectancy about classroom success is influenced by three of the following factors. Which one will probably be least influential?
   a. Whether the student has set short-term or long-term goals
   b. How helpful the student thinks the teacher's instruction will be
   c. How much effort the student thinks will be necessary to succeed
   d. How successful the student has been in the past

•• 15. Which one of the following best illustrates the role of value in motivation?
   a. Angie takes piano lessons mainly because her parents insist that she does.
   b. Beth thinks her teacher asked her to play too hard a piece.
   c. Constance thinks she can impress her friends by playing well.
   d. Dena is afraid of how embarrassed she'll be if she makes a mistake.

• 16. Given what motivation theorists tell us about expectancies and values, which one of the following activities are you least likely to value?
   a. One that will make you look good in front of your peers
   b. One at which you will have to work exceptionally hard to succeed
   c. One that you don't enjoy but is important for career success
   d. One that will enable you to obtain desired reinforcement

•• 17. When Scott was first learning how to write, he wrote quickly and sloppily, without regard for how his papers looked. But his teachers praised him regularly for writing carefully and legibly, and eventually he began to pride himself on his neat and careful handwriting. This transition can best be described as
   a. Acquiring an external locus of control
   b. Developing internalized motivation
   c. Developing situational interest
   d. Developing extrinsic motivation

•• 18. Maggie does her homework primarily to gain her teacher's approval. She has little internal desire to do her homework, although she does feel slight twinges of guilt when she fails to get an assignment done on time. Of the four stages through which internalized motivation evolves, Maggie appears to be in the ________ stage.
   a. External regulation
   b. Introjection
   c. Identification
   d. Integration

• 19. Motivation theorists suggest that three conditions are important for the development of internalized motivation. Which one of the following is probably not an important condition for internalized motivation to occur?
   a. Important people in the student's life have expectations for his or her behavior and will impose consequences for inappropriate behavior.
   b. The student is capable of abstract thought; from a Piagetian perspective, the person has advanced to the formal operations stage.
   c. The student has some autonomy in terms of choosing how to act in various situations.
   d. The student feels the warmth and support of important people in his or her environment.

•• 20. Which one of the following exemplifies situational interest rather than personal interest?
   a. Adam finds the Guinness Book of World Records on a library shelf and is intrigued by the strange people it describes.
   b. Blaine can't think of anything he'd rather do than play video games with his friends.
   c. Chuck spends every Saturday and Sunday working on the 1951 Chevy in his garage.
   d. Dave loves to snorkel and hopes to major in marine biology when he goes to college.

•• 21. Which one of the following illustrates personal interest rather than situational interest?
   a. Jennifer is puzzled when a peeled hardboiled egg is suddenly sucked into a bottle after the teacher lights a fire inside the bottle.
   b. Trent gets totally wrapped up in the adventure novel he reads during free time.
   c. Riley can't wait to find out what's in the big cardboard box his teacher has brought to school today.
   d. Victoria loves ballet and wants to become a ballerina when she grows up.

• 22. Three of the following strategies should engage students' interest in class material. Which one is least likely to do so?
   a. Have each student read a different character's lines when the class is reading the play Our Town.
   b. Asking students to imagine what it must have been like to live in medieval England.
   c. Showing students a scientific phenomenon that isn't what they'd expect to happen given their existing beliefs about the world.
   d. Telling students that occasional failures are probably due to circumstances beyond their control.

•• 23. Considering recommended strategies for promoting interest, which teacher is <u>most</u> likely to capture students' interest in classroom subject matter?

a. In Ms. Gaffery's physical education class, instead of having students warm up with calisthenics, she warms them up by teaching them the popular line dance "The Boot Scootin' Boogie."

b. In her English literature class, Ms. Isaacs has her students compete to see who can memorize Hamlet's soliloquy ("To be or not to be . . .") the fastest.

c. In his history class, Mr. Jacobs intersperses occasional anecdotes about his days as a high school football hero into his lecture on the Renaissance.

d. In his driver education class, Mr. Lancaster lists statistics describing the probabilities of accidents happening when teenagers drive drunk.

•• 24. Which one of the following is most likely to be a <u>core goal</u>?

a. Wanting to find a date for the senior prom

b. Wanting to do well in school

c. Looking desperately for something to drink after field hockey practice

d. Trying to find a misplaced homework assignment that is due tomorrow

•• 25. Identify the student who appears to have a <u>mastery goal</u> rather than a performance goal.

a. When Abby gets a new assignment, she likes to set it aside for a day or so before she actually begins to work on it.

b. Bonnie is a perfectionist who gets upset when her test performance is anything but A+.

c. When given the choice between taking an easy class or a more challenging one, Cora chooses the challenging one.

d. Dana is easily distracted by the many stimuli competing for her attention in the classroom.

•• 26. Four students in Ms. Bennett's social studies class have to give an oral report on a country of their choosing. Which one of the students exhibits behavior consistent with a <u>mastery goal</u>?

a. When Eldon gives his report on Hungary, he stands straight and speaks clearly because he wants to impress his teacher and fellow students with his knowledge and ability.

b. Francis wants to give a good presentation on the United Arab Emirates because he needs to improve his overall class grade.

c. As Holly gives her report on Mongolia, she is very nervous. She is afraid she might make a fool of herself in front of her classmates.

d. John does his report on Spain because that is where his family is from. He has enjoyed talking to his grandfather about what it is like to live in Spain.

•• 27. Four students in Mr. Kent's physical education class have just done poorly on the school district's physical fitness test. Which student is exhibiting a mastery goal?

a. Muriel gets As in all her other classes so she doesn't mind getting a C in physical education.

b. Oliver is going to come back after class to look at his scores and ask Mr. Kent for suggestions about how to improve in his weak areas.

c. Patrice is very upset about her poor performance and plans to work very hard to do better next year because she doesn't want her friends to think that she's a wimp.

d. Robert plans to start working out this very weekend so he will be in better shape. Because his father is the school football coach, everyone expects Robert to excel in athletics.

•• 28. Which one of the following individuals definitely has a mastery goal rather than a performance goal?

a. Andrea is in the pool each day at 6:00 a.m.; she's set her sights on an Olympic gold medal in swimming.

b. Brandon wants to please his parents by doing well in school.

c. Claude studies science so he can understand what makes things "tick."

d. Darlene never asks questions in class; she's afraid they might make her look stupid.

•• 29. Which one of the following students clearly has a performance goal rather than a mastery goal?

a. Alec judges his own performance on the basis of how his classmates do.

b. Blanche always does more than her teacher requires.

c. Christina persists when she encounters a difficult mathematics problem.

d. Devon is bored by easy assignments.

•• 30. Which one of these students has a performance-approach goal?

a. Frank finds a homework assignment too easy to waste his time with.

b. Herb frequently asks questions in class in order to understand the information better.

c. Selena decides to enter the school science fair in hopes of impressing her teacher, classmates, and parents.

d. Rita was somewhat disappointed about her last test score in math. Realizing that people learn from their mistakes, she decides to study harder for the next test using different study strategies.

•• 31. Which one of the following statements indicates that the speaker is focused on a performance-avoidance goal?

a. "This is my chance to show all my classmates how smart I am."

b. "Boy, I hope I don't screw this problem up. If I do, I'll look like an idiot."

c. "I'd really like to become a better math student. I hope the teacher gives me feedback about how I can improve my skills."

d. "I need to do well in my science classes so I can get into a good engineering school."

• 32. Three of the following are typically associated with mastery goals. Which one is associated with <u>performance goals</u> (especially performance-avoidance goals)?
  a. Believing that competent people usually succeed without much effort
  b. Believing that errors are an inevitable part of the learning process
  c. Engaging in such processes as meaningful learning and elaboration
  d. Being satisfied with one's performance if it shows improvement over time

•• 33. Which one of the following students clearly has a <u>mastery goal</u> rather than a performance goal?
  a. Alice stays away from science courses because she's never done very well in science.
  b. Boris wants the recognition that being a star football player will bring him.
  c. Cal is relieved to learn he passed his English composition course.
  d. Dinah doesn't worry about making mistakes as long as she knows she's making progress.

• 34. Three of the following characterize students with a mastery goal. Which one characterizes students with a <u>performance goal</u>?
  a. Thinking that if you have to try hard, you must not be very capable.
  b. Thinking that you're doing well as long as you're making progress, even though you're not totally successful.
  c. Seeking out your teacher's guidance when you're having trouble doing something.
  d. Being bored by easy tasks.

• 35. Three of the following characterize students with a performance goal. Which one characterizes students with a <u>mastery goal</u>?
  a. Looking at classmates' performance as an indication of how well you're doing.
  b. Doing something that you know you will be reinforced for.
  c. Trying to learn something word for word.
  d. Concluding that you need to work harder when you fail.

•• 36. Which one of the following students most clearly has a <u>work-avoidance goal</u>?
  a. Frederick stayed up so late last night watching television that he can hardly stay awake in class.
  b. Loni is so active in student government that she often doesn't have time to get her homework done.
  c. Chris asks for his teacher's help on something he is perfectly capable of doing on his own.
  d. Nancy wonders why she has to work harder than her friends to get the same grades they do.

• 37. Three of the following statements accurately describe the diversity we are likely to see in students' career goals. Which statement is not accurate?

a. Girls are more likely than boys to take their future roles as mothers and spouses into account when considering possible careers to pursue.
b. Many young children reach relatively stable decisions about which career they want to pursue; adolescents change their minds fairly frequently.
c. Girls are more likely than boys to limit their career options to those that are stereotypically appropriate for their gender.
d. Students' career choices are to some extent dependent on the value they assign to various professions.

• 38. Three of the following strategies will enable us to capitalize on students' goals as we try to motivate them to learn and achieve in the classroom. Which strategy is not recommended?

a. Encourage students to focus on long-term rather than short-term goals.
b. Keep students' accomplishments confidential, especially if they are trying to hide their high achievement from their peers.
c. Plan activities through which students can simultaneously meet both their academic goals and their social goals.
d. Show students how the things they learn in class are relevant to their present and future needs.

•• 39. Which one of the following teachers is most likely to promote intrinsic motivation in his or her students?

a. Mr. Albert promises his students that if they all finish their short stories by Friday morning, he will give them a half an hour of free time on Friday afternoon.
b. Ms. Benedetti describes events in history so vividly that her students are captivated during the entire lesson.
c. Ms. Carlsen tells students in her algebra class that she is extremely disappointed in their performance on the last test.
d. Mr. Davidow sends "good news" letters home to parents whenever students have a B average or better.

•• 40. Ms. Nobel says to her creative writing class, "I know you are all eager to become better writers, so I've invited a friend of mine who writes novels to come talk to us about her newest mystery and share some of her writing techniques." Which strategy is Ms. Nobel using to motivate her students?

a. Eliciting students' intrinsic motivation by involving an outside resource person.
b. Communicating the belief that students want to learn.
c. Inducing a strong performance goal.
d. Encouraging students to think about their future academic needs.

•• 41. Which one of the following is the best example of a student attributing success to internal factors?

a. Nita has just gotten an A on her final exam in world history and is feeling very grateful to the teacher for her good grade.
b. Polly's teacher has just told her that she will be the group leader for her reading group next quarter. Polly is glad her teacher is in a good mood today.
c. Renata has just gotten a good grade on her math test and she is glad that her mother got her a math tutor.
d. Sue Ellen has just gotten a good grade on her geography test. She is proud that she did so well and glad that she studied hard.

•• 42. In which one of the following situations is a student attributing failure to stable and uncontrollable factors?

a. Jason tells himself that he failed the last history test because the substitute teacher constructed a bad test. He expects to do better when his regular teacher returns from maternity leave.
b. Kami tells herself that she is getting low grades in math because, like her mom, she just isn't any good at math.
c. Lana thinks that she was the last one to be chosen for the baseball team because she hadn't been practicing enough. She vows to do better next time.
d. Marley believes she is having trouble in music because she has been absent the last two weeks. She knows she'll have to work extra hard to catch up to her class.

•• 43. Which one of the following students is attributing success or failure on a geology test to an <u>internal</u> source and thinks the cause is <u>unstable</u> and <u>controllable</u>?

a. Emily said she did well on her test because she is smart in science.
b. Jane said she failed the test because it was too difficult.
c. Joe said he studied hard, but he failed because he is just not good in geology.
d. Drew said he did well on the test because he studied hard.

•• 44. Francine failed her English literature exam. Given what attribution theory tells us about how students typically interpret failures, how is Francine <u>least</u> likely to explain her failure?

a. She didn't study enough.
b. The teacher writes bad exams.
c. The room was too noisy during the exam.
d. She had bad luck.

•• 45. Roxanne and her teammates consistently lose basketball games by a very close margin. Roxanne believes that their losses are always due to bad calls on the part of the referees. With this information in mind, identify the statement below that is <u>most</u> likely to be an accurate description of Roxanne?

a. She feels guilty about not practicing harder.
b. She feels resentment toward the referees.
c. She has decreasing self-confidence about her ability to play basketball.
d. She intends to ask her coach for suggestions about how to improve her game.

•• 46. Frank is a good student. He attributes his success partly to studying long hours and partly to his intelligence ("It runs in the family," he says). From the perspective of attribution theory, three of the following statements are likely to be accurate descriptions of Frank. Which one is probably <u>not</u> an accurate description?
   a. When he is confused about class material, he is reluctant to ask questions.
   b. He feels proud of his academic accomplishments.
   c. He expects to continue doing well in school over the next few years.
   d. He has high self-efficacy regarding school tasks.

•• 47. John has just failed a test—in a sense, his test performance has been punished. From the perspective of <u>attribution theory</u>, is John likely to work harder to pass his next test?
   a. Definitely not.
   b. Absolutely yes.
   c. Yes, provided that his low test score is accompanied by information about strengths and weaknesses about his performance.
   d. Yes, provided that he believes his test performance is the result of something he didn't do but could do next time.

•• 48. The four boys below have all received As in Algebra 1. From the perspective of attribution theory, which one is most likely to sign up for Algebra 2?
   a. Steve thinks he got an A because he has an older brother who is a math whiz to help him out.
   b. Timmy thinks he got an A because he studied very hard.
   c. Vern thinks his A is due to his natural intelligence.
   d. Willie thinks he got an A because he was lucky on the final exam. His teacher asked questions that he knew and didn't ask questions about topics that he <u>didn't</u> know.

•• 49. Virginia is four years old. Georgia is fourteen years old. Both girls like figure skating, but neither is a very good skater. Given developmental trends in attributions, we can predict that Virginia is more likely than Georgia to believe that:
   a. She has little chance of ever skating professionally.
   b. She can become an excellent skater if she continues to work at it.
   c. Good skating is all a matter of luck.
   d. Professional skating is beyond the reach of all but a few very talented individuals.

•• 50. Which one of the following statements reflects an <u>entity</u> view of intelligence?
   a. "Phoebe is one of the brightest students I know."
   b. "If you keep practicing something, you'll get better at it."
   c. "The more you know about a topic, the more quickly and easily you can learn new things about it."
   d. "If at first you don't succeed, try, try again."

•• 51. Which one of the following boys exhibits learned industriousness?

a. Josiah would much rather make something with his hands than read a book.

b. Zeke would much rather read a book than make something with his hands.

c. Keith continues to work hard on the computer program he's writing, even though he hasn't been able to get it to work right yet.

d. Jamal knows that many of the things he's learning in math and physics will be useful in his future career as an architect, and so he studies these topics with possible architectural applications in mind.

• 52. Which pattern of reinforcement and punishment is most likely to lead children to attribute events to internal and controllable causes?

a. When successes are rewarded and failures are punished.

b. When successes are ignored and failures are punished.

c. When effort is rewarded, regardless of success or failure.

d. When successes are rewarded and failures are ignored.

•• 53. Eileen is reluctant to go out for the school soccer team. We want to enhance her self-confidence about becoming a successful soccer player. If we consider attribution theory, the best thing we can say to Eileen is:

a. "Some people are just naturally good soccer players, and I've seen signs that you're probably one of them."

b. "The game of soccer is largely a matter of luck. Some days are good ones and some days are bad. You just never know how things will go."

c. "Skill in soccer is totally a function of how hard you work at the game."

d. "You have some natural athletic ability, and practice will make you even better."

•• 54. When 14-year-old Valerie discovers that she's gotten an A on the last assignment, she expresses pride to her teacher and explains that she worked very hard on it. On the way home from school, however, she tells her friends that she didn't put much effort into the project at all and so is quite surprised about her high grade. From the perspective of attribution theory, how can we best explain Valerie's conflicting statements?

a. She suspects that her friends have performance goals rather than mastery goals, and she is trying to go along with the crowd.

b. She knows that her teacher is more likely than her friends to have an entity view of intelligence, and she tailors her explanations accordingly.

c. She knows that her teacher values hard work but that her friends do not, and she tailors her explanations accordingly.

d. Her social goals are taking precedence over her academic goals in both incidents.

• 55. Which one of the following examples best describes the differences between students with a mastery orientation and students with learned helplessness?
   a. Students with a mastery orientation expect that they will have to work extremely hard to master new tasks. Students with learned helplessness usually overestimate their abilities.
   b. Students with a mastery orientation set easily attainable goals and become frustrated when they don't attain those goals effortlessly. Students with learned helplessness set goals that are almost impossible to attain.
   c. Students with a mastery orientation attribute their successes to external, uncontrollable factors. Students with an attitude of learned helplessness attribute failures to internal, controllable factors.
   d. Students with a mastery orientation set high goals and seek challenges. Students with learned helplessness underestimate their ability and set low goals.

• 56. Helena has a mastery orientation regarding her ability to be a successful student. With this in mind, choose the statement that is probably least accurate about Helena.
   a. She seeks out easy assignments—ones at which she knows she can succeed.
   b. When she is unfamiliar with a particular procedure, she seeks assistance from her teacher.
   c. She has a realistic sense of what she does well and what she does not.
   d. She approaches new tasks with self-confidence.

•• 57. A student who has developed learned helplessness about his or her spelling ability is most likely to say which of the following?
   a. "I have to work harder than my friends to learn to spell."
   b. "I can learn how to spell words correctly without even trying."
   c. "No matter how much I study words, I can't remember how to spell them."
   d. "I would learn to spell eventually, but it's not worth the time it would take to do so."

• 58. Three of the following statements characterize students with learned helplessness. Which one does not?
   a. They set low goals for themselves.
   b. They become easily discouraged when they fail.
   c. They have little confidence in their ability to succeed.
   d. They know that the few successes they do have are due to their own efforts.

• 59. Ms. Jantzen provides a great deal of academic support to help her students achieve classroom objectives. Why should this strategy help promote a mastery orientation in her students?
   a. All students should be able to learn on their own, but those who are not highly motivated may want the teacher's help.
   b. Students need sufficient resources and support to believe that they can succeed if they really want to.
   c. Students invariably need lots of support to achieve their performance goals.
   d. Students who attribute their accomplishments to internal factors such as ability or effort may need external help in order to learn that they can't do everything by themselves.

• 60. Alexander is doing poorly in class. It seems that no matter how hard he tries, he fails. Finally he just stops trying. As his teacher, you want to motivate Alexander to try again. Considering the textbook's discussion of strategies for increasing students' motivation, which one of the following should you do?
  a. Praise Alexander frequently regardless of what he is or is not doing.
  b. Encourage Alexander to try harder.
  c. Support Alexander's efforts to succeed.
  d. Attribute Alexander's failures to factors beyond his control.

• 61. Mr. Maleska has high expectations for his students' classroom performance. With this in mind, we would expect him to:
  a. Overlook assignments on which they perform poorly.
  b. Give students many opportunities to answer questions.
  c. Give little if any feedback about how students are doing.
  d. Give his students more help than they really need to complete tasks successfully.

•• 62. In which one of the following situations does a teacher's behavior reflect low expectations for a student's classroom performance?
  a. Mr. Oya gives René positive feedback when she performs well.
  b. Ms. Ingalls rarely interacts with Joseph.
  c. Mr. Montoya asks Mei-Yau thought-provoking questions in class.
  d. Ms. Littlefield assigns Owen a difficult math problem.

• 63. Ms. Simons believes that Jeremy has the ability to do better on math tests than he is currently doing. Given the textbook's discussion of <u>teacher attributions</u>, how is Ms. Simons most likely to act toward Jeremy?
  a. She'll be annoyed when he doesn't do well.
  b. She'll express sympathy and pity when he doesn't do well.
  c. She'll completely ignore Jeremy, in an attempt to extinguish his nonproductive behavior.
  d. She'll model learned industriousness for Jeremy.

• 64. Mr. Richardson does not expect much of his students from a poor, inner-city neighborhood. Given what we know about the effects of teacher expectations, which outcome is most likely?
  a. His students are likely to learn information in a rote rather than meaningful fashion.
  b. His students are likely to develop more positive self-concepts than they would otherwise.
  c. His students are more likely to develop a realistic understanding of their own strengths and weaknesses than they would otherwise.
  d. His students are likely to achieve at a lower level than they would otherwise.

• 65. Considering research regarding when teacher expectation effects are most likely to occur, which teachers should be most careful to communicate high expectations for students' performance?
  a. First and second grade teachers
  b. Third and fourth grade teachers
  c. Teachers of students who are beginning their second year of high school
  d. Teachers of students who are finishing their senior year of high school

• 66. Three of the following strategies are consistent with the textbook's recommendations for forming expectations and attributions for students' performance. Which one is not consistent with the textbook's recommendations?

   a. Assume that every student has one or more areas of strength.
   b. Communicate the belief that learning more effective strategies may help students perform more successfully.
   c. Limit your assessments of student achievement to informal observations.
   d. Keep in mind that teachers do make a difference in students' lives.

• 67. From the perspective of attribution theory, in which way are teachers' attributions to effort most likely to backfire?

   a. When students fail at a task they have tried very hard at and are then told that they didn't try hard enough, they may decide they simply don't have the ability to do the task and give up.
   b. When students fail at a task they have not tried very hard to succeed at and are then told that they didn't exert enough effort, they are likely to feel either embarrassed or angry.
   c. When students are told that they didn't try hard enough at a task that they expended quite a bit of effort on, they are likely to decide that the subject area has little relevance to their own lives and needs.
   d. When students are told that they didn't exert enough effort, and they really didn't try very hard, they are likely to attribute their failure to an external factor and not accept responsibility for it.

• 68. Students have just done well on what was obviously an easy assignment. If their teacher praises them for their success, they are likely to:

   a. Have high self-efficacy for academic tasks
   b. Conclude that they will have difficulty with more challenging tasks
   c. Develop a mastery orientation
   d. Exert more effort next time

• 69. Three of the following are true statements about diversity in motivation. Which one is false?

   a. Students who have been raised in mainstream Western culture often attribute school success to stable factors (e.g., intelligence); Asian students are more likely to attribute it to hard work.
   b. Boys tend to underestimate their own competence on tasks, whereas girls tend to overestimate it.
   c. Some African American students have a sense of learned helplessness about their ability to achieve school success, perhaps because of their prior experiences with racial discrimination.
   d. On average, Asian students shoot for higher grades than students from other ethnic groups.

•• 70. Four students—Ann, Barbara, Carl, and David—do very well on a difficult mathematics test. Given what we know about gender differences in attributions, how are these students most likely to interpret their high test scores?

a. Ann and Barbara will say they tried hard; Carl and David will say they're just naturally good in math.

b. Ann and Barbara will say they're naturally good in math; Carl and David will say they tried hard.

c. Ann and Barbara will say they were lucky; Carl and David will say their teacher likes them.

d. Ann and Barbara will say their teacher likes them; Carl and David will say they were lucky.

• 71. Three of the following statements are true with regard to students who have special educational needs. Which one is <u>false</u>?

a. Most students with specific cognitive or academic difficulties have a mastery orientation with regard to their schoolwork.

b. Students with general delays in cognitive functioning have trouble thinking about long-term goals.

c. Students with physical challenges tend to have a lower sense of self-determination than their nondisabled peers.

d. When people respond negatively to the behaviors of students with social or behavioral problems, these students often attribute such responses to uncontrollable causes.

•• 72. You have several students with learning disabilities in your class, and you want to help them improve their reading skills. From the perspective of <u>attribution theory</u>, you should:

a. Reinforce them when they demonstrate proficiency in reading.

b. Punish them when they don't read as well as they are capable of reading.

c. Help them discover that they can improve with effort and practice.

d. Remind them how important reading is for later success in life.

•• 73. Three of the following strategies should promote students' motivation in the classroom. With the textbook's discussion of motivation in mind, choose the strategy that is <u>least</u> likely to motivate students to learn and achieve.

a. Mr. Allen has the students in his history class act out an important event in the nation's history.

b. Ms. Bright says, "I find European history absolutely fascinating. Let me show you some reasons why."

c. Ms. Carmichael says, "I'm sorry you didn't do well on the exam. Better luck next time."

d. Mr. Davis says, "Look at how your handwriting now compares to your handwriting last fall. Thanks to your hard work, you've really improved!"

• 74. Attribution theory considers the expectations that students have about the likelihood of future success or failure. The concept of expectations is most consistent with which one of these theoretical perspectives?
   a. Piaget's theory of cognitive development
   b. Vygotsky's theory of cognitive development
   c. Social cognitive theory of learning
   d. Behaviorist theories of learning

## Essay Questions

• 75. Some motivation theorists believe that two self-perceptions are essential conditions for a student to be intrinsically motivated.
   a. Briefly describe these two conditions, illustrating each with a concrete example.
   b. With the two conditions in mind, describe four strategies for promoting intrinsic motivation in a classroom setting.

• 76. In its discussion of motivation, the textbook describes mastery goals, performance-approach goals, and performance-avoidance goals.
   a. In a short paragraph, explain how these three types of goals are different.
   b. Describe four ways in which students with mastery goals and those with performance goals (especially those with performance-avoidance goals) are likely to think and/or act differently.
   c. List three strategies you might use to promote mastery goals. Illustrate each one with a concrete example of something you might do.

•• 77. Perspectives such as behaviorism and social cognitive theory show us how the consequence (reinforcement or punishment) of a particular behavior affects the extent to which the behavior is likely to appear again. Attribution theory has cast a new light on this notion, maintaining that the consequences of behavior will affect each person's learning and future behavior differently, depending on how the individual interprets those consequences. Within the context of attribution theory:
   a. Explain what motivation theorists mean when they talk about attributions.
   b. Explain how students' responses to failure are likely to be different when they attribute that failure to a controllable cause or to an uncontrollable one. Give a concrete example to illustrate your explanation.
   c. Describe three specific strategies you might use to foster more productive attributions in your students. In each case, use attribution theory to explain why you think the strategy will be effective.

•• 78. Explain each of the following situations in terms of attribution theory.

a. After a history of school failures, Marcus eventually stops trying to do well.

b. A fifth-grade teacher gives her class a difficult mathematics test, and many of her students fail it. She tells her class that she will give them a different test over the same material tomorrow. Many of the boys in the class say they will go home and study again. Some of the girls say that they already studied once, and it didn't do much good, so why bother?

c. Samantha's mother helps her study for an addition test on Tuesday and a subtraction test on Thursday. Samantha passes the Tuesday test and is quite proud of herself. She fails the Thursday test and blames her mother for not helping her enough.

# ANSWER KEY

## Multiple-Choice Questions

1. d
2. c
3. a
4. a
5. d
6. c
7. c
8. a
9. b
10. c
11. b
12. d
13. d
14. a
15. c
16. b
17. b
18. b
19. b
20. a
21. d
22. d
23. a
24. b
25. c
26. d
27. b
28. c
29. a
30. c
31. b
32. a
33. d
34. a
35. d
36. c
37. b
38. a
39. b
40. b
41. d
42. b
43. d
44. a
45. b
46. a
47. d
48. c
49. b
50. a
51. c
52. d
53. d
54. c
55. d
56. a
57. c
58. d
59. b
60. c
61. b
62. b
63. a
64. d
65. a
66. c
67. a
68. b
69. b
70. a
71. a
72. c
73. c
74. c

## Essay Questions

75. Responses to the two parts of the question are as follows:
    a. Students must have high self-efficacy: They must believe that they are capable of successfully accomplishing the task or activity in question. They must also have a sense of self-determination: They must believe that they are in control of their destinies and can make choices regarding the direction that their lives will take. (The response should include a concrete example of each of these concepts.)
    b. The textbook presents a number of possible strategies that should foster either self-efficacy or self-determination (the response should include at least four):
       - Make sure students master basic skills.
       - Help students make noticeable progress on difficult tasks.
       - Communicate confidence in students' abilities through both words and actions.
       - Expose students to successful peers.
       - Provide competence-promoting feedback.
       - Promote mastery on challenging tasks.
       - Promote self-comparison rather than comparison with others.
       - Be sure errors occur within an overall context of success.
       - Present rules and instructions in an informational rather than controlling manner.
       - Provide opportunities for students to make choices.
       - Give students considerable autonomy within their organized extracurricular activities.
       - Evaluate students' performance in a noncontrolling fashion.
       - Minimize reliance on extrinsic reinforcers.
       - Help students keep externally imposed constraints in proper perspective.

       Give credit for other strategies that are equally plausible as means of enhancing self-efficacy or self-determination.

76. Responses to various parts of the question are as follows:
    a. A mastery goal is a desire to acquire new knowledge or skills. A performance goal is a desire either to look good and receive favorable judgments (a performance-approach goal) or else <u>not</u> to look bad and be judged poorly (a performance-avoidance goal).
    b. The response should include at least four of the distinctions listed in Table 12.1 of the textbook.
    c. The response should include three strategies for promoting mastery goals. The textbook specifically identifies the following strategies as ways to promote mastery goals:
       - Point out how the subject matter will be useful in the future.
       - Encourage students to engage in meaningful learning rather than rote learning.
       - Show students that they are making progress.
       - Acknowledge that effective learning requires exerting effort and making mistakes.

       However, strategies that promote interest and other forms of intrinsic motivation are also acceptable. Following are examples:
       - Relate subject matter to students' present and/or future needs and goals.
       - Capitalize on students' existing interests.
       - Promote interest by getting students actively and physically involved.
       - Promote interest by including variety and/or novelty in classroom materials and/or procedures.
       - Promote interest by presenting inconsistent or discrepant information.
       - Promote interest by incorporating fantasy or make-believe into classroom activities.
       - Promote interest by occasionally letting students make choices about what they want to study.
       - Model one's own interest in the subject matter.
       - Communicate the belief that students want to learn.
       - Encourage students to set goals that are challenging yet achievable.
       - Encourage students to use their errors to help them learn.

       Each of the three strategies described should be illustrated with a concrete example involving something a teacher might reasonably do.

77. Responses to various parts of the question are as follows:
    a. An attribution is a student's explanation regarding why a specific event (perhaps a success or failure) has occurred.
    b. Students are more likely to respond appropriately to failure—for example, to try harder or use a different strategy—if they believe they have control over the factors contributing to their failure. They are unlikely to change their behavior if they think the source of the failure is beyond their control. The response should include a concrete example illustrating the difference.
    c. Possible strategies for promoting productive attributions include these (the response should describe three strategies, which may include those listed below and/or other strategies justifiable from the perspective of attribution theory):
        - Reinforce successes but don't make a big deal of failures.
        - Make response-reinforcement contingencies clear.
        - Communicate high yet reasonable expectations for student performance.
        - Attribute students' successes to both high ability and such controllable internal factors as effort or learning strategies.
        - Attribute students' failures to factors that they can control.
        - Attribute students' successes to effort only when they have exerted a great deal of effort.
        - Attribute students' failures to a lack of effort only when they clearly haven't tried very hard.
        - Help students develop more effective learning strategies.
        - Define success as eventual rather than immediate mastery.
        - Minimize competition among students.
        - Evaluate students in terms of the improvement they're making.

    The response should provide a reasonable justification of each strategy it describes from the perspective of attribution theory.

78. Responses to various parts of the question are as follows:
    a. Students with a history of failure are likely to develop the belief that success is beyond their control.
    b. Males tend to attribute their failures to a lack of effort; therefore, they will be relatively optimistic about their chances for future success. In contrast, females tend to attribute their failures to a lack of ability; therefore, they will be relatively pessimistic about their chances for future success. This gender difference is most often observed for traditionally "male" subject areas such as mathematics.
    c. Students have a tendency to attribute their successes to internal causes and their failures to external causes. Samantha's emotional reactions, pride and anger, are consistent with how people tend to react when they attribute their successes to their own efforts and believe their failures are due to outside factors.

## Chapter 13

# INSTRUCTIONAL STRATEGIES

| CHAPTER OUTLINE | RELEVANT TEST BANK ITEMS |
|---|---|
| Introduction | Multiple-Choice 1 |
| OVERVIEW OF INSTRUCTIONAL STRATEGIES | Multiple-Choice 2 |
| PLANNING FOR INSTRUCTION<br>Identifying the Goals of Instruction<br>Conducting a Task Analysis<br>Developing a Lesson Plan | Multiple-Choice 3–27<br>Essay 95 |
| EXPOSITORY APPROACHES<br>Lectures and Textbooks<br>Mastery Learning<br>Direct Instruction<br>Computer-Based Instruction<br>Surfing the Internet | Multiple-Choice 28–49<br>Essay 96–97 |
| HANDS-ON APPROACHES<br>Discovery Learning<br>In-Class Activities<br>Computer Simulations and Applications<br>Homework<br>Authentic Activities | Multiple-Choice 50–61<br>Essay 98 |
| INTERACTIVE AND COLLABORATIVE APPROACHES<br>Teacher Questions<br>Class Discussions<br>Reciprocal Teaching<br>Technology-Based Discussions<br>Cooperative Learning<br>Peer Tutoring | Multiple-Choice 62–85<br>Essay 99–100 |

| | |
|---|---|
| TAKING STUDENT DIVERSITY INTO ACCOUNT<br>Considering Group Differences<br>Accommodating Students with Special Needs | Multiple-Choice 86–89 |
| THE BIG PICTURE | Multiple-Choice 90–94 |
| The items in the "Integrative Questions" chapter of this Test Bank integrate the content of two or more textbook chapters. Within that chapter, the items listed to the right t are relevant to Chapter 13. | Multiple-Choice 14, 17<br>Essay 21, 24, 30–31, 38–39 |

## Multiple-Choice Questions

• 1. Which one of the following statements best summarizes the textbook's discussion of planning, instruction, classroom environment, assessment, and student characteristics?
  a. Student characteristics affect planning, which affects instruction, classroom environment, and assessment.
  b. Planning precedes both instruction and classroom environment, which in turn affects both student characteristics and assessment.
  c. Each of them influences the other four.
  d. How student characteristics will be assessed affects planning, instruction, and the classroom environment.

• 2. The textbook distinguishes between teacher-directed and student-directed forms of instruction. Which one of the following best describes how teachers should view these two approaches?
  a. Generally speaking, teacher-directed instruction is more effective than student-directed instruction.
  b. Generally speaking, student-directed instruction is more effective than teacher-directed instruction.
  c. Teacher-directed instruction is recommended for the elementary and middle school grades; student-directed instruction is recommended for the high school grades.
  d. The best approach depends on the characteristics of the students and the goals of instruction.

• 3. Which one of the following is an advantage of instructional objectives?
  a. Students who are given instructional objectives tend to study more.
  b. Students learn more about subject matter not included in the objectives.
  c. Teachers have a better idea of how to assess student achievement.
  d. Teachers don't have to provide as much direct teaching; the objectives virtually "teach themselves."

•• 4. A teacher has this instructional objective: "Students should know single-digit addition and subtraction facts to a level of automaticity." With this objective in mind, the teacher should focus instruction and assessment on:
   a. Having students apply these number facts to practical, real life applications.
   b. Increasing speed, perhaps by using drill-and-practice and timed tests of these number facts.
   c. Developing students' higher-level thinking skills using these number facts.
   d. Promoting a meaningful understanding of general rules regarding addition and subtraction.

• 5. From the teacher's point of view, objectives are especially useful for:
   a. Focusing on what students should do at the end of instruction
   b. Explaining to parents why certain things are important for students to know
   c. Preventing cheating
   d. Fostering students' interest in the subject matter

• 6. In which one of the following ways are students most likely to benefit from knowing the instructional objectives of a lesson?
   a. Objectives let them know what questions are going to be on the next exam.
   b. Objectives enable them to predict how their teacher will teach the lesson, so they know what to expect.
   c. Objectives give them a good idea of what their grades are going to be.
   d. Objectives tell them what is expected of them so they can direct their efforts wisely.

• 7. As educators define the term, <u>standards</u> are general statements regarding:
   a. Which instructional methods teachers should use
   b. What students should learn and achieve
   c. Why some topics should be included in the curriculum and others should not
   d. How classroom assessment should be conducted

•• 8. "The student will use knowledge of color vision to explain color blindness." This objective falls within the _______ domain.
   a. affective
   b. psychomotor
   c. psychosocial
   d. cognitive

•• 9. "The student will swim the breaststroke for at least 50 meters." This objective falls within the _______ domain.
   a. affective
   b. psychomotor
   c. psychosocial
   d. cognitive

•• 10. "The student will be an active participant in the political party of his or her choice." This objective falls within the _______ domain.

a. affective
b. psychomotor
c. sociocultural
d. cognitive

• 11. An instructional objective that requires students to recite a definition exactly as it has been presented is at the ________ level in Bloom's taxonomy.

a. synthesis
b. knowledge
c. comprehension
d. analysis

• 12. An instructional objective that requires students to rephrase a definition in their own words is at the ________ level in Bloom's taxonomy.

a. application
b. knowledge
c. comprehension
d. analysis

•• 13. An instructional objective that requires students to identify the different parts of speech in a sentence is at the ________ level in Bloom's taxonomy.

a. analysis
b. knowledge
c. comprehension
d. synthesis

•• 14. Which one of the following is the best illustration of <u>synthesis</u> within Bloom's taxonomy?

a. Angela discovers fallacies in her teacher's argument regarding the value of an agricultural economy in Africa.
b. Connie dissects an earthworm and looks for its digestive system.
c. Edgar uses a principle that he learned in physics to develop a new tool to lift a heavy object.
d. Georgette writes a justification for corporal punishment using information from her sociology and psychology classes.

•• 15. "The student will appreciate the fine arts." This educational objective can best be criticized on the grounds that it:

a. Is word magic
b. Focuses on teacher behavior rather than student behavior
c. Cannot be easily measured by a paper-pencil test
d. Is clearly outside the domain of most school curricula

•• 16. Which one of the following instructional objectives focuses on students' higher-level thinking skills?
   a. "Students will describe the laws of momentum and inertia."
   b. "Students will use the laws of momentum and inertia to explain how objects move."
   c. "Students will take accurate readings from an experiment designed to measure momentum."
   d. "Students will learn formulas that involve momentum and inertia."

• 17. As teachers, should we describe each and every behavior we want our students to demonstrate? If we did so, we might generate a long list of relatively trivial behaviors. A reasonable alternative is to:
   a. Forego instructional objectives when we want to focus on higher-level skills.
   b. Emphasize lower-level skills.
   c. Develop a mixture of general and specific objectives.
   d. Develop a few abstract objectives, with examples of behaviors reflecting each one.

• 18. Which one of the following best describes <u>long-term instructional objectives</u>?
   a. Students may make gradual progress toward them but never achieve them completely.
   b. They are inappropriate for elementary school children, who may become frustrated when they don't reach them.
   c. They are inappropriate for high school students, because adolescents' attention is typically focused more on short-term goals.
   d. They are most appropriately used for lower-level skills at all grade levels.

•• 19. From the standpoint of criteria described in the textbook, which one of the following objectives should be most useful?
   a. "Students will complete the first ten chapters of their textbook by the end of the semester."
   b. "The teacher will demonstrate the correct way to use a Bunsen burner."
   c. "Students will study effective government practices."
   d. "Students will write poetry using meter and rhyme."

•• 20. Which one of the following objectives meets criteria described in the textbook?
   a. "Students will study the effects of climate on agricultural and business development in Third World countries."
   b. "Students will practice factoring polynomials for at least 30 minutes per day."
   c. "Students will correctly conjugate regular French verbs in both present and past tenses."
   d. "Students will be shown how to execute an effective overhand throw."

•• 21. Which one of the following objectives meets criteria described in the textbook?
   a. "Teachers will show how to convert decimals to fractions and how to convert fractions to decimals."
   b. "Students will work on problems that involve decimals and fractions."
   c. "Students will correctly convert decimals to fractions and fractions to decimals."
   d. "Students will study the relationship of decimals and fractions."

•• 22. Jonathan is learning to play the guitar. His guitar teacher performs a task analysis of Jonathan's first lesson. Which one of the following best characterizes a behavioral task analysis of a guitar lesson?

a. Hold the neck in the left hand, hold the pick between the right thumb and index finger, and place the fingers of the left hand on the appropriate frets.
b. Learn what the treble and bass clefs are, where the frets are located, and how to play the various chords.
c. Define the task of guitar playing, memorize the finger placements, and retrieve prior knowledge of reading music.
d. Read and interpret the written music, identify the appropriate chords, and mentally keep time.

•• 23. As an art teacher, Ms. Lerner performs a task analysis of a unit in which students will learn to work with clay. She considers the coil and throwing methods of pot making, hand and tooled sculpting, and the effects of different types of clay and firing methods. Which type of task analysis is Ms. Lerner conducting?

a. Behavioral analysis
b. Subject matter analysis
c. Information processing analysis
d. Preliminary cognitive analysis

•• 24. Mr. Nolan is going to teach a unit on Shakespeare to his English literature class. He realizes that his students will need to identify themes and main ideas, elaborate on what they read, and summarize each play. Which type of task analysis is Mr. Nolan conducting?

a. Preliminary cognitive analysis
b. Subject matter analysis
c. Behavioral analysis
d. Information processing analysis

• 25. Which one of the following is considered to be the major advantage of conducting a task analysis for topics taught in the classroom?

a. It ensures accreditation by regional and national associations.
b. It helps teachers determine whether they are treating their male and female students equitably.
c. It helps teachers determine how to teach a topic, and in what order.
d. It helps teachers determine the best way to motivate students to study the topic.

• 26. Three of the following are typically included in a lesson plan. Which one is not usually a part of a lesson plan?

a. A task analysis of the subject in question
b. The instructional objectives of the lesson
c. The procedures to be followed during the lesson
d. A method of assessing what students have learned from the lesson

• 27. Teachers should think of a lesson plan as:
  a. Something that should always include objectives in the cognitive, psychomotor, and affective domains
  b. Something that should always address all six levels of Bloom's taxonomy
  c. A "contract" that they have with their students about what the class will accomplish
  d. A general guide for a lesson that they can modify as necessary

•• 28. Which one of the following best illustrates expository instruction?
  a. Students in Mr. Phillips' English class discuss the themes addressed in Hamlet.
  b. Students in Mr. Richards' science class look at handouts and overhead projections that depict the life cycle of the butterfly.
  c. Students in Ms. Thaller's geometry class work at their desks trying to prove the side-angle-side theorem for triangles.
  d. Students in Ms. Verden's history class write the answers to a series of short questions and then flip the page over to get feedback regarding the correct answers.

• 29. Which one of the following is the best example of expository instruction?
  a. A textbook chapter
  b. A classroom discussion
  c. A problem to solve
  d. A laboratory experiment

• 30. Why have some behaviorists criticized classroom lectures as an approach to instruction?
  a. Shaping does not occur in the proper sequence.
  b. Students are unlikely to generalize to similar stimuli.
  c. Students have no opportunity to make a response.
  d. Students cannot easily discriminate among similar stimuli.

•• 31. Which one of the following is the best example of an advance organizer?
  a. Ms. Hillman tells her students, "Tomorrow we will begin a unit on the Civil War. We will examine the reasons for the war, the strengths and weaknesses of both the North and South, and the reasons for the North's victory."
  b. After describing the characteristics of each of the planets in the solar system, Mr. Jeffrey gives his students a handout that shows the orbits of the planets, their distances from the sun, and their relative sizes.
  c. Ms. Lawford tells her students, "On Monday we will begin a unit on how clouds are formed. Please read the next chapter in your book before then."
  d. Ms. Nicholas writes on the board, "Tell your parents to begin thinking about a costume that they can help you make to wear for our Thanksgiving pageant in three weeks."

•• 32. Which one of the following statements best illustrates <u>prior knowledge activation</u> in a geometry lesson?

a. "Today we will be studying three different kinds of triangles: acute, right, and obtuse."

b. "Calculating the volume of a sphere is similar to a procedure you learned last month—calculating the area of a circle."

c. "Okay, class, it's time to put your reading assignment away so that we can begin our geometry lesson."

d. "Do you know how many square feet you have in your bedroom? After learning how to calculate the area of a rectangle today, you will know how to figure out exactly how big your bedroom is."

•• 33. One of the history teachers below is violating a principle recommended for classroom lectures. Which one?

a. Mr. Annenberg explains to his students how the American Revolution was in some ways similar to the fights children have with one another.

b. Ms. Bartholomew begins her discussion of the American Civil War by drawing some parallels between it and something the class has already studied—the American Revolution.

c. During a unit on World War I, Mr. Cortez often uses maps to show how certain battles were fought at especially strategic locations.

d. Ms. DeLuca talks in a relaxed conversational style, describing different battles of World War II as they come to mind.

•• 34. Which one of the following illustrates a <u>signal</u> in expository instruction?

a. Ms. Allen encourages her students to relate the new material to things they already know.

b. Mr. Berke's enthusiasm about science is evident in every lecture he presents.

c. Mr. Christiansen gives students a list of the important concepts he will describe in class that day.

d. Ms. Driver looks sternly at two whispering students who are obviously not paying attention to the video she is showing.

• 35. Which one of the following is the major rationale underlying a <u>mastery learning</u> approach to instruction?

a. Students have greater self-esteem when they can all work at the same pace.

b. All students should be able to achieve at grade level.

c. Students should learn one topic well before moving on to a more difficult one.

d. Students construct their own understanding of the world from the information they receive.

• 36. Three of the following are typical components of mastery learning. Which one is <u>not</u> necessarily a component of mastery learning?

a. Students demonstrate mastery of each unit before proceeding further.

b. Students have additional, remedial activities when they need them.

c. Topics are arranged in a logical sequence.

d. Students have numerous opportunities to manipulate concrete objects.

•• 37. Judging from the brief descriptions below, which one of these four teachers is using a mastery learning approach?
   a. Mr. Andrews lectures each week on different American novels. Students must attend at least 80% of these lectures.
   b. Ms. Bennett begins each class by asking students what they would most like to study that day.
   c. Mr. Carlton has divided his physics course into 15 discrete units that students study individually at their own rate.
   d. Ms. Dominguez teaches children the basics of mathematics by using such concrete objects as blocks and sticks.

•• 38. Judging from the brief descriptions below, which one of these four teachers is using a mastery learning approach?
   a. Ms. Alfonso gives examinations in which different students are asked different questions, depending on individual student needs and interests.
   b. Mr. Bryant assigns term papers and oral reports rather than in-class examinations.
   c. Ms. Carroll uses the highest four of a student's six exam scores to determine course grades.
   d. Mr. Dickson insists that students pass each test at the 80% level before beginning the next unit.

• 39. In which situation is mastery learning <u>most</u> appropriate?
   a. When instructional objectives lie primarily in the affective domain.
   b. When instructional objectives are at the upper end of Bloom's taxonomy.
   c. When certain skills provide the foundation for future material.
   d. When subject matter is abstract and complex.

• 40. Research indicates that mastery learning approaches are superior to traditional instruction in several ways. Which one of the following conclusions should <u>not</u> be drawn on the basis of research on mastery learning?
   a. Academic achievement is higher in classrooms that emphasize mastery learning.
   b. Mastery learning is more appropriate for high-ability learners than for low-ability learners.
   c. Students have higher self-efficacy about their ability to learn when a mastery approach is used rather than traditional instruction.
   d. Students develop more regular study habits, rather than procrastinating and cramming, with a mastery approach.

•• 41. A mastery learning approach would probably be <u>most</u> suitable for teaching:
   a. Introductory German
   b. A philosophy seminar
   c. Advanced techniques of photography
   d. Controversial issues in history

• 42. Which one of the following are you <u>least</u> likely to see in <u>direct instruction</u>?
   a. Frequent teacher feedback
   b. Opportunities for students to practice a skill independently
   c. A heated discussion of controversial issues
   d. A review of previously learned material

•• 43. When Ms. Krakowski teaches the process of long division, she describes the objective of the lesson and demonstrates the procedure on the chalkboard. Then she has students solve long-division problems at the chalkboard, where she can give them frequent guidance as they work. Later, after the students show some proficiency with long division, she has them work on additional problems at their desks. Ms. Krakowski's approach can best be classified as which of the following?
   a. Discovery learning
   b. Task analysis
   c. Student-directed instruction
   d. Direct instruction

• 44. Direct instruction would be most appropriate for teaching students:
   a. About the human digestive system
   b. How to swing a golf club
   c. Rules for appropriate classroom behavior
   d. Why NATO forces attacked Kosovo in 1999

• 45. Ms. Longman is using programmed instruction to teach basic principles of map interpretation. Which one of the following are students least likely to encounter in their instruction?
   a. One-to-one interactions with their teacher.
   b. A high probability of success when they answer a question.
   c. Immediate feedback about the accuracy of their responses.
   d. A series of frames, each of which presents a small amount of new information.

• 46. Three of the characteristics listed below are frequently found in computer-based instruction. Which characteristic are we least likely to see in CBI?
   a. Questions that ask students to recall what they already know about a topic
   b. Strategies for catching and keeping students' attention
   c. Opportunities for group discussion of the material
   d. Drill-and-practice exercises that promote automaticity

•• 47. The four students described below are all studying classroom subject matter through computer-based instruction. Which one appears to be working with hypermedia?
   a. Tiffani is "dissecting" an earthworm that appears on her computer screen by moving the computer mouse and clicking the mouse button to "cut" or "remove" various parts of the worm.
   b. Sergio is playing a computer game in which he must solve multiplication problems in order to earn the "ammunition" he needs to kill invaders from outer space.
   c. Ron is using electronic mail to exchange ideas with students across the country.
   d. Elisa reads some text about the Gulf War and then clicks on a "button" on the computer screen to view a photograph of Saddam Hussein.

• 48. Three of the following are accurate statements about computer-based instruction. Which statement is false with regard to CBI?
   a. It often promotes more positive attitudes toward school work.
   b. It is recommended even when the same material can be presented in other ways.
   c. It can lead to higher academic achievement than is true for more traditional methods.
   d. It can enhance students' intrinsic motivation to learn.

• 49. Which one of the following statements best describes current views about the value of the Internet in classroom instruction?
   a. It has great potential as a learning tool, but actual effects on learning have not yet been studied systematically.
   b. Many computer experts suggest that its dangers (e.g., exposure to racism and other forms of intolerance) far outweigh the benefits it might have for children and adolescents.
   c. It appears to be far more effective than classroom lectures as a way to promote learning, particularly at the secondary level.
   d. Its effects are minimal unless students each have access to their own computer terminal.

•• 50. Which one of the following is the best example of a discovery learning approach to instruction?
   a. Ms. Markowitz instructs her students to take notes during her lecture and then goes over the notes with them to make sure that they understand the material.
   b. Mr. Tseng gives his students a free day to spend in the library reading about whatever subjects they like.
   c. Mr. Vicker takes his science students to a tide pool and asks them to describe and categorize the different life forms they find there.
   d. Ms. Haxten instructs her drama students to think about what their characters are like as they memorize their lines for a play.

• 51. Which one of the following statements about discovery learning is most accurate?
   a. It makes more efficient use of class time than a lecture does.
   b. It is more appropriate for teaching lower-level skills than for teaching higher-level skills.
   c. It consistently promotes higher achievement than more expository approaches.
   d. It sometimes leads to incorrect understandings about classroom subject matter.

• 52. Which one of the following conditions is recommended for effective learning in a discovery learning session?
   a. Having freedom to explore one's environment without any structure or restraint
   b. Having some prior knowledge about the material being explored
   c. Having a lesson that has been broken down into small, discrete pieces
   d. Having an advance organizer for the lesson

• 53. Three of the following teaching strategies should help students benefit from a discovery learning situation. Which strategy is <u>least</u> likely to be helpful?
   a. Mr. Azama takes his students to the site of a Civil War battle and says, "Okay, look around and see what you can find."
   b. Ms. Berkowitz asks students to write down their discoveries about what happens to a chemical solution when they heat it.
   c. Ms. Clift gives students several guidelines to follow as they conduct a physics experiment.
   d. Mr. DiCicco makes sure students have some knowledge about triangles, including the concepts of <u>base</u> and <u>height</u>, then provides an exercise through which they discover for themselves the formula for calculating a triangle's area.

• 54. Three of the following practices are recommended when assigning in-class activities. Which one is not necessarily recommended?
   a. Provide the support necessary for students to be successful.
   b. Encourage students to evaluate their own work.
   c. Always focus on higher-level thinking skills.
   d. Give frequent feedback about students' progress.

•• 55. Which one of the following uses of a computer in instruction is most similar to an authentic activity?
   a. A computer simulation that allows students to conduct an experiment
   b. A computer-based instructional program that teaches the basics of first aid
   c. A computer-based instructional program that teaches advanced human anatomy
   d. A computer game that promotes automaticity for basic math facts

• 56. Which one of the following statements is most accurate about the value of homework in the elementary grades?
   a. It definitely enhances students' learning.
   b. It seems to promote learning in girls but not in boys, perhaps because girls are more conscientious about doing it.
   c. It has little effect on students' learning but may help them develop self-regulatory skills.
   d. It tends to be effective only when it focuses on drill and practice.

•• 57. The four teachers below are assigning homework to their students. Which teacher is giving an assignment that's inconsistent with general recommendations regarding the appropriate use of homework?
   a. Mr. Rhodes asks his eighth graders to write the answers to a series of questions based on material they've been studying over the past week.
   b. Ms. Wong asks her sixth graders to make up sentences using each of their new spelling words.
   c. Mr. Needham asks his first graders to bring something from home that begins with the letter t.
   d. Ms. Powell asks her high school algebra students to read the next two chapters in their textbook and then do the problems at the end of each chapter.

•• 58. Only one of the teachers below is using a strategy consistent with general recommendations regarding the use of homework. Which one?
   a. Mr. Trahan gives his students a challenging writing assignment and suggests that they ask their parents to help them with it at home.
   b. Mr. Fox sometimes gives students an optional assignment—homework they can do if they want to.
   c. Ms. Hewitt counts homework as being worth 50% of students' final grades.
   d. Mr. Reichel assigns twenty extra math problems after he learns that his class has misbehaved for a substitute teacher.

• 59. Which one of the following statements best describes theorists' rationale for advocating the use of authentic activities?
   a. Authentic activities are the most efficient way of teaching basic skills.
   b. Authentic activities have built-in scaffolding that assures students' success.
   c. Authentic activities help students relate classroom subjects to real-world contexts.
   d. Students' performance in authentic activities is easier to evaluate objectively.

• 60. According to the textbook, an effective authentic activity is most likely to be one that:
   a. Can be accomplished with only a minimal amount of knowledge about the subject matter involved
   b. Helps students refine their gross motor and fine motor skills
   c. Is challenging but ultimately has a single "right" answer
   d. Requires students to gather and integrate information from a variety of sources

•• 61. Which one of the following is the best example of an authentic activity?
   a. Listing four different kinds of sedimentary rocks
   b. Designing a bridge using principles of physics
   c. Putting definitions of new terms in your own words
   d. Discussing reasons why World War I occurred

• 62. Three of the following are purposes that asking questions in class can serve. Which one is not a typical use of asking questions?
   a. To decrease the extent to which students need to process the material.
   b. To promote students' elaboration of the material.
   c. To help students monitor their own comprehension of the material.
   d. To determine whether students understand the material.

• 63. Class discussions can serve several useful purposes. For which of the following purposes is a class discussion least likely to be helpful?
   a. In promoting transfer of mathematical principles to real-world problems
   b. In helping students discover that history is not necessarily all "fact"
   c. In promoting conceptual change in science
   d. In facilitating the memorization of a poem

•• 64. Using the guidelines presented in the textbook, choose the topic below that would be most appropriate for a classroom discussion.
   a. Interpreting Edgar Allan Poe's poem The Raven
   b. Learning the various tenses of the verb to be
   c. Studying the history of the United Nations
   d. Learning how gravity affects the speed with which an object falls to the earth

• 65. Three of the following strategies are recommended for conducting class discussions. Which one is not recommended?
   a. Communicate the idea that changing one's mind about an issue is a sign of thoughtful reflection.
   b. Ask students to try to identify a compromise position that takes diverse perspectives into account.
   c. Use a class discussion to explore a topic that students know nothing about.
   d. Bring some kind of closure on the topic at the end of the discussion.

•• 66. Three of the teachers below are using strategies consistent with the textbook's recommendations for holding class discussions. Which teacher is using a strategy that is <u>inconsistent</u> with the textbook's recommendations?

a. Mr. Poston assures students that it's OK if they change their minds about an issue.
b. Mr. Morris allows students to remain silent throughout the discussion if they choose to do so.
c. Mr. Sheehan reminds students that they can criticize ideas but not people.
d. Mr. Retzlaff divides his class into groups of four students each to discuss a controversial issue.

• 67. Three of the following are strategies that good readers use to enhance their comprehension. Which one is <u>not</u>?

a. They ask themselves questions to make sure they understand.
b. They take steps to clarify possible sources of confusion.
c. They anticipate what is likely to come next in the passage.
d. They read through material fairly rapidly.

•• 68. Which one of the following teachers is using <u>reciprocal teaching</u>?

a. Mr. Armando has students work in pairs, testing each other's knowledge about a topic.
b. Working with a small group, Mr. Bromley gives each student a chance to ask questions of his or her classmates regarding a section of text they are reading.
c. When students ask questions about things they don't understand, Ms. Cromwell asks if others can answer those questions before answering them herself.
d. Before a test, Ms. Dievers has each student describe the strategies he or she plans to use while studying.

• 69. If we consider the effectiveness of reciprocal teaching from a <u>metacognitive</u> perspective, why do students in a reciprocal teaching situation show improvements in reading comprehension?

a. They become increasingly capable of abstract thought.
b. They have numerous opportunities to practice using visual imagery.
c. They can observe the ways that their classmates process information.
d. They feel they must compete with others and therefore work harder.

•• 70. As a teacher, you want to improve your students' ability to learn from their textbooks. Considering research results described in the textbook, which technique should you use?

a. Reciprocal teaching
b. Authentic activities
c. Cooperative learning
d. Expository instruction

• 71. Which one of the following best reflects <u>technology-based discussions</u> as the textbook describes them?

a. Students share their work on a classroom data base, give one another feedback, and build on one another's ideas.
b. At a predesignated time, students sit at computer terminals in pairs or trios and converse with their peers across the nation.
c. Students "meet" in Internet "chat rooms" during the evening hours to work on cooperative group projects.
d. Two classes in distant locations use telephone lines and video technology to exchange ideas about a topic of mutual interest.

• 72. Cooperative learning can be justified from three of the following theoretical concepts. Which one of the underlined concepts that follow is <u>least</u> relevant to cooperative learning?

a. Students in a cooperative group provide <u>scaffolding</u> for one another as they attempt challenging tasks.
b. Students are getting <u>continuous reinforcement</u> for their responses.
c. Social interaction among students facilitates <u>knowledge construction</u>.
d. Students' <u>self-efficacy</u> increases when they see their classmates succeed.

• 73. Which concept from behaviorism figures prominently in cooperative learning?

a. Intrinsic reinforcement
b. Continuous reinforcement
c. Group contingency
d. Conditioned response

• 74. Three of the following are reasons why cooperative learning is successful. Which one is <u>not</u> a reason?

a. Higher-ability students do much of the work for lower-ability students.
b. Students help one another learn and understand the material at a meaningful level.
c. Students model effective thinking skills for one another.
d. Students reinforce one another for achieving at a high level.

• 75. Three of the following are accurate statements about the benefits of cooperative learning. Which statement is <u>not</u> accurate?

a. Students are more likely to develop friendships with students of diverse cultural backgrounds.
b. Students often show higher academic achievement in comparison to students instructed in more traditional ways.
c. Students rarely get off-task during cooperative learning activities.
d. Students show greater interest in classroom subject matter.

•• 76. As a teacher, you want two students who have physical disabilities to develop closer friendships with their nondisabled classmates. Of the following choices, the <u>best</u> instructional approach to use for this purpose is:

a. Hypermedia
b. Mastery learning
c. Cooperative learning
d. Expository instruction

• 77. Many advocates of cooperative learning recommend that the most effective cooperative groups are those that include a wide range of student ability levels. How can we best summarize research findings regarding the effectiveness of different kinds of groups?

a. These advocates are correct; heterogeneous grouping maximizes student achievement.
b. Low-ability students do better when placed with high-ability students, but middle-ability students work best with students very similar to themselves in ability.
c. High-ability students rarely, if ever, benefit from working with low-ability students.
d. Research results are inconclusive with regard to the optimal range of ability levels within a particular group.

• 78. Three of the following are typical elements of cooperative learning. Which one is <u>not</u> typical of cooperative learning?

a. Group members depend on one another for their learning.
b. Each group member is working on a different instructional objective.
c. Group members must individually demonstrate what they have learned.
d. Groups work toward clear, concrete objectives.

•• 79. Which one of the following cooperative groups is using the <u>jigsaw</u> technique?

a. When studying types of mountains (volcanic, dome, fold, and block), each student studies one type and teaches what he or she has learned to other group members.
b. When attempting to solve several challenging mathematics problems, group members brainstorm possible ways of solving each one.
c. As it prepares for a debate about capital punishment, a cooperative group decides which member will present which argument.
d. After everyone has read Shakespeare's <u>Julius Caesar</u>, group members divide up the scenes of the play, and each student skims through his or her scenes for examples of symbolism.

•• 80. The students in Mr. Cohen's class have formed cooperative groups of three students each to study a chapter in their science book. Which one of the following best illustrates how the students might use <u>scripted cooperation</u> during the activity?

a. The students divide the chapter up into sections that each contain roughly one-third of the material. They read their allotted sections and then plan how they can best teach the material to their fellow group members.
b. The students work actively to help one another learn because they know that their final grade for the activity will depend not only on how much they learn, but also on how much the other two group members learn.
c. One student reads a paragraph aloud, a second summarizes it, and the third listens for any errors or omissions the second student might have made. The three students change roles for each successive paragraph.
d. At the end of the cooperative learning activity, Mr. Cohen asks each group to evaluate its effectiveness in terms of these questions: "Did they all actively participate?" "Did they listen to one another?" "Did they criticize ideas rather than people?"

•• 81. Which one of the following teachers is using the recommended approach to evaluating students' achievement in a cooperative learning situation?
   a. Ms. Au has students take notes on what they are learning throughout a cooperative learning session.
   b. Mr. Baer's cooperative groups turn in a research paper co-authored by all group members.
   c. Mr. Craighead's students meet with him in their cooperative groups to explain to him what they have learned during the session.
   d. Ms. Donaldson gives students a quiz over the material that groups have studied; students get extra credit if everyone in their group scores high.

• 82. Which one of the following most accurately describes a <u>base group</u> in cooperative learning?
   a. A group that works on knowledge and skills that are prerequisites for later material
   b. A group that provides ongoing academic support for its members
   c. A group that convenes for an entire day to plan and carry out a lengthy project
   d. A group that meets once a month to discuss each student's academic progress

• 83. Three of the following statements about peer tutoring are true. Which one is <u>false</u>?
   a. It provides a context in which students feel more at ease asking questions.
   b. It fosters friendships among students from diverse backgrounds.
   c. In some cases, it leads to higher achievement than whole-class instruction.
   d. There are academic benefits for the students being tutored but not for the tutors.

• 84. Three of the following are consistent with the textbook's recommendations for using peer tutoring. Which one is <u>not</u> consistent with the textbook's recommendations?
   a. Peer tutoring can be used effectively to help students who have been identified as having learning disabilities.
   b. Tutors function most effectively when they are allowed to use teaching strategies that they develop on their own.
   c. Teachers should continually monitor the effects of peer tutoring to be sure that both the tutors and the students being tutored are learning from the process.
   d. Tutors are most effective when they have learned the subject matter very well.

• 85. Which one of the following <u>best</u> illustrates how teachers can effectively structure a peer tutoring session?
   a. Give students examples of the kinds of questions they should ask one another.
   b. Tell tutors how long they should spend on each topic they are tutoring.
   c. Give the students being tutored an upper limit on the number of questions they can ask their tutor.
   d. Remind tutors that they should ask at least ten questions during a tutoring session.

• 86. Which one of the following teaching strategies is probably <u>least</u> likely to be effective for a class of students from diverse ethnic backgrounds?
   a. Conducting peer tutoring sessions
   b. Assigning textbook readings
   c. Assigning cooperative learning activities
   d. Having small-group discussions

• 87. In cooperative learning, you would be most likely to form all-male and all-female cooperative groups if your goal was to:
   a. Maximize the heterogeneity of group members' ability levels
   b. Use scripted cooperation to facilitate the activity
   c. Establish base groups for the entire school year
   d. Encourage all group members to participate actively

• 88. Three of the following statements are accurate regarding recommended teaching strategies for students with special needs. Which statement is <u>not</u> accurate?
   a. Students with specific cognitive difficulties can use grammar and spell checkers to compensate for possible deficits in their language skills.
   b. Expository instruction can be an effective method for students with advanced cognitive development.
   c. Students with general delays in cognitive development benefit most from discovery learning approaches.
   d. Hypermedia provides a means through which students with specific cognitive difficulties can learn through multiple modalities.

• 89. For which students with special needs are <u>homogeneous</u> cooperative groups sometimes recommended?
   a. Students who have a variety of physical and sensory disabilities
   b. Students who are gifted
   c. Students with mental retardation
   d. Students with social or behavioral problems

•• 90. As a teacher, you want your students to learn basic concepts in chemistry well enough that they can use them when studying more advanced topics. Of the following choices, the <u>best</u> instructional approach to use for this purpose is:
   a. Discovery learning
   b. Lecture
   c. Cooperative learning
   d. Direct instruction

•• 91. As a teacher, you want to accommodate students' diverse ability levels in mathematics. Of the following choices, the <u>best</u> instructional approach to use for this purpose is:
   a. Surfing the Internet
   b. Class discussion
   c. Peer tutoring
   d. Reciprocal teaching

•• 92. As a teacher, you want your students to pull together their knowledge and skills from a variety of different disciplines to solve real-world problems. Of the following choices, the <u>best</u> instructional approach to use for this purpose is:
   a. Mastery learning
   b. An authentic activity
   c. Discovery learning
   d. Hypermedia

• 93. Which one of the following instructional strategies would probably be <u>least</u> appropriate for students who have little or no prior knowledge about the topic they are studying?
   a. Class discussion
   b. Computer-based instruction
   c. Mastery learning
   d. Lecture

•• 94. When we choose an instructional strategy, we should consider the extent to which our students are self-regulated learners. Which of the following approaches would be <u>most</u> effective if our students show little or no ability to regulate their own learning?
   a. Hypermedia
   b. An authentic activity
   c. Discovery learning
   d. Direct instruction

## <u>Essay Questions</u>

•• 95. Identify a particular topic that you may someday teach. Now:
   a. Write three instructional objectives for your topic, including at least one that addresses a higher-level skill. Be sure that your objectives meet the criteria presented in the textbook.
   b. Determine whether each of your objectives lies in the cognitive, psychomotor, or affective domain. Justify your decisions.
   c. Choose a suitable approach to instruction for each of your objectives. Justify your decisions.

•• 96. Choose a topic with which you are familiar and imagine that you have to give a half-hour lecture on that topic. Describe your topic, then explain in concrete terms <u>four</u> different things you should do in your lecture to facilitate students' ability to process the information effectively.

•• 97. Describe the mastery learning approach to instruction, identifying at least <u>four</u> major components that are typically included. Then give a concrete example of how you might use mastery learning to teach a specific topic, being sure to illustrate all four of the components you listed.

•• 98. Identify a grade level at which you might teach. Pick a topic you might teach at that grade level and explain how you might teach it through <u>discovery learning</u>. In your explanation, incorporate the two strategies that the textbook recommends for discovery learning.

•• 99. Pick a topic that you might effectively teach through a cooperative learning approach. Then, using guidelines presented in the textbook, describe how you will:
   a. Form your cooperative groups.
   b. Foster interdependence of group members.
   c. Assess what students have learned.

• 100. Describe <u>reciprocal teaching</u> and its effects on student achievement. Explain its effectiveness using principles of learning from cognitive psychology, being sure to address <u>metacognition</u> in your discussion.

# ANSWER KEY

## Multiple-Choice Questions

1. c
2. d
3. c
4. b
5. a
6. d
7. b
8. d
9. b
10. a
11. b
12. c
13. a
14. d
15. a
16. b
17. d
18. a
19. d
20. c
21. c
22. a
23. b
24. d
25. c
26. a
27. d
28. b
29. a
30. c
31. a
32. b
33. d
34. c
35. c
36. d
37. c
38. d
39. c
40. b
41. a
42. c
43. d
44. b
45. a
46. c
47. d
48. b
49. a
50. c
51. d
52. b
53. a
54. c
55. a
56. c
57. d
58. b
59. c
60. d
61. b
62. a
63. d
64. a
65. c
66. b
67. d
68. b
69. c
70. a
71. a
72. b
73. c
74. a
75. c
76. c
77. d
78. b
79. a
80. c
81. d
82. b
83. d
84. b
85. a
86. b
87. d
88. c
89. b
90. d
91. c
92. b
93. a
94. d

## Essay Questions

95. The response should first identify a particular topic to be taught. Then:
    a. The response should present three objectives that describe observable student outcomes.
    b. The response should accurately categorize each objective as belonging in the cognitive domain (knowledge and ways of mentally processing it), psychomotor domain (physical movements and actions), or affective domain (attitudes and values). It should also justify why each objective falls in the chosen domain.
    c. Responses will vary widely here. The method of instruction described should be clearly appropriate for helping students achieve each objective.

96. The response should identify the specific topic to be taught and then describe four concrete strategies that reflect at least three of the following elements:
    - An advance organizer
    - Connections to students' prior knowledge
    - Analogies
    - A coherent organization
    - Signals about what's important
    - Visual aids
    - Appropriate pacing
    - A summary at the end

97. Mastery learning approaches are those that ensure that students learn one topic thoroughly before proceeding to the next one. Components of mastery learning approaches include these (the response should identify at least four):
    - Small, discrete units
    - A logical sequence of topics
    - Demonstration of mastery at the completion of each unit
    - A concrete, observable criterion for mastery of each unit
    - Remedial activities for students needing extra assistance to achieve mastery

    The response should include a concrete example of how a mastery learning approach might be implemented in the classroom; this example should illustrate the four components of mastery learning identified previously.

98. The response should include a specific grade level and a specific topic to be taught at that level. It should describe how that topic might be taught using discovery learning in sufficiently concrete terms that you have a fairly good idea of what would occur during the lesson. Although students' responses are apt to vary considerably, their approaches should incorporate the following two ideas:
    - Students have the knowledge they need to interpret their findings appropriately.
    - The teacher should provide some structure to guide students' discovery activities.

99. The response should first identify a specific topic that might realistically be taught with a cooperative learning approach. Parts a-c below should be addressed within the context of this topic.
    a. The procedure used to form cooperative groups should ensure that students in each group can work effectively together. The groups should be heterogeneous with respect to gender and ethnic background. The response should include an explanation of how heterogeneous the groups are with respect to ability level and offer a rationale for the decision.
    b. Interdependence of group members can be achieved by: (1) assigning different roles to different group members (e.g., through scripted cooperation), or (2) using a jigsaw technique in which each group member receives information that he or she must then teach to the rest of the group. The response needs to describe only one of these strategies.
    c. Cooperative learning is most effective when students are individually accountable for their own learning but also receive rewards for achievement of the group as a whole (the response should reflect both individual accountability and rewards for group success).

100. Reciprocal teaching is an approach to teaching reading comprehension whereby a group of students and their teacher read passages from expository text, stopping periodically to ask teacher-like questions of one another. The teacher initially models appropriate questions, but gradually turns the role of "teacher" over to students; each student has a turn asking questions about the text and encouraging other group members to do likewise. Reciprocal teaching has been shown to have dramatic effects on students' reading comprehension skills. Reciprocal teaching promotes four information processing strategies—summarizing, questioning, clarifying, and predicting. By verbalizing these strategies aloud, and by observing how classmates process the material they read, students develop greater metacognitive awareness of how reading material can be effectively processed.

Chapter 14

# CREATING AND MAINTAINING A PRODUCTIVE CLASSROOM ENVIRONMENT

| CHAPTER OUTLINE | RELEVANT TEST BANK ITEMS |
|---|---|
| CREATING AN ENVIRONMENT CONDUCIVE TO LEARNING<br>Arranging the Classroom<br>Creating an Effective Classroom Climate<br>Setting Limits<br>Planning Activities That Keep Students on Task<br>Monitoring What Students Are Doing<br>Modifying Instructional Strategies When Necessary | Multiple-Choice 1–19<br>Essay 41 |
| DEALING WITH MISBEHAVIORS<br>Ignoring the Behavior<br>Cueing the Student<br>Discussing the Problem Privately with the Student<br>Promoting Self-Regulation<br>Using Behaviorist Approaches<br>Conferring with Parents | Multiple-Choice 20–30<br>Essay 42 |
| TAKING STUDENT DIVERSITY INTO ACCOUNT<br>Creating a Supportive Climate<br>Defining and Responding to Misbehaviors<br>Accommodating Students with Special Needs | Multiple-Choice 31–33<br>Essay 43 |
| COORDINATING EFFORTS WITH OTHERS<br>Working with Other Teachers<br>Working with the Community at Large<br>Working with Parents | Multiple-Choice 34–40 |
| The items in the "Integrative Questions" chapter of this Test Bank integrate the content of two or more textbook chapters. Within that chapter, the item listed to the right is relevant to Chapter 14. | Multiple-Choice 18<br>Essay 23 |

## Multiple-Choice Questions

•• 1. From the perspective of the textbook, which one of the following classrooms clearly reflects effective classroom management?
   a. While Mr. Alton works with a reading group, most of his other students are doing their assigned seatwork, although a handful of them are giggling in the corner about something that happened in the lunchroom earlier.
   b. Ms. Berg's students are busily working on their math assignments in groups of three or four students each. The classroom gets a bit noisy at times when a group disagrees about how to do a problem.
   c. While Ms. Carrera sits at her desk in the front of the classroom, her students are doing assignments independently at their desks. She overlooks the whispering, note passing, and mindless doodling that is occurring as long as the classroom is quiet.
   d. In his physical education class, Mr. Dupuis works with the students who seem truly interested in learning the long jump. Those students who don't want to try the jump are allowed to sit on the sidelines and talk quietly among themselves.

• 2. From a classroom management standpoint, which one of the following statements describes the most suitable physical arrangement of a classroom?
   a. One that minimizes distractions and facilitates teacher-student interactions
   b. One that has as little furniture as possible so that students can move about in an unrestricted fashion
   c. One that is structured and orderly enough to communicate the message that the teacher must ultimately be in control of what happens in the classroom
   d. One that allows students to feel as relaxed as possible

•• 3. Ms. Parisi, a fifth grade teacher, wants all her students to be able to see her easily. She has read that the students nearest the teacher are more likely to pay attention and learn in class. So as she arranges her classroom at the beginning of the year, she puts her desk in the center of the room and puts the students' desks in three concentric circles around hers. With the textbook's discussion about arranging the classroom in mind, identify the biggest problem with Ms. Parisi's arrangement.
   a. Students in the second and third rows will be unlikely to pay attention.
   b. Students will be confused by the irregularity of the classroom arrangement and feel anxious as a result.
   c. Students will be facing other students as well as her.
   d. Ms. Parisi will not be able to see the entire class from where she is seated.

•• 4. Which one of the following examples is most consistent with educators' view of an effective <u>classroom climate</u>?
   a. In Ms. Puzio's fifth grade classroom, students work quietly at their desks most of the day on independent assignments she has tailored to match their individual needs and skill levels.
   b. Mr. Kavanoze's fifth graders are free to do whatever they want as long as they pass weekly classroom quizzes and are relatively quiet.
   c. Ms. Sommarstrom encourages her fifth graders to express their opinions about various topics, even though such opinions may differ from her own.
   d. Mr. Evers begins the school year telling students in his fifth grade class exactly what to expect in terms of assignments and tests and reminds them how important it is for them to do well on these assessments.

•• 5. Four students are talking in the cafeteria about their new teachers. From the perspective of the textbook, which student is describing the most effective classroom climate?
   a. Adele says, "My teacher is really cool. He pretty much lets us do our own thing. He doesn't pressure us if we don't feel like paying attention. In fact, one chick was crying in the corner the other day, and he didn't say a word to her."
   b. Brandon says, "My teacher is a little scary at times. When Harry came in late one day, she looked over her reading glasses at him until he crawled into his seat, and she suggested that if he was late again, he might as well not show up."
   c. Chelsey says, "My teacher makes class really fun. He tells lots of jokes to make us laugh. If we don't get anything done one day, we just try to do twice as much the next day."
   d. Darren says, "Marianne came in late yesterday looking really upset. My teacher stopped for a minute to talk quietly with her but didn't give her too much static about being late for class."

• 6. Which one of the following does the textbook suggest as a strategy that teachers can use to demonstrate that they care for and respect their students?
   a. Greet each student with a smile as he or she enters the classroom at the beginning of the day or class period.
   b. Give each student at least three compliments every day.
   c. Take students aside individually at least once a week and ask them how things are going at home.
   d. Remind students periodically that if they need someone to talk to, they should feel free to make an appointment to see the school counselor.

•• 7. Which one of the following examples is consistent with what the textbook means by giving students a sense of control?
   a. Jason can turn his homework in whenever he wants to, even if he waits until the last day of school to turn all his assignments in.
   b. Kenda asks her teacher for help whenever she finds a word she doesn't know the meaning of, or whenever she runs into a problem she hasn't seen before.
   c. Lonnie knows that he can demonstrate his mastery of an instructional objective in his social studies class in either of two ways—by taking an exam or completing a project.
   d. In art class, Marie only needs to work on her art project on days when she feels particularly creative.

• 8. Three of the following strategies may help promote a sense of community in the classroom. Which strategy is least likely to promote this sense of community?
   a. Encouraging prosocial behavior
   b. Providing opportunities for students to tutor one another on difficult subject matter
   c. Incorporating students' ideas into classroom discussions
   d. Publicly praising students who show high academic achievement

• 9. Which one of the following is consistent with the textbook's recommendations regarding the best approach to setting limits for classroom behavior?
   a. Begin with a few basic rules and procedures; as the year goes on, involve students in decision making about additional issues that arise.
   b. Allow students to establish all rules for daily classroom routines and procedures.
   c. Make a complete list of expectations for students' behavior; distribute and explain it on the first day of class.
   d. In fifth grade and above, have a full academic lesson on the first day; most students at this level already know what behaviors are acceptable in the classroom.

•• 10. Which one of the following teacher statements is most consistent with the recommendation that classroom rules and procedures should be presented in an informational, rather than controlling, manner?
   a. "You should always do your math homework on wide-ruled paper and make sure your answers are lined up in rows that are easy for me to grade."
   b. "When you write your compositions, remember that I can read what you've written more easily and can give you more useful feedback if you write clearly."
   c. "Remember to do your own work on this assignment. This is not like the cooperative activity we did yesterday."
   d. "Tomorrow you should bring in a newspaper or magazine article about one of the countries we are studying in current events this week."

•• 11. Our students are most likely to follow classroom rules if they understand the reasons behind the rules. Below are four possible ways we might help students learn why we establish certain rules for classroom behavior. Which one is most consistent with recommendations offered in the textbook?
   a. If students are capable of deductive reasoning, explain the logic behind each rule and procedure.
   b. Have students discuss problems that arise in the classroom and develop possible ways of solving them.
   c. Describe what a classroom with no rules and procedures would be like.
   d. Let the class operate <u>without</u> rules for the first week or two.

•• 12. Which one of the following statements is consistent with the textbook's recommendation regarding how to deal with students' feelings about classroom assignments and activities?
   a. "I know you won't mind sitting quietly for an hour this morning while we have a guest speaker."
   b. "If you think about it, you'll certainly conclude that your language assignment and your math problems are a more useful way to spend the evening than watching television."
   c. "I'm sure you won't mind staying in from recess today to finish this assignment. It's too hot to play baseball anyway."
   d. "It isn't always fun to rewrite something you've already written once, but practice in editing will help you become better writers."

•• 13. One strategy for maintaining a productive classroom environment is to keep students busy and engaged at all times. Three of the following practices reflect this strategy. Which one does not?

a. Ms. Aguilar makes sure that all the equipment that students need for their science lab is ready for them before they arrive.

b. Mr. Barnard keeps his art lesson moving along at a steady pace.

c. Ms. Cunitz takes time out from her math lesson to help Sam with a difficult concept until he thoroughly understands it.

d. Mr. Dunbar plans several simple activities for his students on their first day of kindergarten.

• 14. As we have discovered, challenging tasks are often the ones that are most likely to promote students' learning and cognitive development. Yet students sometimes resist such challenges. Which one of the following is consistent with the textbook's recommendation for how to incorporate challenging activities into the classroom curriculum?

a. Start the year with relatively easy tasks that give students a sense of success, then gradually increase the difficulty level of assignments.

b. Start the year with few if any requirements, allowing students to feel comfortable in their new classroom, and then begin assigning challenging tasks after a week or two.

c. Start the year with extremely difficult assignments, then make them slightly easier after a few days.

d. Explain to students that they have little to gain from doing things they already know how to do.

• 15. Which one of the following strategies is consistent with how teacher planning contributes to effective classroom management?

a. Have a general idea of what you want to do each day, but don't plan specific activities ahead of time.

b. Plan exactly what you want to do each day and stick to your plan.

c. Plan the day's activities carefully, but be flexible if student questions or concerns arise.

d. At the beginning of each day, find out what students' interests are and spontaneously develop activities that capitalize on those interests.

• 16. Vygotsky's concept of scaffolding provides a strategy for structuring classroom activities. Which one of the following best describes scaffolding?

a. Providing structure for some activities but not for others, allowing students to develop a sense of independence in some aspects of the curriculum.

b. Giving students considerable freedom in the first few days, then increasing structure as they feel more secure in their new classroom.

c. Telling students what they need to accomplish, but letting them make their own decisions about how best to accomplish it.

d. Providing considerable structure for activities early in the school year, then gradually reducing it as students become more skilled.

•• 17. Students are especially likely to misbehave during transitions from one activity to another. Which one of the following high school teachers is handling a transition in a recommended fashion?

a. Mr. Antuna has his geography students come into the classroom and sit quietly until everyone is seated and ready to work.
b. Ms. Bartholomew asks a student to erase the chalkboard at the beginning of class.
c. Mr. Chinn's students know that as soon as they get to class, they should copy the outline and key concepts written on the chalkboard.
d. Five minutes before the end of each class period, Ms. Dahl has her students put away their notebooks and other materials and wait quietly for the bell to ring.

•• 18. Ms. Girardi, a sixth grade teacher, is explaining an assignment. She notices two students passing notes to one another. While continuing to discuss the assignment, she moves toward the students and confiscates the written notes. Then she walks back to the front of the class without discontinuing her lecture and asks Mark, who is daydreaming, to answer a question. This scenario best illustrates which one of the following classroom management skills?

a. Negative reinforcement
b. Withitness
c. Scaffolding
d. Planning for transitions

• 19. When we compare beginning teachers with experienced teachers in terms of how they think about student misbehaviors, we find that experienced teachers are more likely to:

a. Consider how to change instruction to avert future problems
b. Plan and implement complex behavior management programs
c. Attribute students' behaviors to internal but unstable causes
d. Depend heavily on extrinsic reinforcers

• 20. Which one of the following issues is usually <u>most</u> important to consider when a student behaves in an unacceptable fashion in the classroom?

a. Why the student has decided to behave that way
b. How much the behavior disrupts learning
c. Whether the student has been a chronic behavior problem
d. What the misbehaving student's mood is

•• 21. Which one of the following examples is most consistent with the textbook's definition of a <u>misbehavior</u>?

a. Ashley is chewing gum in art class.
b. Brian is doodling in the margins of his notebook as he takes notes on a lecture.
c. Caroline has forgotten to bring her lunch today and must borrow a dollar from a friend to buy a hot lunch.
d. Duncan is using a rubber band as a slingshot during music.

•• 22. In which one of the following situations would it be best to <u>ignore</u> a student's misbehavior?

a. Fritz and Irene are throwing paper airplanes across the room at each other.
b. Jim keeps pulling Jackie's hair while she is trying to work at her desk.
c. Harriet gets up to sharpen her pencil at least once every ten minutes.
d. Mary asks a classmate to clarify an assignment and then returns to her work.

•• 23. In three of the following situations, ignoring a student's misbehavior might be the best approach to take. Considering the textbook's discussion of this strategy, in which situation would ignoring not be advisable?

a. Anita has whispered a juicy (and apparently hilarious) piece of gossip to her friend, who in turn is passing it along to two others.
b. Bill breaks a beaker and seems very remorseful that he has done so; he vows to be more careful in the future.
c. Cathy is usually very attentive in class, but today when the teacher asks her a question, it's clear that she hasn't been listening.
d. An entire class seems to be on a "sugar high" the day after Halloween.

• 24. In which one of the following situations is cueing an appropriate means of dealing with misbehavior in the classroom?

a. When the behavior interferes with learning but is not serious in nature
b. When the behavior is already being punished by a natural consequence
c. When the misbehaving student has a history of defiance and disobedience
d. When you want to set an "example" from which other students can learn

•• 25. Stanley pokes his pencil point in Sharon's arm. The teacher gives him a stern look, and Stanley quickly puts his pencil back in his desk. The teacher's behavior is an example of:

a. Vicarious punishment
b. Cueing
c. Ignoring
d. Positive behavioral support

• 26. The textbook recommends that when a teacher talks with a student about a chronic pattern of misbehavior, he or she should do so in private rather than in front of classmates. Why?

a. Because students need to know that a teacher will devote as much time to misbehavior as necessary.
b. Because the teacher's remarks will be easier for the student to hear clearly.
c. Because calling attention to the behavior in front of classmates may be reinforcing.
d. Because the behavior may be typical for the student's age group.

• 27. Mr. Jacobs is speaking privately with Alicia, who has obviously been having trouble paying attention in class over the past two weeks. Three of the following strategies are appropriate things for Mr. Jacobs to do. Which strategy is not recommended for a private conference with a student?

a. Mr. Jacobs should communicate an openness to hearing what Alicia has to say.
b. Mr. Jacobs might explain that he feels hurt that she doesn't find class very interesting.
c. Mr. Jacobs can give Alicia a choice regarding how the problem might best be solved.
d. Mr. Jacobs should remind Alicia that he is ultimately in charge in the classroom.

•• 28. Three of the following are examples of <u>self-regulation</u> as social cognitive theorists describe it. Which one is <u>not</u> a good example of self-regulation?

a. A student tries hard to earn the reinforcer his teacher has told him he will get for good behavior.
b. A student reminds herself in a whisper that she should raise her hand before speaking in class.
c. A student thinks, "I paid better attention in class today. I'm going to reward myself by watching television when I get home from school."
d. A student keeps track of the number of times he's gone to the pencil sharpener in a single day.

• 29. Applied behavior analysis, functional analysis, and positive behavioral support are most often recommended as a means of dealing with misbehavior when:

a. The student recognizes that there is a problem and wants to change, but doesn't know how to go about doing so
b. The behavior falls in the "affective" domain, rather than in either the "cognitive" or "psychomotor" domains
c. The behavior continues to interfere with a student's classroom performance despite other interventions
d. The student's parents say that the behavior occurs at home as well

• 30. Under what circumstances should teachers confer with parents about a student's misbehavior?

a. Any time the student shows disregard for the feelings of fellow students
b. Only when the misbehavior is in clear violation of the law
c. Whenever the student shows no interest in improving his or her behavior
d. When a collaborative effort is likely to help bring about a behavior change

• 31. From the textbook's perspective, which one of the following classroom management strategies is probably most important for students from diverse ethnic backgrounds?

a. Demonstrating withitness
b. Creating a supportive classroom climate
c. Setting limits
d. Planning effectively for transitions

• 32. As the textbook points out, we must consider cultural differences when we deal with inappropriate classroom behavior. More specifically, we should remember that:

a. Some behaviors we think are inappropriate may be perfectly acceptable in another culture.
b. Many cultures place little value on the importance of education.
c. Students from some minority cultures will actively resist being taught in any language except their native tongue.
d. In most cultures, parents deal severely with children when they misbehave at home.

• 33. Three of the following describe recommendations that the textbook offers for helping students with special needs. Which statement is <u>inconsistent</u> with the textbook's recommendations?
   a. When students have mental retardation, give them explicit feedback about their behavior.
   b. When students have specific cognitive or academic difficulties, teach them strategies for organizing their time more effectively.
   c. When students have social or behavioral problems, lower your expectations for their classroom behavior.
   d. Give students with physical disabilities the additional time they may need to complete assigned tasks.

• 34. Which one of the following best describes a <u>sense of school community</u>, as educators define the term?
   a. A common set of rules shared by classrooms throughout the school building
   b. The joining of two or more classes on a daily basis, with the teachers of those classes team-teaching a subject area
   c. A shared understanding that teachers and students are all working together to promote learning
   d. A system in which students have increasing involvement in school decision making as they advance through the grade levels

•• 35. Which one of the following best illustrates <u>collective self-efficacy</u> of teachers?
   a. The teachers at West Middle School confer weekly about students who they believe are at risk for academic failure, and they are confident that, by working together, they can help these students be successful at school.
   b. The teachers at South Elementary School have coordinated what they do at each grade level so that at any particular grade, students master the knowledge and skills they will need in the following grade.
   c. The English teachers at East High School have agreed on how they will teach the required freshman English class. That way, students will have a similar classroom experience no matter which teacher they have for the course.
   d. A third-grade teacher and a fourth-grade teacher at North Elementary School have combined their two classes into one large class. Sometimes they team-teach the entire group. At other times they divide the class into two smaller groups, one of which is ready for more advanced work than the other.

•• 36. The textbook author recommends that teachers coordinate their efforts with people in the community at large. Which one of the following examples most clearly illustrates the spirit of her recommendation?
   a. Ms. Argersinger asks students to use their new vocabulary words when they have conversations at home with their parents.
   b. Mr. Byers spends one Saturday a month in the local university library keeping up to date on the latest educational research.
   c. Ms. Chimenis brings a newspaper article to class that describes recent advances in genetic engineering.
   d. Mr. Deyermond consults with a parole officer about how they might work together to keep several at-risk students in school.

- 37. Three of the following strategies are recommended for conducting effective parent-teacher conferences. Which strategy is not necessarily recommended?
    a. Prepare ahead of time by reviewing what you know about the student.
    b. Emphasize that the student's education is ultimately your responsibility rather than that of parents.
    c. Minimize your use of educational jargon.
    d. Be honest about how the student is performing in class.

- 38. As a teacher, you are likely to find that the parents of a few of your students will have little involvement in their children's education. Three of the following statements are accurate with regard to such parents. Which statement is not accurate?
    a. Their lack of involvement usually reflects a lack of interest in their child's academic performance.
    b. Inadequate child care may prevent them from getting involved in school activities.
    c. They may think that they shouldn't bother school personnel with their questions and concerns.
    d. They may have had bad experiences at school when they themselves were children.

- 39. Three of the following are recommended strategies for getting students' parents involved in school activities. Which one is not recommended?
    a. Visit students' families at home if such visits are welcome.
    b. Invite parents to share their unique talents with your students.
    c. Ask that visits to class be limited primarily to immediate family members.
    d. Find people who can interpret for parents who speak little or no English.

- 40. Three of the following strategies are recommended when teachers confer with a student's parents about a chronic behavior problem. Which one is not recommended?
    a. Ask for the parents' opinions regarding possible reasons for the misbehavior.
    b. Acknowledge that raising children in this day and age is a challenging task.
    c. Try to reach an agreement with the parents regarding an appropriate strategy for dealing with the misbehavior.
    d. Point out that the parents are somewhat responsible for the misbehavior.

## Essay Questions

- 41. It's the first day of class, and you want to start off the school year on the right foot. Describe five different strategies that the textbook recommends for establishing a productive classroom—one in which students are working consistently toward achieving your instructional objectives. Describe each of these strategies in a short paragraph, being specific and concrete as to what you might do.

- 42. Mary, a student in your class, has difficulty keeping her attention on classroom activities. Describe four different strategies that you might use to help her keep her attention better focused on class. Base your strategies on those presented in the textbook as being effective.

- 43. As teachers, we should keep in regular contact with parents about how their children are performing and progressing in our classrooms. Describe four different strategies that you might use to open and/or maintain lines of communication with your students' parents.

## ANSWER KEY

### Multiple-Choice Questions

| | | | | |
|---|---|---|---|---|
| 1. b | 9. a | 17. c | 25. b | 33. c |
| 2. a | 10. b | 18. b | 26. c | 34. c |
| 3. d | 11. b | 19. a | 27. d | 35. a |
| 4. c | 12. d | 20. b | 28. a | 36. d |
| 5. d | 13. c | 21. d | 29. c | 37. b |
| 6. a | 14. a | 22. d | 30. d | 38. a |
| 7. c | 15. c | 23. a | 31. b | 39. c |
| 8. d | 16. d | 24. a | 32. a | 40. d |

### Essay Questions

41. Strategies for establishing and maintaining a productive learning environment include these (the response should describe five specific strategies that reflect at least five of the ideas below):
    - Arrange the classroom in a way that minimizes possible distractions (e.g., one that establishes appropriate traffic patterns).
    - Arrange furniture to facilitate your interaction with all students.
    - Place misbehaving and/or uninvolved students near you.
    - Situate yourself where you can see all your students.
    - Communicate your care and concern for students.
    - Maintain a businesslike atmosphere, focusing on students' achievement of instructional objectives.
    - Refrain from threatening behaviors.
    - Communicate the value of classroom subject matter in students' own lives; focus students' attention on mastery goals rather than performance goals.
    - Let students control some aspects of classroom life.
    - Create a sense of community among students.
    - Establish a few rules for appropriate classroom behavior at the beginning of the school year.
    - Create routines for accomplishing classroom tasks.
    - Describe rules and procedures in an informational rather than controlling manner.
    - Involve students in decision making about classroom rules and procedures.
    - Acknowledge students' feelings about unpleasant tasks.
    - Plan classroom activities in advance.
    - Keep students busy and engaged.
    - Choose tasks and assignments at an appropriate level for students.
    - Begin the school year with easy and familiar tasks; introduce more difficult ones only after a supportive classroom climate has been established.
    - Provide some structure for classroom activities.
    - Give students something to do during transition times.
    - Monitor what students are doing at all times (i.e., demonstrate withitness).
    - Modify instruction in ways that are more likely to keep students on task.

42. Possible strategies are these (the response should include four strategies and incorporate at least three of the ideas listed below):
    - Seat Mary near the teacher.
    - Cue Mary when she's off-task.
    - Discuss the problem privately with Mary.
    - Teach Mary self-observation and/or self-evaluation techniques.
    - Teach Mary self-instruction techniques.
    - Use applied behavior analysis (e.g., reinforce Mary for paying attention).
    - Use functional analysis or positive behavioral support (e.g., identify and address any purposes that Mary's inattentive behavior may serve for her).
    - Confer with Mary's parents about possible reasons for the inattentiveness and possible solutions to the problem.

43. Possible strategies include these (the response should describe at least four of them):
    - Get parents involved in school activities.
    - Invite parents to share their special talents with your class.
    - Hold parent-teacher conferences.
    - Send notes or newsletters home.
    - Call parents on the telephone.
    - Communicate by e-mail *if* working in a relatively affluent community.
    - Conduct parent discussion groups.
    - Make home visits if such visits are welcome.
    - Make an effort to get parents' trust and confidence.
    - Encourage parents to be assertive when they have questions or concerns.
    - Keep other important family members (e.g., grandparents) in the loop, especially if these individuals appear to play a major role in students' care and upbringing.
    - Give parents suggestions about learning activities they can easily do with their children at home.
    - Conduct conferences and other discussions at times and locations convenient for families.
    - Offer resources for parents at the school building.
    - Find someone who can interpret for non-English-speaking parents.
    - Give recognition to parents when their children do well at school.

# Chapter 15

# BASIC CONCEPTS AND ISSUES IN ASSESSMENT

| CHAPTER OUTLINE | RELEVANT TEST BANK ITEMS |
|---|---|
| ASSESSMENTS AS TOOLS | Multiple-Choice 1–2 |
| THE VARIOUS FORMS OF EDUCATIONAL ASSESSMENT | Multiple-Choice 3–10 |
| USING ASSESSMENT FOR DIFFERENT PURPOSES<br>Using Assessments to Promote Learning<br>Using Assessments to Guide Instructional Decision Making<br>Using Assessments to Diagnose Learning and Performance Problems<br>Using Assessments to Promote Self-Regulation<br>Using Assessments to Determine What Students Have Learned | Multiple-Choice 11–20<br>Essay 101 |
| IMPORTANT QUALITIES OF GOOD ASSESSMENTS<br>Reliability<br>Standardization<br>Validity<br>Practicality | Multiple-Choice 21–46<br>Essay 102–103 |
| STANDARDIZED TESTS<br>Types of Standardized Tests<br>Technology and Assessment<br>General Guidelines for Choosing and Using Standardized Tests | Multiple-Choice 47–57 |
| TYPES OF TEST SCORES<br>Raw Scores<br>Criterion-Referenced Scores<br>Norm-Referenced Scores<br>Using Norm-Referenced and Criterion-Referenced Scores in the Classroom<br>Interpreting Test Scores Appropriately | Multiple-Choice 58–83<br>Essay 104 |
| HIGH-STAKES TESTING AND ACCOUNTABILITY<br>Problems with High-Stakes Testing<br>Potential Solutions to the Problems | Multiple-Choice 84–87 |

| | |
|---|---|
| CONFIDENTIALITY AND COMMUNICATION ABOUT ASSESSMENT RESULTS<br>Communicating Classroom Assessment Results to Students and Parents<br>Explaining the Results of Standardized Tests | Multiple-Choice 88–91<br>Essay 105 |
| TAKING STUDENT DIVERSITY INTO ACCOUNT<br>Developmental Differences<br>Test Anxiety<br>Cultural Bias<br>Language Differences<br>Testwiseness<br>Accommodating Students with Special Needs | Multiple-Choice 92–100<br>Essay 106 |
| The items in the "Integrative Questions" chapter of this Test Bank integrate the content of two or more textbook chapters. Within that chapter, the items listed to the right are relevant to Chapter 15. | Multiple-Choice 17<br>Essay 39 |

## Multiple-Choice Questions

•• 1. Which one of the following examples is most consistent with the textbook's definition of assessment?

a. Having a student swim two laps using the breast stroke
b. Having a student form a visual image of a nine-sided polygon
c. Having a student describe how long she studied
d. Having a high school student read two chapters of a college-level textbook

•• 2. Several decades ago, it was common practice to place any student with an IQ score of 70 or below in a class for the mentally retarded. This practice resulted in many children who did not have mental retardation being placed inappropriately in such classes. From the perspective of the textbook, who or what would be at fault for these misplacements?

a. Government officials who wanted more ability grouping of students
b. Poorly constructed intelligence tests
c. Inaccurate norms for the intelligence tests that were used
d. The individuals who made the placement decisions

•• 3. Which one of the following examples illustrates informal assessment?

a. Asking students to submit their cooperative group projects to be evaluated
b. Observing how various students handle the ball as they play soccer
c. Giving a quiz that counts for only a small fraction of students' grades
d. Giving a five-item short-answer test

•• 4. Which one of the following is the best example of performance assessment?
   a. Having students solve several arithmetic word problems
   b. Giving students a standardized reading comprehension test
   c. Having students write an essay explaining why there are always 180 degrees in the three angles of a triangle
   d. Having students do as many push-ups as they can

• 5. What is the major argument for the use of authentic assessment rather than traditional assessment to determine what students have learned?
   a. Authentic assessment measures are easier to score and therefore more practical.
   b. Authentic assessment looks at behaviors similar to those required in the outside world.
   c. Authentic assessment methods are more likely to provide a representative sample of the various topics that have been studied in class.
   d. Authentic assessment makes more sense from a behaviorist point of view, because the task is clear-cut and the reward is tangible.

•• 6. Which one of the following is the best example of authentic assessment?
   a. Giving students written comments about the strengths and weaknesses of their test papers
   b. Asking essay questions rather than multiple-choice questions
   c. Giving students a flashlight that doesn't work and asking them to fix it using what they've learned about electricity
   d. Giving a pretest to assess students' knowledge about invertebrates before the unit on invertebrates begins

•• 7. Which one of the following is the best example of authentic assessment of students' knowledge of ten spelling words?
   a. Having them write a composition that includes all ten words.
   b. Asking them to participate in a spelling bee where they spell the words orally.
   c. Giving a traditional spelling test in which the teacher says the word, presents it in a sentence, then says the word again; students write the words on a piece of paper.
   d. Giving students a multiple-choice test in which they choose the correct spelling of each word from a set of four possible spellings.

• 8. Which one of the following is definitely not an example of authentic assessment?
   a. Writing an opinion essay
   b. Preparing a graph from data
   c. Conducting an experiment
   d. Taking a multiple-choice test

•• 9. Which one of the following is most likely to be what educators refer to as a <u>standardized test</u>?

a. Ms. Argon's students are taking a test asking them to find the diameter, circumference, and area of a circle with a radius of 5 centimeters; Ms. Argon wants to find out if her students know this material well enough to proceed on to spheres.
b. Mr. Basili's students are taking a multiple-choice test, developed by a testing company, that assesses students' knowledge of language, mathematics, and logic; scores on the test have been shown to predict college success with some degree of accuracy.
c. Mr. Conway's fifth graders are taking a test of mathematical word problems requiring addition and subtraction. Mr. Conway has instructed his students to work as quickly as they can so that he can get an idea of whether they have developed automaticity in their ability to solve such problems.
d. Mr. Delano's eighth graders are taking an objective test over what they have learned in their geography unit on Asia. Students are marking their answers on a bubble sheet with a number two pencil so that Mr. Delano can have the school district's computer center score the tests for him.

•• 10. Which one of the following would typically be most appropriate for assessing the specific things students have learned in a three-week unit about rocks and minerals?

a. A standardized test
b. An assessment instrument with norm-referenced scores
c. A teacher-developed assessment instrument
d. Informal assessment

•• 11. Which one of the following illustrates the use of <u>formative evaluation</u>?

a. A teacher gives students an unexpected ("pop") quiz that will be worth extra points toward their grade.
b. A teacher gives students an unexpected quiz in order to find out what things they need more work on; it won't count toward final grades.
c. A university uses students' SAT scores to determine which students to accept; only the top 5% are admitted.
d. A university uses students' SAT scores to determine which students to accept; all students who score at or above a certain cutoff score are admitted.

•• 12. Midway through a unit on how mountains are formed, Mr. McDonald gives a brief quiz to find out what students do and do not understand. He plans to focus the next few classes on the things about which students are most confused. Which one of the following does Mr. McDonald's quiz exemplify?

a. A norm-referenced test
b. Authentic assessment
c. A performance assessment
d. Formative evaluation

•• 13. Which one of the following is the best example of <u>summative evaluation</u>?
   a. Ms. Vickery gives her social studies students a test at the end of a unit to determine how well they have learned the material in the unit.
   b. Mr. Waters gives his history students a test at midterm to determine whether he needs to spend more time on certain aspects of the Constitution.
   c. Ms. Yarborough gives her German students weekly exams to make sure they are keeping up with the material.
   d. Mr. Zeller gives his science students a pretest before beginning a unit on water to determine how much they already know.

• 14. Three of the following are accurate statements about how classroom assessments affect students' learning. Which one is <u>not</u> accurate?
   a. Studying for an assessment encourages students to review material they have previously learned.
   b. Students are more motivated to study classroom material when they know their knowledge of the material will be assessed.
   c. Studying for an assessment facilitates students' memory even for information that they do not specifically study.
   d. Assessments can provide valuable feedback about what students know and what they need to work on.

• 15. Which one of the following statements accurately describes the effect of classroom tests on students' motivation?
   a. They promote greater extrinsic motivation for studying classroom material.
   b. They promote greater intrinsic motivation for studying classroom material.
   c. Essay tests enhance students' motivation to study classroom material; multiple choice tests undermine it.
   d. Only performance tests promote facilitating anxiety; paper-pencil tests typically lead to debilitating anxiety.

•• 16. On a weekly quiz, Mr. Harris asks students in his auto mechanics class to figure out what is probably wrong with a car when it has a certain set of "symptoms." His students have never considered this particular combination of symptoms before, but they know everything they need to know in order to determine what must be wrong. Mr. Harris's test question illustrates the value of a classroom assessment as a:
   a. Form of review
   b. Learning experience in and of itself
   c. Way of giving concrete feedback to students
   d. Way of minimizing the negative impact of high-stakes testing

•• 17. As a teacher, you want your students to use effective information processing strategies as they study classroom subject matter. You consider research about the effects of classroom assessment tasks on learning, and you conclude that you should:
   a. Ask many short questions rather than a few lengthy ones.
   b. Give assessment tasks that require meaningful understanding of the material.
   c. Assess students' rote knowledge of the material first, then ask higher-level questions about the material in a subsequent assessment.
   d. Not give paper-pencil tests at all.

- 18. A classroom teacher and school psychologist are conferring about Gregory, a boy who works very hard in class yet shows consistently poor performance in any assignments that require reading or writing. Which sources of data should the teacher and psychologist look at as they try to pinpoint the source of Gregory's difficulty?
    a. The should focus on standardized test results, which have specifically been developed to assess learning disabilities and other sources of learning difficulty.
    b. They should focus on Gregory's performance on weekly classroom tests, which provide ongoing assessment of Gregory's progress.
    c. They should conduct an in-depth analysis of Gregory's writing samples, which will be much more informative than test scores.
    d. They should look for clues about Gregory's difficulties in both his standardized test results and his classroom tests and assignments.

- 19. By encouraging students to evaluate their <u>own</u> performance during assessment activities, we are <u>most</u> likely to:
    a. Facilitate meaningful learning
    b. Promote self-regulation
    c. Increase the reliability of our assessment instruments
    d. Increase the validity of our assessment instruments

- 20. A good summative assessment instrument is one that:
    a. Always ties academic content to real-world issues
    b. Assesses everything a student should know
    c. Is at least thirty minutes long
    d. Reflects instructional objectives

- 21. The <u>reliability</u> of an assessment instrument tells us:
    a. Whether the instrument predicts a future behavior
    b. Whether the instrument assesses something consistently
    c. How norms for the instrument were obtained
    d. Whether the instrument actually measures what it is intended to measure

- 22. If we say that a particular classroom assessment instrument is highly reliable, we mean that it:
    a. Accurately assesses whether students have attained our instructional objectives
    b. Yields scores that fall in a normal distribution
    c. Predicts future success in school
    d. Gives us similar results on different occasions

•• 23. In which one of the following situations do we definitely have a problem with the reliability of a classroom assessment?
   a. Ms. Arthur assesses her students' overall physical fitness on Monday; she then assesses it the following Monday. Students who perform well one week are not the same ones who perform well the following week.
   b. Ms. Benavidez uses a test of mechanical aptitude to determine which students are ready for her physics class. She finds out later that the students who scored worst on the mechanical aptitude test are some of the best students in physics.
   c. Ms. Candelaria tells students to study Chapter 14 but mistakenly gives them a test over Chapter 15 instead.
   d. Ms. D'Amato devises a test for her class of 35 students that must be given to students one at a time and requires 2 hours for each student.

• 24. Three of the following conditions are likely to affect the reliability of classroom assessment instruments. Which condition is likely to have little or no effect on reliability?
   a. Whether the teacher responds consistently to various students' questions about the assessment tasks
   b. Whether the teacher gives the same or different instructions to different students
   c. Whether students have learned what they were supposed to learn
   d. Whether students are distracted by noise outside the classroom windows

• 25. One disadvantage of assessment tasks that must be scored subjectively rather than objectively is that the _____ of the assessment instrument is likely to decrease.
   a. content validity
   b. reliability
   c. authentic nature
   d. predictive validity

•• 26. Some school districts regularly administer writing assessments: They ask students to write an essay on a particular topic and then evaluate the students' performance in terms of such qualities as grammar, spelling, organization, persuasiveness, and so on. Typically, the school districts have at least two (and sometimes three) people score each student's essay. By doing so, they are showing their concern for:
   a. Internal consistency reliability
   b. Predictive validity
   c. Construct validity
   d. Scorer reliability

•• 27. The publisher of a standardized test of reading comprehension gives the test to the same group of students on two different occasions. The publisher computes the correlation coefficient between the two sets of scores and obtains a coefficient of .93. Teachers who read this information in the test manual should conclude that the test has:
   a. High validity
   b. Low validity
   c. High reliability
   d. Low reliability

• 28. Tests are rarely perfect—the scores they give us are usually not completely accurate reflections of what we are trying to measure. To get an idea of how far off our test scores are likely to be, we should look at:
   a. Students' true scores
   b. The test's predictive validity
   c. The test's norms
   d. The test's standard error of measurement

• 29. A student's test performance is sometimes indicated by a <u>confidence interval</u> rather than by a single score. The rationale behind this practice is that:
   a. The computation of a single score is not possible for some tests.
   b. A single test score is always subject to error.
   c. Some tests have extremely vague scoring criteria.
   d. Tests typically have low reliability (.50 or less).

• 30. Which one of the following best characterizes how <u>confidence intervals</u> are used in reporting students' scores on standardized tests?
   a. They indicate the norm group to which students are being compared.
   b. They show the range of ten percentile points in which each student's score falls.
   c. They indicate how likely it is that each student has mastered a particular topic.
   d. They show the range within which each student's true score probably falls.

• 31. Three of the following strategies are likely to increase the reliability of a classroom assessment instrument. Which one is <u>unlikely</u> to do so?
   a. Give the same instructions to everyone about how to complete the assessment tasks.
   b. Decide on the specific criteria you will use to evaluate students' responses to each task.
   c. Make sure that students know exactly what they are being asked to do.
   d. Incorporate knowledge of students' previous achievement levels into judgments about their current performance.

• 32. Three of the following are questions that arise related to the <u>standardization</u> of an assessment instrument. Which question is <u>not</u> an aspect of standardization?
   a. Are all students being assessed over equivalent content?
   b. Are all students being judged on the basis of similar criteria?
   c. Are students' scores lower when points are taken off for spelling errors?
   d. Are time limits the same for everyone performing the assessment task?

•• 33. For a standardized test, test administration procedures are often very rigid: All students must take the test with the same directions and under the same conditions. This practice should have the effect of increasing the test's:
   a. Subjectivity
   b. Reliability
   c. Content validity
   d. Practicality

• 34. As teachers, we need to be concerned that any assessment tool we use is actually assessing what it is supposed to assess. Here we are concerned about the ______ of our assessment practices.
  a. Validity
  b. Practicality
  c. Standardization
  d. Reliability

•• 35. If students complain that a history test was not a good reflection of what they knew about history, then the test may have low:
  a. Reliability
  b. Objectivity
  c. Validity
  d. Variability

• 36. The content validity of an assessment instrument tells us whether the instrument:
  a. Is representative of the domain being measured
  b. Predicts how well students will perform in a particular situation
  c. Will be relatively easy and inexpensive to use
  d. Measures something in a consistent manner

•• 37. In which one of the following situations do we definitely have a problem with the content validity of a classroom assessment?
  a. Ms. Arthur assesses her students' overall physical fitness on Monday; she then assesses it the following Monday. Students who perform well one week are not the same ones who perform well the following week.
  b. Ms. Benavidez uses a test of mechanical aptitude to determine which students are ready for her physics class. She finds out later that the students who scored worst on the mechanical aptitude test are some of the best students in physics.
  c. Ms. Candelaria tells students to study Chapter 14 but mistakenly gives them a test over Chapter 15 instead.
  d. Ms. D'Amato devises a test for her class of 35 students that must be given to students one at a time and requires 2 hours for each student.

• 38. Ms. Edgerton wants to construct an assessment instrument that is a good reflection of what her students have learned from a recent unit on the history of their state. To do so, she might best begin by constructing a table of specifications that includes both:
  a. The kinds of questions she wants to ask and the scoring criteria she wants to apply.
  b. The kinds of questions she wants to ask and the types of instructions she intends to give students about how to respond.
  c. The topics students have studied and the order in which they have studied them.
  d. The topics students have studied and the things they should be able to do with each topic.

•• 39. Mr. Hatch wants to assess what his students have learned in a recent unit on four-sided figures. He realizes that the unit included four figures—squares, rectangles, parallelograms, and trapezoids. He also knows that he wants students to do three things for each of these figures: (1) recognize examples, (2) calculate the perimeter, and (3) calculate the area. In essence, Mr. Hatch is:

a. Constructing a table of specifications for his assessment instrument
b. Maximizing the likelihood that his assessment instrument will have predictive validity
c. Increasing the extent to which his assessment instrument is standardized
d. Determining the standard error of measurement for his assessment instrument

•• 40. Mr. O'Hara has developed a test of mechanical aptitude. At the beginning of a course in auto mechanics, he gives this test to his students. At the end of the year, he compares students' scores on the test with their actual achievement in his course. What is he probably trying to find out about his test?

a. Its practicality
b. Its reliability
c. Its content validity
d. Its predictive validity

•• 41. In which one of the following situations do we <u>definitely</u> have a problem with the <u>predictive validity</u> of a classroom assessment?

a. Ms. Arthur assesses her students' overall physical fitness on Monday; she then assesses it the following Monday. Students who perform well one week are not the same ones who perform well the following week.
b. Ms. Benavidez uses a test of mechanical aptitude to determine which students are ready for her physics class. She finds out later that the students who scored worst on the mechanical aptitude test are some of the best students in physics.
c. Ms. Candelaria tells students to study Chapter 14 but mistakenly gives them a test over Chapter 15 instead.
d. Ms. D'Amato devises a test for her class of 35 students that must be given to students one at a time and requires 2 hours for each student.

•• 42. Which one of the following is a question about the <u>construct validity</u> of an assessment instrument?

a. Does a teacher-developed test of algebraic reasoning measure what students have learned in their algebra class?
b. Does a teacher-developed test of algebraic reasoning predict students' performance in the calculus class they take the following year?
c. Does an instrument called the "Test Anxiety Scale" actually measure test anxiety?
d. Does a performance test in instrumental music tap a representative sample of how much students have learned in their instrumental music class?

• 43. Classroom assessment instruments can only be valid when they are also:

a. performance-based
b. practical
c. authentic
d. reliable

• 44. Which one of the following is a consideration related to an assessment instrument's practicality?
   a. What the instrument assesses
   b. What the instrument's name says it assesses
   c. How easy it is to administer
   d. How consistent students' performance is from one time to the next

•• 45. The school district of Wattville, Delaware, is considering using the Colorado Achievement Test (CAT) this year. This test must be administered by a school psychologist to each student individually, with each student's testing time being about two hours. Without knowing anything else about the CAT, the Wattville school district should probably question the test's:
   a. Practicality
   b. Content validity
   c. Standardization
   d. Reliability

•• 46. Which one of the following best reflects the trade-off between practicality and validity?
   a. Mr. Andrade is trying to decide whether to assess his students' knowledge about tennis either by giving them a paper-pencil test about the rules of the game or by having them get on the tennis court to show how well they can play the game.
   b. Mr. Bowman is trying to decide whether an essay question about Romeo and Juliet or one about The Merchant of Venice would be more suitable for finding out what his students have learned in a unit on Shakespeare.
   c. Ms. Chisholm is trying to decide whether to use true-false or multiple-choice questions to assess her science students' understanding of physics principles related to force, velocity, and acceleration.
   d. Ms. Dorrell is trying to decide whether or not she should take points off for misspellings when she grades students' history essay exams.

• 47. When we say that an assessment instrument has norms, we mean that it:
   a. Has cutoffs regarding what is acceptable performance
   b. Has a distribution of test scores that fit a bell curve
   c. Can be interpreted with reference to others who have taken the assessment
   d. Has a manual that provides information about reliability and validity

• 48. Standardized achievement tests are most helpful to teachers as:
   a. A good overall assessment of what students have learned in a particular class or at a particular grade level
   b. A way of monitoring students' general progress in various subject areas over time
   c. A means of determining whether learning problems are due to learning disabilities or, instead, to serious social-emotional problems
   d. A general indication of which students are likely to do well in college and which are not

• 49. How can a teacher most accurately assess the content validity of a standardized achievement test?
   a. Consult the test manual regarding content validity data for the norm group.
   b. Compare the curriculum to a table of specifications for the test.
   c. Calculate the correlation coefficient between the students' scores on the test and their scores on a similar achievement test.
   d. Calculate the correlation coefficient between the scores of the norm group and the scores of the students in the classroom.

• 50. With the major use of scholastic aptitude tests in mind, choose the kind of validity that is probably most important for such tests.
   a. Norm-referenced validity
   b. Predictive validity
   c. Content validity
   d. Face validity

• 51. Scholastic aptitude tests differ from achievement tests in that they:
   a. Measure innate ability
   b. Are more heavily dependent on reading and language skills
   c. Yield scores that can be used for a long period of time
   d. Are less likely to measure what students have learned in school

•• 52. Which one of the following questions is more likely to be found on a scholastic aptitude test than on an achievement test?
   a. How does one calculate the circumference of a circle?
   b. What significant historical event happened at Waterloo, Belgium, in 1815?
   c. What's missing in this picture of a turtle?
   d. Of what two elements does water consist?

•• 53. The mathematics teachers of a large high school want to use a test that will help them select students who could benefit from an accelerated math class that will include advanced algebra and calculus. Which kind of test is probably most suitable for this purpose?
   a. A teacher-developed test of general algebra skills
   b. A standardized test that assesses students' automaticity for basic arithmetic facts
   c. A mathematics aptitude test
   d. A general intelligence test

•• 54. Which one of the following is the best example of adaptive testing as the textbook describes it?
   a. Marvin takes an aptitude test on a computer. The specific questions that the computer gives him depend on how well he has answered previous questions.
   b. A school psychologist asks Darrell a series of questions that assess his knowledge of social skills and his interpretation of various social situations.
   c. A teacher gives different tests to different students, depending on their specific skill levels.
   d. When giving a final exam, a high school teacher makes special accommodations for a student with a learning disability.

• 55. Three of the following are advantages of using computer technology in standardized testing. Which one is <u>not</u> necessarily an advantage?
   a. Computer-administered tests can include videos and audiotaped messages.
   b. Computer-administered tests yield higher construct validity than traditional paper-pencil tests.
   c. Students' performance on computer-administered tests can be scored immediately.
   d. The computer can easily determine not only whether students answer a question correctly but also how quickly they answer it.

• 56. When choosing a standardized achievement test to administer in your own school, three of the following are important considerations. Which one is <u>least</u> likely to be of concern?
   a. Does the test have high test-retest reliability?
   b. Is the norm group similar to the students at your school?
   c. Does the test manual provide clear directions for administering the test?
   d. Have the test items been written by people with at least five years of teaching experience?

•• 57. Other things being equal, the norm groups used for standardized tests should be quite large. Why?
   a. To ensure that the norm group reflects the population it represents
   b. To ensure that the norm group contains some of the students being tested
   c. To ensure that the test is of practical value
   d. To ensure higher content validity

• 58. Ms. Beloit wants to describe her students' performance on a classroom achievement test in a way that her students can understand, so she scores it in terms of the percentage of correct items. Which type of score is Ms. Beloit using?
   a. A norm-referenced score
   b. A percentile rank
   c. A true score
   d. A raw score

•• 59. In Ms. Chapman's math class, students who take a classroom assessment receive scores of either "Mastered" or "Not mastered" in four different areas: addition, subtraction, multiplication, and division. What type of scores is Ms. Chapman using?
   a. Criterion-referenced scores
   b. Raw scores
   c. Norm-referenced scores
   d. Stanine scores

•• 60. Which one of the following assessments will definitely be scored in a criterion-referenced fashion?

a. Ivy is taking an achievement test in English. Her score will tell her how her performance compares with that of her classmates.
b. John is taking a math test with questions involving ratios. He will get three separate scores reflecting how much he knows about fractions, decimals, and proportions.
c. Quatrain is taking a physical fitness test in which she and her classmates run a quarter mile, and their times are compared at the end of the test.
d. Leon is taking a Spanish test that will determine whether he should be placed in an advanced section of Spanish II designed for students who have achieved at an especially high level in Spanish I.

•• 61. In which of the following situations would criterion-referenced scores always be more appropriate than norm-referenced scores?

a. To choose students for a program for gifted and talented youth.
b. To select students for a highly prestigious university.
c. To pretest students' knowledge so that you know where to begin instruction.
d. To place students in reading groups based on relative ability.

•• 62. Which one of the following teachers is definitely scoring students' performance in a norm-referenced fashion?

a. Mr. Applebee asks his fifth-graders to spell the 20 words in this week's spelling assignment.
b. Mr. Burghs asks his physical education students to do as many chin-ups and push-ups as they can, and he records the number that each student can do.
c. Mr. Car has his second-graders take a quiz on the addition number facts over and over again until they can answer all 100 facts correctly within three minutes' time.
d. Mr. Duchess grades students' essays on the causes of the American Revolution, giving the five best essays an A, the next five best a B, and so on.

•• 63. Which one of the following tests definitely has norm-referenced scores?

a. Melanie is taking a music test in which she has to play the C-major scale on her trumpet correctly.
b. Noreen is taking a multiple choice history test covering the last two weeks' lectures on the Civil War.
c. Owen is taking a reading comprehension test that will tell his teacher whether he is performing at grade level in reading.
d. Paul is taking an essay test in English composition that will show his teacher whether he is using appropriate grammar and punctuation.

• 64. Which one of the following reflects the use of a grade-equivalent score?
   a. Mr. Rosenthal's fifth graders are given a mathematics achievement test in which they are compared to a norm group of fifth graders only.
   b. Ms. Eskers' fifth graders are given a writing achievement test in which they are compared to norms for a variety of grade levels.
   c. Mr. Huang's eighth graders are given a physical fitness test in which their scores are reported in terms of the percentage of people getting the same or lower score.
   d. Ms. Richard's eighth grade students are given a history achievement test for which each student's test performance is compared to students at exactly the same age level.

• 65. Which one of the following best describes how an age-equivalent for a standardized achievement test is determined?
   a. The student's performance is compared to the average performance of students at various grade levels.
   b. The student's performance is compared to the average performance of students at various age levels.
   c. The student's performance is compared to that of other students at the same age level, and a percentile rank is calculated.
   d. The student's performance is compared to that of other students at the same age level, and a criterion-referenced score is calculated.

•• 66. As a second-grade teacher, you receive the standardized achievement test scores for Molly and discover that she has gotten a grade-equivalent score of 4 on the reading subtest. You should conclude that Molly:
   a. Had slightly below-average performance on the subtest.
   b. Showed performance in the "gifted" range on the subtest.
   c. Performed as well as the average 4th grader on the subtest.
   d. Answered 40% of the questions on the subtest correctly.

•• 67. Three of the following are true statements about age- and/or grade-equivalents. Which statement is false?
   a. They tell us which students are currently placed at an inappropriate grade level.
   b. If Mary gets an age-equivalent of 10, she has performed as well as the average ten-year-old.
   c. If John gets a grade-equivalent of 5, he has performed as well as the average fifth grader.
   d. They are sometimes used inappropriately as standards for all students' achievement.

• 68. You receive the standardized test scores for Muhammed and learn that he has gotten a percentile rank of 75 on the geography subtest. You should conclude that Muhammed:
   a. Performed better than 75% of the students at all grade levels who took the test.
   b. Performed better than 75% of the students at his grade level who took the test.
   c. Answered 75% of the questions on the subtest correctly.
   d. Responded to only 75% of the questions on the subtest.

• 69. What is the major drawback of using percentile ranks to describe students' performance on a standardized test?

a. Percentiles allow students to make comparisons between their own performance and that of their classmates—comparisons that standard scores prevent.
b. Percentiles tend to underestimate how much students have actually learned.
c. Because most students get fairly low scores, they become easily discouraged and their self-efficacy decreases.
d. Students in the middle range can be similar in achievement and yet have scores that are quite dissimilar.

• 70. Why are <u>standard scores</u> often preferred to percentile ranks?

a. Because they are usually easier for parents to understand.
b. Because they always have a mean of 100 and a standard deviation of 15.
c. Because they are a more accurate reflection of differences among students.
d. Because they give us a better idea of what students do and do not know.

• 71. When we represent students' test performance in terms of standard scores, we must first know the <u>standard deviation</u> of those scores, This statistic tells us:

a. What the average student's performance was.
b. How close together or far apart the scores are.
c. Whether the test has high predictive validity.
d. Whether the test has high reliability.

•• 72. Erica received these scores on various subtests of a national achievement test:

| Test | Erica's Raw Score | Mean for Norm Group |
|---|---|---|
| Algebra | 52 | 54 |
| Physics | 116 | 120 |
| Reading | 163 | 163 |
| French | 84 | 72 |

On a norm-referenced basis, Erica is achieving at the highest level in:

a. Algebra
b. Physics
c. Reading
d. French

• 73. Which one of the following statements best describes how a <u>standard score</u> is derived?

a. By identifying the grade level to which the student's test performance is most similar.
b. By counting the total number of points the student has earned on all test items.
c. By determining how far from average the student's raw score is in terms of standard deviation units.
d. By finding out how many students at the same age or grade level obtained lower scores.

• 74. Approximately how many students will get scores within one standard deviation of the mean (either above or below the mean) on a given standardized achievement test?

a. About two thirds of them
b. About one third of them
c. About twenty percent of them
d. About half of them

• 75. Which one of the following most accurately characterizes IQ scores?
   a. In the range of scores between 90 and 110, more people get a score of 110 than any other score within the range.
   b. If you divide the IQ score by 2, you get a person's percentile rank on the intelligence test.
   c. The average score is 100, with equal numbers of people getting every score between 70 and 130.
   d. The average score is 100, with more people getting scores near 100 and fewer people getting scores farther away.

•• 76. David takes an intelligence test, and gets an IQ score of 85. David's percentile rank on this test is about:
   a. 14th percentile
   b. 16th percentile
   c. 34th percentile
   d. 65th percentile

•• 77. As a third-grade teacher, you receive the standardized test scores for Marie and learn that she has gotten a stanine of 1 on the spelling subtest and a stanine of 3 on the math subtest. You should conclude that Marie:
   a. Had below-average performance on the spelling subtest, but above-average performance on the math subtest.
   b. Performed above average among her peers on both subtests.
   c. Performed below average among her peers on both subtests.
   d. Performed below grade level on the spelling subtest, but at grade level on the math subtest.

•• 78. Greg took the district-wide achievement test and got a stanine score of 9. Which one of the following is closest to Greg's percentile rank?
   a. 14
   b. 16
   c. 84
   d. 98

•• 79. Which one of the following test scores shows the greatest deviation from the mean?
   a. A z-score of 3
   b. An SAT score of 600
   c. A stanine of 7
   d. An IQ score of 120

•• 80. Todd takes an achievement test that yields standard scores. The mean of the test scores is 200, and the standard deviation is 50. If Todd does better than 84% of the people his age who take the test, his standard score is:
   a. 150
   b. 200
   c. 250
   d. 300

• 81. Which one of the following is something you should consider when you decide whether to use criterion-referenced scores or norm-referenced scores to reflect what your students have learned on a classroom assessment?
   a. Criterion-referenced scores are more useful when you need to compare your students to one another.
   b. Criterion-referenced scores are more useful when you need to compare your students' learning to that of "typical" students nationwide.
   c. Norm-referenced scores are more useful when you want to assess students' mastery of your instructional objectives.
   d. Norm-referenced scores may be helpful when you need to assess a complex skill that is difficult to define in terms of mastery.

•• 82. Ralph has just taken two achievement tests. He scored at the 90th percentile on the Ohio Reading Test (ORT). He scored at the 50th percentile on the California Mathematics Inventory (CMI). Can we conclude that Ralph has higher achievement in reading than in mathematics?
   a. Yes, because a percentile rank of 90 is above average, whereas a percentile rank of 50 is only average.
   b. Yes, provided that both tests have been shown to have content validity for the curriculum at Ralph's school.
   c. No, because the two percentile ranks are both essentially "average" scores.
   d. No, because the norm groups of the two tests are apparently different.

•• 83. Bayside High School requires freshmen to take an English composition course. However, the school faculty agree that a few students are sufficiently skilled in writing that they really don't need to take the course—that the students would essentially be studying things they already know. At a weekly faculty meeting, one teacher suggests that the school use the results of the standardized language arts achievement test given to all eighth graders to determine which students should be exempted from the freshmen composition course the following year. The faculty agree that any ninth grader who earns a score at the 80th percentile or higher on the eighth-grade test does not have to take the course. Which one of the following mistakes have the faculty <u>definitely</u> made here?
   a. Language arts achievement tests have no predictive validity for performance in writing a year later.
   b. The teachers have no clear rationale for choosing their cut-off score.
   c. The test's construct validity is the validity of most concern here, but it has not been determined.
   d. Standardized achievement tests in language arts have notoriously poor reliability.

•• 84. Which one of the following is the best example of <u>high-stakes testing</u> as educators typically use this term?
   a. A high school awards diplomas only to students who score above predetermined cutoffs on tests of writing, math, science, and history.
   b. A high school teacher gives exams that, in the opinion of students and their parents, are far too difficult for most 16- and 17-year-olds.
   c. When administering a series of tests to a middle school student to determine if he has a learning disability, a school psychologist asks questions about the student's religious beliefs, sexual activity, and other very personal issues.
   d. A school district wants to track students' progress in various content domains. It administers a standardized achievement test to students at all grade levels, even first and second grade.

•• 85. Which one of the following is an example of <u>accountability</u> as educators most often use the term?
   a. Asking test publishers to justify the specific items they include on their standardized achievement tests
   b. Reporting standardized test results only within the context of information about the standard error of measurement and confidence interval for each test score
   c. Making teachers' pay raises contingent on their students' standardized test scores
   d. Making sure that a standardized achievement test is a good reflection of the local school curriculum

• 86. Three of the following are commonly cited problems with high-stakes testing. Which one is usually <u>not</u> a problem?
   a. We may reach different conclusions depending on which criterion we use to determine "good" performance.
   b. Teachers focus almost exclusively on higher-level skills and neglect the more basic knowledge and skills that students need.
   c. The tests that are used do not always have content validity for the local curriculum.
   d. School officials may find reasons not to include low achievers in the assessment process and thereby distort school averages.

• 87. Which one of the following is probably the <u>best</u> alternative to high-stakes testing?
   a. Convincing lawmakers that standardized tests are essentially useless
   b. Using only performance assessments when making important decisions
   c. Making sure that any test used has a reliability coefficient of at least .70
   d. Using multiple measures whenever important decisions are to be made

• 88. In 1974 Congress passed the Family Educational Rights and Privacy Act. This act makes which one of these common classroom practices <u>illegal</u>?
   a. Students taking a history test are penalized if they misspell words.
   b. Students are required to take a three-day, standardized achievement test.
   c. Students grade one another's test papers.
   d. Students' standardized test scores are reported to their parents.

• 89. Only <u>one</u> of the following practices is permissible under the Family Educational Rights and Privacy Act. Which one?

a. Sharing a student's school records with parents upon their request
b. Asking students to write an essay test defending their choice of political party
c. Posting test grades using student's birth dates rather than their names
d. Placing graded tests in a basket for students to sort through

•• 90. Which one of the following teachers is violating the <u>Family Educational Rights and Privacy Act</u> of 1974?

a. A teacher has students put a star on a large wall chart every time they earn an A on a weekly quiz.
b. A teacher posts each student's test score by using a pseudonym that only he and the student know.
c. A teacher writes comments on the top of each test paper that tell students about what they have done well.
d. A teacher uses a teacher-made test that has a reliability coefficient of .70.

•• 91. Only one of the following teachers is behaving in accordance with the textbook's guidelines as he/she explains a student's standardized test results to parents at a parent-teacher conference. Which one?

a. Ms. Sculley suggests that parents take a basic statistics course at the local community college so that they can better understand their child's standard scores.
b. Mr. Muldar smiles and confesses, "I'm not sure what these scores mean myself. Let's look at the booklet I have about the test and see if we can figure them out."
c. Mr. Spock gives parents a detailed description of the test items and shows how a table of specifications for the test closely matches his classroom curriculum.
d. Mr. Kirk provides the confidence intervals for the scores a student has obtained and explains what the intervals mean.

• 92. Three of the following accurately describe issues that we should take into account when using standardized paper-pencil assessment instruments with young children. Which statement is <u>not</u> accurate?

a. It is more difficult to standardize testing conditions for young children than for students in the middle and high school grades.
b. Tests used to assess children's readiness for kindergarten are good predictors of their later performance in kindergarten.
c. Young children's erratic behavior (due to short attention span, poor motivation, etc.) can adversely affect a test's reliability.
d. Young children's erratic behavior (due to short attention span, poor motivation, etc.) can adversely affect a test's validity.

• 93. Which one of the following statements best characterizes the effects of test anxiety?

a. A small amount of anxiety about a classroom assessment is likely to facilitate most students' performance.
b. Even the smallest amount of anxiety tends to interfere with students' performance.
c. Anxiety facilitates students' performance on essay tests but interferes with their performance on multiple-choice tests.
d. Anxiety facilitates creative problem solving but interferes with recall for specific facts.

•• 94. Which one of the following statements is most likely to keep students' anxiety about a classroom assessment at a facilitative level?

a. "On Friday, we'll have a quiz on what we've covered this week. It should give us all feedback about how well you're learning and what things we still need to work on."

b. "We're having a quiz this Friday so that I can evaluate how well you know the material we've covered."

c. "This Friday we will be having our usual Friday spelling test. It's extremely important that you get all your spelling words right, so I expect you to study hard this week."

d. "This Friday we will be having a quiz in French. Your performance will help me decide which of you will be eligible for the school trip to France next summer."

• 95. If one group of students performs better on an assessment instrument than another group for reasons unrelated to the characteristic being measured, then the instrument:

a. Probably has low reliability

b. Is obviously not standardized

c. Clearly has low predictive validity

d. May be culturally biased

•• 96. Which one of the following test items is most likely to have <u>cultural bias</u>?

a. How are a puppy and a kitten alike?

b. Croquet is to mallet as racquetball is to _____.

c. What is the next number in the following series? 5 8 11 14 __

d. What's missing in this picture of a person's foot?

•• 97. Eduardo immigrated to the United States from Ecuador last summer and began fourth grade in California in September. He still has very little knowledge of English, as he has always spoken Spanish at home and with his friends. Concerned about his low achievement in class, school staff give him a general intelligence test and several specific aptitude tests. The staff administer the tests to Eduardo one-on-one in a private, quiet office where he can concentrate. Because students in the norm groups for the tests were all native English speakers, the staff give Eduardo the test items in English but use gestures in an attempt to help him understand what the items are asking of him. Which one of the following mistakes have the school staff <u>definitely</u> made?

a. They have administered the tests outside of Eduardo's regular classroom environment.

b. They have omitted an assessment of Eduardo's personality characteristics.

c. They have violated IDEA by not administering the tests in Eduardo's primary language.

d. They should have administered a general intelligence test <u>or</u> specific aptitude tests, but not both.

•• 98. Which one of the following students is displaying testwiseness as psychologists typically use the term?
   a. Malika brings her lucky pencil to a test and makes sure she sits next to her best friend, who is very good at the subject.
   b. Nancy starts with the first question of the test and works on each question until she gets the answer, even if it takes a long time.
   c. When stumped on a multiple-choice question, Oliver eliminates alternatives that are impossible and then guesses one of the remaining alternatives.
   d. Pauline gets copies of previous tests that the teacher has given, and she and her friends look at them as they prepare for the test in their study group.

• 99. Three of the following are recommended strategies for accommodating students' special needs during educational assessments. Which one is not necessarily recommended?
   a. Excusing a student from an assessment
   b. Using a different assessment instrument from the one given to nondisabled classmates
   c. Dictating questions that other students in the class instead must read
   d. Giving a shorter version of an assessment than that given to nondisabled classmates

• 100. Whenever we modify an assessment to accommodate a student's special needs, we must remember that we are inevitably reducing:
   a. reliability
   b. standardization
   c. validity
   d. practicality

## Essay Questions

• 101. Our classroom assessments will not only measure students' learning, they will also affect students' learning. In three short paragraphs, describe three different ways in which they might do so.

•• 102. In four short paragraphs, describe the four RSVP characteristics of good classroom assessment. In each paragraph, present two concrete examples of assessment practices: one that is likely to have the particular characteristic you are describing, and one that is unlikely to have it.

• 103. Psychologists distinguish between the content validity and predictive validity of tests.
   a. Describe the nature of these two types of validity.
   b. Describe a situation in which the content validity of a test would be more important than predictive validity, and why.
   c. Describe a situation in which the predictive validity of a test would be more important than content validity, and why.

- 104. Psychologists distinguish between norm-referenced and criterion-referenced scores.
    a. Explain the difference between these two types of scores.
    b. Describe a situation in which norm-referenced scores would clearly be more appropriate, and why.
    c. Describe a situation in which criterion-referenced scores would clearly be more appropriate, and why.

- 105. In 1974, the U. S. Congress passed the Family Educational Rights and Privacy Act. In two paragraphs, describe the implications of this legislation for:
    a. Your use of educational tests and test scores in the classroom
    b. Your communications with students' parents

- 106. Explain what psychologists mean when they say that a classroom assessment instrument is culturally biased. Then describe three strategies that you might use to minimize the presence of cultural bias on your classroom assessments.

## ANSWER KEY

### Multiple-Choice Questions

| | | | | |
|---|---|---|---|---|
| 1. a | 21. b | 41. b | 61. c | 81. d |
| 2. d | 22. d | 42. c | 62. d | 82. d |
| 3. b | 23. a | 43. d | 63. c | 83. b |
| 4. d | 24. c | 44. c | 64. b | 84. a |
| 5. b | 25. b | 45. a | 65. b | 85. c |
| 6. c | 26. d | 46. a | 66. c | 86. b |
| 7. a | 27. c | 47. c | 67. a | 87. d |
| 8. d | 28. d | 48. b | 68. b | 88. c |
| 9. b | 29. b | 49. b | 69. d | 89. a |
| 10. c | 30. d | 50. b | 70. c | 90. a |
| 11. b | 31. d | 51. d | 71. b | 91. d |
| 12. d | 32. c | 52. c | 72. d | 92. b |
| 13. a | 33. b | 53. c | 73. c | 93. a |
| 14. c | 34. a | 54. a | 74. a | 94. a |
| 15. a | 35. c | 55. b | 75. d | 95. d |
| 16. b | 36. a | 56. d | 76. b | 96. b |
| 17. b | 37. c | 57. a | 77. c | 97. c |
| 18. d | 38. d | 58. d | 78. d | 98. c |
| 19. b | 39. a | 59. a | 79. a | 99. a |
| 20. d | 40. d | 60. b | 80. c | 100. b |

### Essay Questions

101. In three paragraphs, the response should present and explain three of the following ideas (details for each of these ideas can be found in the section "Using Assessments to Promote Learning" in Chapter 15):
- Assessments enhance motivation (usually extrinsic in nature).
- Assessments provide mechanisms for review.
- Assessments influence how students cognitively process classroom material.
- Assessment tasks can be learning experiences in and of themselves.
- Assessments provide feedback about what students have and have not learned.

102. In four paragraphs, the student should accurately describe the concepts of reliability, standardization, validity, and practicality, providing definitions along these lines:
- Reliability: Extent to which an instrument yields consistent information about the knowledge, skills, or abilities allegedly being assessed
- Standardization: Extent to which an instrument involves similar content and format and is administered and scored in the same way for everyone
- Validity: Extent to which an instrument actually assesses what it is being used to assess
- Practicality: Extent to which assessment instruments and procedures are inexpensive and relatively easy to use and take only a reasonable amount of time to administer and score

Each paragraph should include both an example and a counterexample of the characteristic being described. To illustrate, a teacher who specifies the scoring criteria for an essay in specific, concrete terms is enhancing reliability. In contrast, a teacher who grades some essays while fresh and alert in the morning but grades other essays while tired and groggy at night is reducing reliability.

103. Responses to various parts of the question are as follows:
   a. Content validity is the extent to which a test is a representative sample of the content being assessed. Predictive validity is the extent to which a test predicts some future behavior.
   b. The response should describe a situation in which a test is used to measure what has been learned in the classroom (e.g., as would be true for a teacher-made classroom test or a standardized achievement test).
   c. The response should describe a situation in which a test is used to predict a future behavior (e.g., as would be true for a general scholastic aptitude test, a specific aptitude test, or a kindergarten readiness test).

104. Responses to various parts of the question are as follows:
   a. Norm-referenced scores indicate how students compare with one another. Criterion-referenced scores indicate what and/or how much students have learned.
   b. The response should describe a situation in which students must be compared to one another (e.g., selecting students for a program with limited spaces, assessing performance in a domain where mastery is very difficult to define in absolute terms).
   c. The response should describe a situation in which it is important to know exactly what students do and do not know (e.g., giving a pretest to determine where to begin instruction, assessing learning in a mastery situation).

105. Responses to the two parts of the question are as follows:
   a. The handling of test papers and test scores must limit knowledge of students' test results to the teacher, other school personnel directly involved in the student's education, the student, and the student's parents.
   b. Parents have a right to know their children's test scores (as do children of majority age); they must also be shown their children's school records if they request to see them. Furthermore, school personnel must present and interpret test results and school records in ways that parents and students can understand.

106. An assessment instrument has cultural bias if any of its items either offend or unfairly penalize some students on the basis of their ethnicity, gender, or socioeconomic status. Examples of strategies that can help minimize cultural bias are the following (the response should include three of them or other equally justifiable strategies):
- Scrutinize assessment instruments carefully for tasks that students might find offensive because of their ethnicity, gender, or socioeconomic status.
- Scrutinize assessment instruments carefully for tasks that students might have difficulty answering because of their ethnicity, gender, or socioeconomic status.
- If students have limited English proficiency, minimize your dependence on language to assess achievement in subject areas other than English per se.
- Teach students test-taking strategies.
- Encourage students to ask questions if they are unfamiliar with the content or procedures required for assessment tasks.

## Chapter 16
# CLASSROOM ASSESSMENT STRATEGIES

| CHAPTER OUTLINE | RELEVANT TEST BANK ITEMS |
|---|---|
| ASSESSMENT, COGNITION, AND METACOGNITION | Multiple-Choice 1 |
| INFORMAL ASSESSMENT<br>RSVP Characteristics of Informal Assessment | Multiple-Choice 2–6 |
| PLANNING A FORMAL ASSESSMENT<br>Selecting Appropriate Tasks<br>Obtaining a Representative Sample | Multiple-Choice 7–9 |
| PAPER-PENCIL ASSESSMENT<br>Constructing the Assessment Instrument<br>Administering the Assessment<br>Scoring Students' Responses<br>RSVP Characteristics of Paper-Pencil Assessment | Multiple-Choice 10–35<br>Essay 77–78 |
| PERFORMANCE ASSESSMENT<br>Choosing Appropriate Performance Tasks<br>Planning and Administering the Assessment<br>Scoring Students' Responses<br>RSVP Characteristics of Performance Assessment | Multiple-Choice 36–50<br>Essay 79 |
| INCLUDING STUDENTS IN THE ASSESSMENT PROCESS | Multiple-Choice 51 |
| ENCOURAGING RISK TAKING | Multiple-Choice 52–55 |
| EVALUATING AN ASSESSMENT TOOL'S EFFECTIVENESS AFTER THE FACT | Multiple-Choice 56–60 |
| SUMMARIZING STUDENTS' ACHIEVEMENT<br>Determining Final Class Grades<br>Using Portfolios | Multiple-Choice 61–71<br>Essay 80 |

| | |
|---|---|
| TAKING STUDENT DIVERSITY INTO ACCOUNT<br>Accommodating Students with Special Needs | Multiple-Choice 72–73 |
| THE BIG PICTURE<br>Learning, Motivation, and Assessment<br>General Guidelines for Classroom Assessment | Multiple-Choice 74–76<br>Essay 81 |
| The items in the "Integrative Questions" chapter of this Test Bank integrate the content of two or more textbook chapters. Within that chapter, the items listed to the right are relevant to Chapter 16. | Multiple-Choice 15–16, 18<br>Essay 39 |

## Multiple-Choice Questions

•• 1. Which one of the following illustrates how classroom assessments can affect students' epistemological beliefs?

a. Susan thinks that "art appreciation" means memorizing the names of paintings and the artists who painted them because every test in her art appreciation class asks her to label a series of paintings and identify the painter of each one.

b. Because Geraldine consistently receives low marks on assignments in her history class, she is convinced that her teacher is "out to get her."

c. Duncan mistakenly believes that how well he does on his weekly spelling tests will be the determining factor in whether he gets promoted to fourth grade.

d. Martin has heard that "Mr. Stewart's tests are really picky," so he is very anxious when he prepares for his first test in Mr. Stewart's class.

• 2. When teachers ask different questions of different students during a class discussion, they are conducting _____ assessment.

a. authentic

b. informal

c. standardized

d. invalid

• 3. Three of the following are accurate statements regarding the advantages of <u>informal assessment</u>. Which statement is <u>not</u> necessarily accurate?

a. It is sometimes the only way we can assess students' attitudes and values.

b. It often requires little, if any, advance preparation of materials.

c. It is usually more valid than formal assessment.

d. It provides ongoing information about students' progress.

• 4. Of the four RSVP characteristics, informal assessment strategies are strongest with respect to:

a. reliability

b. standardization

c. validity

d. practicality

•• 5. Which one of the following teachers provides the best example of the halo effect?
   a. Mr. Gregg likes Frank better than Mark because Frank is the more polite of the two students.
   b. Ms. Noonan always gives her students the benefit of the doubt when they exhibit "borderline" test performance.
   c. Mr. Urquhart overrates Cathy's gymnastic skills because she is head cheerleader.
   d. Ms. Rabinowitz believes that all students can learn calculus if they study hard enough.

• 6. For which kind of assessment are teachers' expectations for students most likely to influence their judgments of students' performance?
   a. true-false tests
   b. multiple-choice tests
   c. standardized performance assessments
   d. informal assessments

•• 7. As we plan our classroom assessments, one of the decisions we will have to make is whether to use a paper-pencil or performance assessment. Keeping both practicality and validity in mind, we should probably use a performance assessment:
   a. Whenever we want to assess recall rather than recognition.
   b. Whenever we want to assess students' achievement of higher-level objectives.
   c. Only when a paper-pencil assessment cannot give us sufficient content validity.
   d. As often as possible.

•• 8. For which one of the following instructional objectives is a paper-pencil assessment probably least appropriate?
   a. Students will use a Bunsen burner safely.
   b. Students will correctly spell 90% of the words on the fifth-grade spelling list.
   c. Students will identify the main idea of a paragraph.
   d. Students will recall single-digit addition facts with 100% accuracy.

•• 9. As a teacher, perhaps you don't want your students only to know information. You may also want them to be able to analyze information and apply it to new situations. To ensure that a classroom assessment measures all of your instructional objectives, you probably should:
   a. Use only authentic assessment
   b. Develop a table of specifications
   c. Use subjective rather than objective assessment tasks whenever possible
   d. Ask recall questions rather than recognition questions

• 10. Multiple choice tests have a reputation for being "multiple guess"—for being picky questions that focus on trivial details. How has such a reputation probably developed?
   a. Because lower-level questions are easier to write and so are more common
   b. Because it's probably not possible to write higher-level multiple choice questions
   c. Because multiple choice questions involve recall rather than recognition
   d. Because most teachers' instructional objectives are exclusively lower-level

• 11. Imagine that, as a teacher, you want to assess students' knowledge of many specific facts. You will be able to ask them more questions in a limited amount of time if you ask:
   a. Short-answer questions rather than true-false questions
   b. Norm-referenced questions rather than criterion-referenced questions
   c. Performance tasks rather than paper-pencil tasks
   d. Recognition questions rather than recall questions

• 12. In which one of the following situations is assessing recall of isolated facts most likely to be <u>in</u>appropriate?
   a. Mr. Wang wants his physics students to know the elements and their symbols by the end of the semester.
   b. Ms. Grunwald wants her history students to understand how various events contributed to the outcome of World War II.
   c. Mr. Sorenson wants his math students to know their addition facts up through the number nine.
   d. Ms. Filo wants her geography students to know the capitals of all fifty of the United States.

• 13. Why are recognition items on a paper-pencil assessment instrument usually easier for students to answer than recall items?
   a. Because recognition items provide students with more retrieval cues to facilitate recall.
   b. Because recall items include irrelevant information that may confuse students.
   c. Because recognition items increase the likelihood that students will use higher-level thinking skills effectively.
   d. Because recall items require retrieval of things students have learned several weeks or months earlier, whereas recognition items focus on recently learned material.

• 14. Which one of the following is an advantage of <u>recognition</u> assessment items in comparison to recall items?
   a. They are more likely to encourage students to learn things in a meaningful rather than rote fashion.
   b. They have greater predictive validity of students' future test performance.
   c. They allow wider sampling of students' knowledge and skills.
   d. They can be more easily used to measure how well students can apply the things they've learned to new situations.

•• 15. As a chemistry teacher, you want your students to be able to remember the symbols for any chemical element (e.g., <u>O</u> is oxygen, <u>C</u> is carbon, <u>Na</u> is sodium, <u>Au</u> is gold) without having any hints as to what each symbol might be. With this objective in mind, you will want to assess your students' knowledge using:
   a. Recognition questions rather than recall questions
   b. Recall questions rather than recognition questions
   c. Multiple-choice questions rather than true-false questions
   d. True-false questions rather than multiple-choice questions

•• 16. Following is an excerpt from your educational psychology textbook:

> The main disadvantage in using rehearsal is that we make few if any connections between new information and the knowledge already in our long-term memory. Thus, we are engaging in rote learning: We are learning information verbatim, without attaching any meaning to it. Contrary to what many students think, rote (meaningless) learning is a slow and relatively ineffective way of storing information in long-term memory. Furthermore, for reasons you will discover later, information stored by rote learning is more difficult to retrieve later on.

An instructor writes several true-false items to assess what students have learned about rehearsal after reading the textbook. Only one of them is consistent with guidelines presented in the textbook. Which one?

a. The term rehearsal means learning information verbatim, without attaching any meaning to it. (The item is true.)

b. Information learned in a rote fashion is not more difficult to retrieve later on. (The item is false.)

c. Rote learning is a slow and relatively ineffective way of storing information in long-term memory. (The item is true.)

d. Rehearsing information enables students to make many connections between what they are learning and what they already know. (The item is false.)

•• 17. For which one of the following topics would matching items be most appropriate?

a. Meanings of vocabulary words (in a foreign language class)

b. Causes of the French and Indian War (in a history class)

c. Rules for playing softball (in a physical education class)

d. Strategies for solving algebraic equations (in a math class)

• 18. Multiple-choice questions are more often seen on standardized achievement tests than are alternative-response and matching items. Why?

a. Because students are more familiar with their format, so testwiseness is less likely to affect students' performance.

b. Because they are more useful in assessing higher-level skills.

c. Because they eliminate the guessing factor that plagues other recognition items.

d. Because they are easier to write.

• 19. Only one of the following is a recommended practice in constructing multiple-choice items. Which one?

a. Make the correct answer more precise than the other alternatives.

b. Use distractors that reflect common misconceptions about the topic.

c. When in doubt, use items from the test bank that a textbook publisher provides.

d. Put negative words and prefixes (no, not, un-, etc.) in both the stem and the possible answers to assess students' logical reasoning ability.

•• 20. Which one of the following is the best example of an interpretive exercise?

a. "What is the square root of 64?"

b. "Drawing on ideas we identified in class, discuss the underlying themes of Charles Dickens's A Tale of Two Cities."

c. "Using the map presented above, estimate the distance between Toronto and Boston."

d. "Give three reasons why many experts believe that a capitalist society must impose certain regulations on free enterprise."

• 21. Which one of the following is an advantage of essay questions over recognition questions?
   a. Essays can be scored with greater reliability.
   b. Essays allow a broader sampling of the content domain.
   c. Essays typically have greater predictive validity.
   d. Essays allow easier assessment of higher-level skills.

•• 22. Which one of the following is a drawback of using essay questions on a paper-pencil assessment?
   a. Guessing is likely to inflate students' scores considerably.
   b. The administration of essay questions is difficult to standardize.
   c. It is difficult to write essay questions that assess higher-level skills.
   d. Reliability tends to be lower than that for more objective items.

•• 23. With the textbook's discussion of constructing essay questions in mind, identify the best essay question among the four questions below.
   a. List three causes of the French Revolution.
   b. Summarize the aftermath of the American Revolution.
   c. Define the following terms: (1) metamorphosis, (2) cocoon, (3) chrysalis.
   d. In five or six sentences, describe three ways in which the attack on the World Trade Center changed American diplomatic efforts in the Middle East.

• 24. From the textbook's perspective, which one of the following is the primary advantage of allowing students to use reference materials during a paper-pencil assessment?
   a. Students don't have to study the material ahead of time; they can simply learn it during the assessment session.
   b. Students are more likely to learn material meaningfully if they know they are going to have an "open book" test rather than a "closed book" test.
   c. Such a procedure better assesses students' ability to apply material that they don't necessarily need to commit to memory.
   d. Such a procedure is less likely to lead to test anxiety than would be true otherwise.

• 25. You have just written a paper-pencil quiz for a unit on map reading skills. Following the textbook's advice, you arrange the items by:
   a. Putting easier items, and those that can be answered quickly, at the beginning of the test.
   b. Putting more difficult items, and those that require considerable thought, at the beginning of the test.
   c. Testing lower-level skills first and higher-level skills last.
   d. Interspersing shorter and easier items among longer, more difficult ones.

• 26. When we give high school students instructions about a summative classroom assessment, we should:
   a. Assume they have had experience with such standard item types as true-false and multiple-choice.
   b. Give them considerable freedom about how to respond.
   c. Always deduct points for any grammatical or spelling errors.
   d. Communicate clear guidelines about how they should respond.

• 27. You have just developed a series of problems and two essays to assess what your students have learned about liquids and gases. You must also develop scoring criteria to guide you as you grade your students' responses. Three of the following are important things to consider as you develop these criteria. Which one is <u>not</u>?

   a. How long each student has spent answering each question
   b. Whether you will take off points for misspellings
   c. What elements are essential for a correct answer
   d. Whether you will penalize students who answer a question correctly but include additional information that is incorrect

•• 28. On the day you give a paper-pencil test, your classroom is unusually cold, and a construction crew is working noisily just outside the building. For which one of the following students are such conditions likely to adversely affect test performance?

   a. Andrea, who thinks tests are challenging and fun
   b. Brittany, who doesn't really care how she does on the test
   c. Corbin, who has done well on similar tests in the past
   d. Dennis, who is receiving special educational services for students who are gifted

• 29. Three of the following are accurate statements about cheating in the classroom. Which one is <u>not</u> necessarily accurate?

   a. Students are more likely to cheat if they have performance goals rather than mastery goals.
   b. Students are more likely to cheat if they think an assessment instrument doesn't reflect classroom objectives.
   c. Students are more likely to cheat if they think their teacher is a "softie" who grades leniently.
   d. Students are more likely to cheat if they think their teacher's expectations for them are unreasonably high.

•• 30. Which one of the following illustrates use of a <u>rubric</u> in a classroom assessment?

   a. Responses to a 10-point essay in a history class are given 5 points for describing historical events accurately, 4 points for explaining how the events are interrelated, and 1 point for using complete sentences throughout the essay.
   b. In a swimming test, students are asked to swim one lap each of the breaststroke, backstroke, and crawl.
   c. A science test has 30 multiple questions, 10 alternative-response questions, 3 short-answer questions, and one essay.
   d. A math assignment presents a complex problem with several parts and asks students to break it down into at least five simpler problems.

•• 31. Which one of the following teachers is most likely to score his or her essay tests reliably?

a. Mr. Achziger scores students' responses to each question on a scale of 1 to 5, where 1 means "inadequate" and 5 means "excellent."
b. Ms. Brodzinski scores each student's test in its entirety before moving to the next student's test.
c. Ms. Cullen arranges the tests with her higher-achieving students' responses at the top; their responses will give her an idea of what a "good" response is like as she continues to grade other students' papers.
d. Mr. Duning identifies the components that a good response should include and awards a specific number of points for each component he finds in a student's response.

•• 32. The four students below have just received feedback about their test performance. With the textbook's discussion of assessment and feedback in mind, choose the student who is most likely to benefit from the feedback he or she has received.

a. Garry got his multiple-choice science test back with the errors circled in red and the comment, "You need to study harder for the next test" written at the top of the page.
b. Harry received his history essay test with the comment, "You have a thorough knowledge of history, but your discussion is vague and disorganized."
c. Jerry cannot see his geography test after it has been scored, as his teacher plans to use the test again with next year's class. However, he's gotten the feedback, "You need to work more on the characteristics of the countries we're studying."
d. Kerrie received her math test with any incorrect answers corrected in red, and with the comment, "You do well on addition problems but are having trouble with borrowing in subtraction problems."

•• 33. Which one of the following statements is most accurate with regard to the RSVP characteristics of paper-pencil assessments?

a. Although reliability, standardization, and practicality are almost always high, validity is typically rather low.
b. Such assessments are typically practical and easily standardized; reliability and validity will vary, depending on the circumstances.
c. Reliability will be high only if validity is high; standardization and practicality will vary, depending on the circumstances.
d. There is a trade-off between reliability and validity; to the extent that one is high, the other will be relatively low.

•• 34. Which one of the following paper-pencil assessments is most likely to have a reliability problem when the teacher scores students' responses?

a. Ms. Gibbons asks students to describe the "first Thanksgiving" in one or two pages.
b. Mr. Hammond gives 50 true-false questions about the geography of Russia.
c. Ms. Sonnenschein administers a 30-item multiple-choice test about invertebrates.
d. Mr. Strauch gives a 10-word spelling test.

•• 35. Which one of the four "RSVP" characteristics is definitely compromised when we ask students to complete an assessment activity at home in the evening?
   a. Reliability
   b. Standardization
   c. Validity
   d. Practicality

•• 36. Which one of the following best reflects performance assessment?
   a. Reading a science fiction novel that applies principles currently being studied in a physics class
   b. Explaining in a couple of paragraphs how you solved a geometry problem
   c. Identifying the problem in a car engine that has stalled
   d. Writing an essay explaining how one might address health care issues in developing nations

• 37. Three of the following are advantages of performance assessment. Which one is not?
   a. It has greater practicality than paper-pencil assessment.
   b. It is more likely than paper-pencil assessment to resemble real-world tasks.
   c. It is often more motivating than paper-pencil assessment.
   d. It is especially suitable for assessing students' ability to handle complex tasks.

•• 38. Some performance assessments focus on processes, whereas others focus on products. Which of the following pairs best illustrates this distinction?
   a. Observing how a student solves algebra problems vs. observing how a student tackles geometry proofs
   b. Observing how a student goes about developing a computer program vs. observing how well the final program actually works
   c. Observing how a student speaks during an oral presentation in class vs. observing how the student interacts with peers informally in class and at lunch
   d. Observing a student's watercolor painting vs. observing a student's clay sculpture

•• 39. We show Antoinette two identical glasses containing equal amounts of water. We pour the water from one glass into a wide, shallow bowl. Antoinette tells us that the other glass has more water than the bowl does. (You may recognize this as Piaget's conservation of liquid task.) We ask Antoinette to explain why she thinks the glass and bowl have different amounts of water so that we can identify possible strategies to help her develop conservation of liquid. By doing so, we are engaging in performance assessment of a _______ for purposes of _______ evaluation.
   a. product; formative
   b. product; summative
   c. process; formative
   d. process; summative

•• 40. Which one of the following performance tasks best reflects restricted performance?
   a. Conducting a survey of senior citizens in the local community
   b. Raising rabbits using two different diets to see which diet leads to faster growth
   c. Creating costumes for the school play
   d. Playing Beethoven's "Ode to Joy" on a clarinet

•• 41. Which one of the following performance tasks best reflects extended performance?
   a. Testing the variables that possibly affect a pendulum's oscillation rate
   b. Collecting and analyzing data about the frequency of violent crimes in one's community
   c. Making a Valentine's Day card out of construction paper and paper lace
   d. Doing 10 pushups and 20 pull-ups as quickly as possible

•• 42. Which one of the following is the best example of dynamic assessment?
   a. Mr. Thiessen asks Macy to show him how to use a microscope properly.
   b. Ms. Ursinas asks her students to work in groups of three to write a paper evaluating the effectiveness of the United States' attacks on Iraq in 1990.
   c. Ms. Vincenti gives her students twenty multiple-choice questions; she then gives twenty more difficult questions to students who've done very well on the first set, as a way of assessing the upper limits of their knowledge.
   d. Mr. Warren observes and records how Erica's logical thinking changes over time as she experiments with a pendulum.

• 43. In some situations, teachers can incorporate performance assessments into their everyday classroom activities. Which statement below most accurately reflects the advantages and disadvantages of doing so?
   a. We can use classroom time more efficiently, but standardization may suffer.
   b. Validity is likely to be higher, but at the expense of practicality.
   c. Validity is maintained only if different students are asked to perform different tasks.
   d. Although reliability will increase, we will have difficulty developing a sufficiently practical task.

•• 44. Three of the teachers below are using strategies consistent with the textbook's recommendations for giving performance assessments. Which teacher is using a strategy that is inconsistent with the textbook's recommendations?
   a. Mr. Mervin lists several components that students' science fair projects should include.
   b. Ms. Pujo uses a checklist to evaluate how well each of her students perform on the parallel bars.
   c. Ms. Jensen asks students to wait patiently and quietly while they wait for their turn to perform.
   d. Mr. Ramos tells his students that he will be assessing their ability to project their voices as they try out for the school choir.

•• 45. Which one of the following best reflects analytic scoring during a performance assessment?
   a. Ms. Andretti evaluates students' oral presentations by using a 7-point rating scale that ranges from "unsatisfactory" to "superior."
   b. Mr. Barnes evaluates students' science projects with separate rating scales for effort, creativity, and use of scientific method.
   c. Mr. Cavanagh divides students' metalwork projects into three categories: "exceeds expectations," "meets expectations," and "needs improvement."
   d. Ms. D'Angelo determines students' grades in her art class by averaging the scores they have earned for eight projects using at least four different media.

•• 46. Which one of the following best reflects holistic scoring during a performance assessment?

a. Using a checklist to indicate whether students have mastered various swimming skills
b. Rating each student's performance in a classroom debate in terms of three criteria: participation, logic, and persuasiveness
c. Rating students' performance of several gymnastics skills in terms of strength, agility, and effort
d. Evaluating students' performance on a particular musical instrument by identifying the best player, the second-best player, and third-best, and so on

• 47. When identifying the criteria to use in evaluating students' responses to a performance task, the textbook recommends that we:

a. Identify a few criteria that best embody what skilled performance entails
b. Focus on three general criteria: accuracy, efficiency, and effort
c. Identify as many criteria as possible so that we can capture all aspects of students' performance
d. Identify at least 10 criteria, but no more than 15

• 48. Which one of the following is a legitimate concern about the use of performance assessment?

a. It focuses more on rote learning than on meaningful learning.
b. It undermines students' performance goals.
c. It underestimates how much students have learned.
d. Its reliability and content validity are sometimes questionable.

• 49. Which one of the following is a potential drawback of performance assessment?

a. The tasks typically require only a narrow search of long-term memory.
b. Guessing is likely to raise students' scores considerably.
c. The tasks are often time-consuming to administer.
d. The tasks are rarely authentic in nature.

•• 50. Which one of the following classroom assessment instruments is most likely to have high reliability?

a. A multiple-choice test that has a large number of questions, each of which is worth one point.
b. An essay test that a teacher grades over a three-day weekend, doing a few now, a few more after lunch, etc.
c. A short-answer test that is graded by a teacher and student teacher; each of these individuals grades half of the test papers.
d. A performance assessment that the teacher grades subjectively based on a general impression of each student's overall performance.

•• 51. Which one of the following teaching strategies is most consistent with the textbook's discussion of promoting self-regulation through classroom assessment practices?

a. At the beginning of a cooperative group problem-solving activity, Mr. Hays tells the students in each group that they should submit one set of problem solutions that represents the consensus of all group members.

b. Mr. Weller has his students exchange and grade one another's homework assignments.

c. Mr. Rushing gives his art students several criteria to use as they examine the clay sculptures they've just created.

d. Mr. Bickling gives his students the answer key for a multiple-choice quiz he has just given and asks them to score their own responses.

• 52. Which one of the following statements best reflects the textbook author's position with regard to assessment and student risk-taking?

a. Classroom assessment practices should make allowances for the fact that students learn more when they occasionally take risks related to academic subject matter.

b. Authentic assessment gives students greater latitude for risk-taking than does traditional assessment.

c. Although students should certainly be encouraged to take risks during practice activities, they should be discouraged from doing so during formal assessment.

d. Students should be given credit for responses that, although clearly incorrect, reflect a willingness to go out on a limb on occasion.

• 53. Three of the following are advantages of giving classroom assessments frequently rather than infrequently. Which one is an inaccurate statement?

a. Frequent assessment makes cheating less likely.

b. Frequent assessment is less likely to tax students' long-term memory capabilities.

c. Frequent assessment makes students less anxious because each assessment score is less important.

d. Frequent assessment enables students to get frequent feedback about their performance.

•• 54. Kevin and Ron are taking the same physics course but with different teachers. Kevin's teacher gives a short quiz over class material every Friday. Ron's teacher gives a lengthy test the first Monday of every month. Which boy is likely to learn physics more effectively, and why?

a. Kevin, because frequent testing promotes intrinsic motivation to learn

b. Kevin, because he must review what he has learned more often

c. Ron, because students do better on tests given at the beginning of the week than at the end of the week

d. Ron, because it's virtually impossible to ask higher-level questions on a weekly basis

•• 55. The four teachers below are using a mastery learning approach in their classrooms. With the textbook's discussion of classroom assessment practices in mind, choose the teacher who has the best policy regarding retakes of assessments.

a. Mr. Ingersol allows his students to retake the same assessment as many times as they need to in order to pass a unit.
b. Ms. Saldano knows that students will study more thoroughly if they know they have one chance to be assessed, so she does not allow retakes under any circumstances.
c. Ms. Huang has all students take the same assessment at least twice so that testing procedures will be fair for everyone.
d. When students don't demonstrate mastery the first time, Mr. Firenze gives them a different assessment instrument the second time.

• 56. An item analysis of an assessment instrument involves:

a. Looking at the information covered in class, making sure that everything is covered by the questions and tasks presented
b. Re-reading the instrument before giving it to make sure all items are clearly stated
c. Checking item content to determine if any cultural bias is present
d. Looking at students' response patterns to various items for possibly poor items

•• 57. Why might you decide to conduct an item analysis for one of your classroom tests?

a. To determine the number of test items that you should include on the test
b. To detect invalid test items and items that are too easy or too difficult
c. To determine the content validity of your test
d. To determine whether to use recall or recognition items on the test

•• 58. You have just finished a unit on basic material that you want your students to know thoroughly before you proceed to more difficult material. You construct what you believe is a challenging test over the material and administer it to your class. You then score the test and conduct an item analysis. You find that item difficulty values for all the items are between .90 and 1.00. You should conclude that:

a. The test questions were easy for students, so apparently your class has learned the material well.
b. On the average, the test was moderately difficult for students, so perhaps some students know the material and others do not.
c. The test questions were extremely difficult for students, so you probably should devote additional instructional time to the material.
d. Low-achieving students did better on the test questions than high-ability students did, so you may have made errors in your scoring key.

• 59. What role do item discrimination values from an item analysis play in our use of classroom assessments?

a. They tell us whether items distinguish between high-scoring and low-scoring students.
b. They tell us whether each item assesses lower-level or higher-level thinking skills.
c. They tell us how many students in the class got each item correct.
d. They give students feedback about how well they did on different kinds of test items.

•• 60. You are looking at the information an item analysis provides about a quiz you gave this morning. Most of the test items have D values of between .20 and .50. However, question #12 has a D value of -.60. You should conclude that the item:

a. Was easier for students than the other items were
b. Was more difficult for students than the other items were
c. Was poorly written or incorrectly scored
d. Is measuring rote memorization rather than meaningful learning

• 61. A potential disadvantage of giving grades in the classroom is that:

a. They are usually unrelated to a teacher's instructional objectives.
b. They are typically not correlated with students' success in college or a professional career.
c. They may focus students' attention on performance goals rather than mastery goals.
d. Most students believe that their grades are poor reflections of what they have learned.

• 62. Three of the statements below describe problems inherent in assigning final grades that reflect students' achievement in the classroom. Which statement is not accurate about grading?

a. Grading practices discourage students from taking risks that may lower their GPA.
b. Grades from different teachers do not always reflect the same level of achievement.
c. Students learn less when they know they are being graded.
d. Course grades, like test scores, rarely if ever have perfect reliability.

•• 63. With the textbook's discussion of grading in mind, identify the high school teacher who is assigning class grades in an appropriate manner.

a. Ms. Norrell bases her final grades on fifteen in-class projects and test scores; although she doesn't grade the accuracy of students' homework assignments, she takes into account whether they have turned in their homework regularly.
b. Ms. Lansing uses a single final exam that has high content validity for the curriculum she has covered and yields highly reliable scores.
c. Mr. Pottier uses as much data about each student as he can get his hands on; in addition to using test scores and homework assignments, he also rates students' performance in question-answer sessions and cooperative learning groups.
d. Mr. Robbins grades his students on three major exams, giving equal weight to each one. He has made sure that each exam has content validity for the material it is meant to cover.

• 64. Which one of the following is consistent with the textbook's recommendation for taking improvement into account in assigning final class grades?

a. Comparing students' standardized achievement test scores obtained this year with their standardized achievement test scores obtained last year
b. Giving a pretest and a posttest for each unit of study, and using the difference between the two test scores
c. Giving one test midway through a unit and another at the end of the unit, and using the difference between the two test scores
d. Assigning greater weight to assessments conducted at the end of the semester or school year

•• 65. Ms. Zaborowski considers how hard students have worked when she assigns her grades. For example, she gives an A to low-ability students who have performed at the highest level she thinks they are capable of. In contrast, she will give only a B or C to high-ability students who achieve at that same level because she knows they are not performing up to their potential. From the textbook's perspective, is Ms. Zaborowski's grading policy appropriate?

a. Yes, because it gives lower-ability students a chance to receive higher grades in relation to their peers and therefore increases their self-esteem.
b. No, because it penalizes those students who are more knowledgeable to begin with.
c. Yes, but only if she is teaching at the secondary level. The policy is inappropriate at the elementary level.
d. No, because it involves a subjective judgment of effort. It would be appropriate if she defined effort objectively, such as by the number of hours students spend on their homework.

• 66. The textbook author suggests that it is <u>not</u> a good idea to incorporate more than a few extra-credit points into students' grades. Why?

a. Incorporating extra-credit work into classroom grades typically affects only the grades of high-achieving students, so it is not worth the time and trouble.
b. Scores on extra-credit projects frequently suffer from low reliability.
c. The time spent on extra-credit assignments is better spent planning classroom activities.
d. Too many opportunities for extra-credit points allow students who have not met class objectives to get good grades.

•• 67. Which one of the following teachers is using a <u>norm-referenced</u> grading system?

a. In Ms. Albrecht's class, students who have completely mastered the topic and are able to apply it receive an A. Students who have thoroughly mastered the material but cannot apply it receive a B. Students who have mastered only the basics of the topic receive a C. Students who have learned little about the topic receive a D or F.
b. In Mr. Buchanan's class, the ten students with the highest accumulation of points receive an A, the next ten receive a B, and so on.
c. In Ms. Chan's class, students who get an average of at least 90% correct on tests and assignments get an A. Those with an average of 80% to 89% get a B, those between 70% and 79% get a C, and so on.
d. In Mr. Davenport's class, students who have achieved all of his instructional objectives get a grade of "Pass"; students who have not achieved all objectives get a grade of "In progress."

• 68. Which one of the following statements best reflects the textbook's recommendation with regard to assigning criterion-referenced or norm-referenced grades?

a. Assign criterion-referenced grades at the elementary level, but assign norm-referenced grades at the high school level.
b. Assign criterion-referenced grades in the lower elementary grades and in all low-ability classes; assign norm-referenced grades in high-ability classes at the upper elementary and secondary grades.
c. Assign criterion-referenced grades at all grade levels to the extent that such is possible.
d. Assign norm-referenced grades at all grade levels to the extent that such is possible.

• 69. Three of the following statements are accurate with regard to the advantages of portfolios. Which statement is false?
   a. Portfolios are useful for promoting students' self-evaluation.
   b. Portfolios can reflect the complex nature of students' achievement.
   c. Portfolios provide a means through which instruction and assessment can be easily interrelated.
   d. As a means of summarizing students' achievement, portfolios have greater practicality than final grades.

• 70. Three of the following statements are accurate with regard to the disadvantages of portfolios. Which statement is not necessarily accurate?
   a. Evaluations of portfolios often have low reliability.
   b. Portfolios discourage students from being creative in their classwork.
   c. Portfolios often contain different products for different students, reflecting a problem with standardization.
   d. Portfolios that contain only a few items may have poor content validity.

•• 71. Three of the teachers below are using strategies consistent with the textbook's recommendations regarding the use of portfolios. Which one is not?
   a. Ms. James urges her students to include anything they would like in their portfolios.
   b. Ms. Gaudet lists the criteria that she will use to evaluate students' portfolios.
   c. Ms. Shaklee asks her students to include a brief statement about each of the entries they include in their portfolios.
   d. Ms. Salih asks students to include a writing sample from each month of the school year to show how they have improved over time.

• 72. Three of the following accurately describe how student diversity is likely to affect our ability to assess students' learning fairly and validly. Which statement is not accurate?
   a. Some students may think that classroom assessment tasks are irrelevant to their lives outside of school.
   b. Boys put forth more effort on assigned tasks than girls do.
   c. Students from some cultures prefer to work in groups rather than alone.
   d. Students from some cultures are reluctant to perform in public until they have completely mastered a skill.

• 73. Three of the following strategies are consistent with the textbook's recommendations for accommodating students with special needs regarding classroom assessment practices. Which strategy is not consistent with the textbook's recommendations?
   a. Reward high-achieving students by announcing how well they've done.
   b. Minimize reliance on reading skills when students have low reading ability.
   c. Use informal assessment to either confirm or disconfirm the results of formal assessments.
   d. Give students with cognitive difficulties extra time to complete paper-pencil tasks that require considerable thought.

•• 74. Given what we have learned about the strengths and weaknesses of various forms of classroom assessment, which one of the following is probably the most appropriate course of action for us?

a. Use assessment instruments with either high or low validity as long as they have high reliability.
b. Use assessment instruments with either high or low reliability as long as they have high validity.
c. Interpret assessment results within the context of other information we have about students.
d. Engage in as little formal assessment as possible; teachers are better off making subjective judgments about students' achievement.

•• 75. Mr. Jones, a parent of one of your students, criticizes the fact that you base your grades partly on students' paper-pencil test scores. You need to defend your use of such tests as a way of evaluating students. Three of the following are appropriate ways you might respond to Mr. Jones' concern. Which statement is not accurate?

a. Your tests provide a way of obtaining systematic samples of your students' performance.
b. You have determined that your tests have content validity for the material you cover in class.
c. Your tests have been shown to have perfect reliability.
d. Using tests is a fairer and more objective way to evaluate students than grading simply on the basis of your subjective impressions.

• 76. Which one of the following statements is consistent with the textbook's discussion of the scoring criteria for a formal classroom assessment?

a. When students know the teacher's criteria for scoring their performance, content validity is apt to be jeopardized.
b. Students perform better when given only general guidance (e.g., "Answer as completely as you can") about how to respond.
c. Students should be informed regarding the specific scoring criteria a teacher will use.
d. Telling students the scoring criteria ahead of time is likely to make them unnecessarily anxious about the assessment.

## Essay Questions

•• 77. As a health teacher, you want your students to know which foods go in each of the food groups so well that they can classify any food almost without thinking. (In the following unit you will begin teaching students to develop balanced meals based on these groups.) Describe the kind of assessment instrument you should develop to assess students' achievement of your objective, including a discussion of whether your assessment should:

a. Focus on lower-level or higher-level thinking skills
b. Be paper-pencil or performance-based
c. Assess recall or recognition

In each case, justify your choice.

•• 78. As a geography teacher, you want your students to be able to use their map-reading skills when interpreting local city maps, road maps, bus route maps, weather maps, and so on. Describe an appropriate method you can use to assess students' achievement of this objective, being sure to indicate whether your method should:

a. Focus on lower-level or higher-level thinking skills
b. Be paper-pencil or performance-based
c. Assess recall or recognition

In each case, justify your choice.

•• 79. In four paragraphs, compare paper-pencil and performance assessment with regard to reliability, standardization, validity, and reliability. Your answer should focus on the use of the two forms of assessment for measuring classroom learning and achievement.

• 80. As a teacher, you will almost inevitably be asked to assign final grades that summarize your students' achievement. Keeping the textbook's discussion of recommended grading practices in mind, describe four guidelines that you will follow when you assign your grades.

• 81. As a teacher, you want your classroom assessment practices to help students learn classroom subject matter more effectively. Describe three strategies you can use to make your assessment instruments valuable learning tools for your students.

# ANSWER KEY

## Multiple-Choice Questions

| | | | | |
|---|---|---|---|---|
| 1. a | 17. a | 33. b | 49. c | 65. b |
| 2. b | 18. b | 34. a | 50. a | 66. d |
| 3. c | 19. b | 35. b | 51. c | 67. b |
| 4. d | 20. c | 36. c | 52. a | 68. c |
| 5. c | 21. d | 37. a | 53. b | 69. d |
| 6. d | 22. d | 38. b | 54. b | 70. b |
| 7. c | 23. d | 39. c | 55. d | 71. a |
| 8. a | 24. c | 40. d | 56. d | 72. b |
| 9. b | 25. a | 41. b | 57. b | 73. a |
| 10. a | 26. d | 42. d | 58. a | 74. c |
| 11. d | 27. a | 43. a | 59. a | 75. c |
| 12. b | 28. b | 44. c | 60. c | 76. c |
| 13. a | 29. c | 45. b | 61. c | |
| 14. c | 30. a | 46. d | 62. c | |
| 15. b | 31. d | 47. a | 63. a | |
| 16. d | 32. d | 48. d | 64. d | |

## Essay Questions

77. Responses to various parts of the question are as follows:
    a. The instrument should focus on lower-level skills because you simply want to find out whether students know the food groups.
    b. A paper-pencil assessment is a valid and practical way of assessing such basic knowledge.
    c. Recall items may be preferable in that they provide fewer retrieval cues. Recognition items may be preferable in that students can respond to a greater number of items in a limited amount of time. (Either choice is acceptable if it is adequately justified.)

78. Responses to various parts of the question are as follows:
    a. The assessment should focus on higher-level skills—more specifically, on the application of map reading skills when interpreting various kinds of maps.
    b. A paper-pencil assessment is more practical. A performance assessment may in some situations have greater content validity (e.g., if the objective is for students to use a city map to find their way around a city.) (Either choice is acceptable if it is adequately justified.)
    c. Recall items have greater content validity because they more closely approximate map usage in a real-life situation.

79. In four separate paragraphs, the student should compare paper-pencil and performance assessment with respect to reliability, standardization, validity (especially content validity), and practicality. Following are general points that might be made:
    - Reliability: For paper-pencil assessment, scorer reliability depends on the extent to which items are objectively scorable; thus, recognition tasks tend to be more reliable than recall tasks (the latter often give considerable latitude in how students respond). Performance assessments often have low scorer reliability (different teachers rate the same performance differently, especially if criteria are not clearly spelled out) and low test-retest reliability (students'.performance on complex tasks can be inconsistent across time, especially if an assessment taps only a small sample of behavior).
    - Standardization: Generally speaking, paper-pencil assessments are easily standardized. Some performance assessments (e.g., a typing test) are easily standardized, but others (e.g., an art project) are not.
    - Validity: Content validity is of primary concern when assessing classroom achievement. Recognition and short-answer paper-pencil tests allow wider sampling of the content domain; in this sense, they provide greater content validity. Yet tasks requiring complex responses—perhaps interpretive exercises, essays, or performance tasks—may have greater content validity if they more closely match instructional objectives.
    - Practicality: Paper-pencil assessment is typically more practical than performance assessment; for instance, it requires no "equipment" other than paper and writing implements, and teachers can easily assess the knowledge and skills of all of their students at the same time. Some paper-pencil assessments have the additional advantage of being relatively quick and easy to score.

80. The response should include at least four guidelines consistent with the textbook's discussion of grading in Chapter 16. Examples of appropriate guidelines are these:
    - Take the job of grading seriously.
    - Base grades on hard data (e.g., on the results of formal assessments).
    - Base grades on assessment instruments that are reliable and standardized, and that have content validity for your instructional objectives.
    - Be selective about the data used to determine grades (i.e., don't include everything).
    - Give little, if any, credit for effort, improvement, or extra-credit projects.
    - Stick to your grading system.
    - Assign criterion-referenced grades unless there is a compelling reason to do otherwise.

81. Examples of assessment practices that facilitate learning are these (the response should include three of these or equally justifiable strategies):
    - Use tasks that assess meaningful learning rather than rote learning.
    - Focus assessment on important objectives rather than trivial details.
    - Use tasks that require higher-level skills.
    - Use authentic assessment to promote connections between classroom subject matter and real-world contexts.
    - Give a pretest to determine an appropriate place to begin instruction.
    - Use assessment results to determine which content areas need additional coverage and which student behaviors need additional practice.
    - Use recall tasks rather than recognition tasks when you want students to remember material with minimal retrieval cues.
    - Involve students in the assessment process (e.g., solicit their input about appropriate scoring criteria) to promote self-regulation.
    - Provide concrete feedback about the strengths and weaknesses of students' performance.

Chapters 1–16

# INTEGRATIVE QUESTIONS

| TEST ITEM | CHAPTERS | TEST ITEM | CHAPTERS |
|---|---|---|---|
| Multiple-Choice 1 | Chapters 2, 3 | Essay 20 | Chapters 2, 3, 10, 13 |
| Multiple-Choice 2 | Chapters 2, 3 | Essay 21 | Chapters 3, 4 |
| Multiple-Choice 3 | Chapters 2, 3 | Essay 22 | Chapters 3, 9, 10, 12, 14 |
| Multiple-Choice 4 | Chapters 2, 3 | Essay 23 | Chapters 4, 13 |
| Multiple-Choice 5 | Chapters 2, 3 | Essay 24 | Chapters 6, 7 |
| Multiple-Choice 6 | Chapters 2, 5 | Essay 25 | Chapters 6, 8 |
| Multiple-Choice 7 | Chapters 2, 6 | Essay 26 | Chapters 6, 8, 9, 10 |
| Multiple-Choice 8 | Chapters 2, 6, 9, 10 | Essay 27 | Chapters 6, 8, 10 |
| Multiple-Choice 9 | Chapters 2, 9, 10 | Essay 28 | Chapters 6, 9, 10 |
| Multiple-Choice 10 | Chapters 6, 8, 9 | Essay 29 | Chapters 6, 13 |
| Multiple-Choice 11 | Chapters 6, 9, 10, 11 | Essay 30 | Chapters 6, 13 |
| Multiple-Choice 12 | Chapters 6, 11 | Essay 31 | Chapters 9, 10 |
| Multiple-Choice 13 | Chapters 9, 13 | Essay 32 | Chapters 9, 10 |
| Multiple-Choice 14 | Chapters 12, 16 | Essay 33 | Chapters 9, 10 |
| Multiple-Choice 15 | Chapters 12, 16 | Essay 34 | Chapters 9, 10 |
| Multiple-Choice 16 | Chapters 13, 15 | Essay 35 | Chapters 9, 10 |
| Multiple-Choice 17 | Chapters 14, 16 | Essay 36 | Chapters 9, 10, 11, 12 |
| Essay 18 | Chapters 2, 3 | Essay 37 | Chapters 9, 13 |
| Essay 19 | Chapters 2, 10, 12 | Essay 38 | Chapters 2, 3, 6, 7, 8, 9, 10, 12, 13, 15, 16 |

## Multiple-Choice Questions

• 1. Social interaction (such as interaction with adults and/or classmates) is definitely important for three of the developmental tasks below. For which task is extensive social interaction probably least important?

a. To accomplish a task within one's zone of proximal development
b. To progress to a more advanced stage of moral reasoning
c. To reduce preoperational egocentrism
d. To develop conservation

• 2. Erik Erikson's stage of identity vs. role confusion occurs at about the same time as Jean Piaget's stage of:

a. Concrete operations
b. Conservation
c. Preoperational thinking
d. Formal operations

• 3. The developmental theories of Piaget, Vygotsky, and Kohlberg all have something in common. Which one of the following ideas is true of all three perspectives?

a. Students cannot move to a more mature level of development until they are physiologically capable of doing so.
b. Students advance developmentally only when their environment challenges them to do so.
c. Students are incapable of formal operational thought until adolescence.
d. Students must see the relevance of information for their own lives.

• 4. Paul is a fifteen-year-old student. Based on what we have learned about adolescents, which one of the following is least likely to be true of Paul?

a. He has difficulty thinking abstractly.
b. He thinks that no one else can possibly understand his problems.
c. He thinks that everyone in class has noticed the hole in the toe of his shoe.
d. He is struggling with concerns about who he is and how he fits into the world.

•• 5. Three characteristics of adolescence are idealism, the imaginary audience, and the personal fable. Considering these characteristics, three of the following statements are typical of an adolescent's way of thinking. Which one is not typical?

a. "The world would be a lot better if we could all just love one another."
b. "Things are going so badly in my life, I might as well just kill myself."
c. "Getting pregnant only happens to other girls; it won't happen to me."
d. "Everyone in school is going to notice the bad haircut I just got."

•• 6. From the perspective of Piaget's theory, the cognitive development of a child with mental retardation can best be described as:

a. Having a different sequence of stages than that of a child with average intelligence.
b. Involving assimilation but not accommodation.
c. Probably not reaching the preoperational stage.
d. Probably not reaching the formal operational stage.

• 7. From the perspective of both Piaget's theory of cognitive development and contemporary cognitive psychology, students can only learn something meaningfully and effectively when they know:
   a. That they will be evaluated on the basis of how much they know and how well they know it.
   b. That their teachers consider the information important enough to spend classroom time on.
   c. How the information relates to what they already know.
   d. How different the information is from things they have learned previously.

• 8. Identify the learning theorists most likely to describe learning as "S —> R."
   a. Social cognitive theorists
   b. Cognitive theorists
   c. Behaviorists
   d. Piagetian theorists

•• 9. Ms. Olson wants to teach her first-year algebra students how to solve a quadratic equation. She begins by having her students learn to solve each small step in the equation, then she writes a quadratic equation on the board and has students work together to solve it with help. She has her students work several problems this way, providing them with a little less help each time. Which theory is Ms. Olson most clearly using?
   a. Skinner's operant conditioning theory
   b. Bandura's social cognitive theory
   c. Piaget's theory of cognitive development
   d. Vygotsky's theory of cognitive development

•• 10. When Fred reads about the American Revolution in his history book, he stops to think about how the colonists must have resented their treatment by the King of England and how the American soldiers must have been fearful about going into battle. The ideas Fred has generated related to the revolution are an example of:
   a. Positive reinforcement, which should help him learn.
   b. Negative reinforcement, which should interfere with his learning.
   c. Elaboration, which should help him learn.
   d. Negative transfer, which should interfere with his learning.

• 11. Three of the following statements describe accurate comparisons among cognitive psychology, behaviorism, and/or social cognitive theory. Which one is <u>not</u> an accurate comparison?
   a. Cognitive psychologists are more concerned about motivation than either social cognitive theorists or behaviorists are.
   b. In comparison with cognitive psychology, behaviorism and social cognitive theory place more emphasis on how the consequences of the learner's responses affect future behavior.
   c. Both cognitive psychologists and social cognitive theorists consider the role that mental processes play in learning.
   d. In comparison with behaviorism and cognitive psychology, social cognitive theory looks more closely at what people can learn by watching others.

•• 12. Given what we know about how highly anxious students process information, which learning strategy would we expect them to use most often?

a. Elaboration
b. Rehearsal
c. Meaningful learning
d. Organization

•• 13. Students' thought processes clearly play an important role in learning. For which one of the following classroom strategies are students' mental processes <u>least</u> likely to be a consideration?

a. Expository instruction
b. Discovery learning
c. Reciprocal teaching
d. Applied behavior analysis

•• 14. A potential disadvantage of giving grades for classroom achievement is that:

a. They are usually unrelated to a teacher's instructional objectives.
b. They are typically not correlated with students' success in college or a professional career.
c. They may focus students' attention on performance goals rather than mastery goals.
d. Most students believe their grades are poor reflections of what they have learned.

•• 15. If we consider research findings that the textbook describes regarding how teachers' <u>expectations</u> can affect their assessment of students' behaviors, we should reach which one of the following conclusions?

a. We should base our evaluations of student achievement on objective data.
b. We should assess students' learning at least once every day.
c. In most situations, evaluating students' learning in group situations is preferable to evaluating their learning on individual tasks.
d. We can better evaluate students' learning when we talk with them informally than when we give them a paper-pencil test.

•• 16. If you have implemented a mastery learning program in your classroom, you should <u>definitely</u> use ________ scores when you assess your students' achievement.

a. criterion-referenced
b. norm-referenced
c. raw
d. subjective

• 17. Occasionally students may be tempted to cheat during a formal classroom assessment. With the textbook's recommendations for classroom management and classroom assessment practices in mind, choose the best strategy for addressing cheating.

a. Watch students like a hawk and immediately remove the test paper of anyone who appears to be looking at someone else's paper.
b. Watch students subtly throughout the test, and impose a reasonable consequence in private when you are sure that cheating occurred.
c. Punish a cheating student in front of classmates so that others learn the importance of honesty vicariously.
d. Ignore cheating the first or second time it occurs because students are not likely to repeat this type of behavior.

## Essay Questions

•• 18. Students at different ages and grade levels are certainly very different from one another, but just how different are they? Identify a particular grade at which you might be teaching (kindergarten, third grade, etc.); if you like, you may also identify a specific subject area you will be teaching. Then describe age-related characteristics you are likely to find in your students in the following aspects of development, and give a specific example to illustrate each characteristic you describe:

a. Cognitive development (describe two characteristics from a Piagetian perspective and two characteristics from an information processing perspective)
b. Language development (describe one characteristic)
c. Personal or social development (describe one characteristic)
d. Moral development (describe one characteristic)

Note: An "age-related characteristic" is one that is found at some ages and/or developmental stages but not at others.

• 19. In four short paragraphs, describe the role of challenge with respect to:

a. Piaget's theory of cognitive development
b. Vygotsky's theory of cognitive development
c. Self-efficacy
d. Motivation

• 20. In five short paragraphs, explain why social interaction is important within the context of:

a. Piaget's theory of cognitive development
b. Vygotsky's theory of cognitive development
c. Kohlberg's theory of moral development
d. Social cognitive theory
e. Reciprocal teaching

•• 21. Hope has had a consistent record of high achievement in all areas until recently. Now, at the beginning of junior high school, her self-confidence has fallen dramatically. Mr. Lester, her science teacher, sees signs of intelligence lurking under the surface but doesn't know why Hope's self-esteem is dropping. He consults with her math teacher, Ms. Frank, who says, "Hope didn't do very well on the pretest I gave her, so I've been going easy on her and trying not to push her too hard." Considering the various topics your textbook has covered, speculate on at least two different reasons why Hope's self-esteem has dropped.

•• 22. One essential component of effective teaching is classroom management: teachers must create and maintain an environment conducive to all students' learning. Describe at least one classroom management strategy that can be derived from each of the following perspectives:
   a. Principles of social development
   b. Principles of moral development
   c. Principles of operant conditioning
   d. Principles of learning from social cognitive theory
   e. Principles related to intrinsic motivation

•• 23. As a beginning teacher, you discover that your first class consists of students from a variety of ethnic backgrounds, including a few students with limited English proficiency. Drawing on the discussion of teaching strategies in Chapter 13, describe at least four different instructional strategies that are likely to be effective in your class. For each strategy, present a rationale as to why it is likely to be effective for your diverse group of students.

•• 24. Many learning theorists propose that elaboration sometimes occurs in learning. Define what they mean by the term elaboration, and give a concrete example to illustrate it. Then explain:
   a. Why cognitive psychologists recommend that students elaborate as much as possible.
   b. Why different people elaborate the same information differently.
   c. Why elaboration sometimes leads to the storage of inaccurate information.

• 25. Explain the difference between rote learning and meaningful learning from the perspective of cognitive psychology. Now distinguish between the two forms of learning in terms of the following:
   a. Which one leads to faster storage in long-term memory, and why?
   b. Which one leads to faster retrieval from long-term memory, and why?
   c. Which one promotes better transfer and problem solving, and why?

•• 26. Choose a particular grade level at which you might eventually be teaching. Then identify a specific topic or skill that you might teach students at this grade level, describing its nature and scope in a sentence or two. Then explain how you might teach your topic using at least three of the following concepts:

- Positive reinforcement
- Modeling
- Meaningful learning
- Elaboration
- Transfer

As you describe your instructional approach, identify the specific concepts and/or learning principles on which your approach is based.

•• 27. Students in your classroom are having difficulty studying. Describe four study strategies you might teach them. Explain why each strategy should be effective from the perspective of cognitive psychology or social cognitive theory. You do not necessarily have to use the same theory to explain each strategy, although you may limit yourself to a single theory if you wish.

• 28. Compare the cognitive, behaviorist, and social cognitive perspectives of learning with regard to each of the following:

a. How does each perspective define learning?
b. On what does each perspective's general principles of learning focus?
c. Give an example of a specific teaching strategy that can be derived from each perspective.

•• 29. You are giving a lecture on a topic that you know is difficult for your students. Describe at least one specific strategy you can use to maximize the probability that:

a. Your students will store the information in their working memories.
b. The information you present doesn't exceed the limits of students' working memory capacities.
c. Your students will engage in meaningful learning.
d. Your students will organize the material effectively.
e. Your students will elaborate on the things you talk about.

• 30. Expository instruction may or may not be an effective way of helping students to store information in their long-term memories; its effectiveness depends on how the instruction is carried out. Describe:

a. At least two processes through which information can be stored effectively in long-term memory.
b. At least four strategies you might use to promote effective long-term memory storage during expository instruction. Describe each strategy in specific and concrete terms, and explain how it should facilitate students' long-term memory storage.

• 31. Reinforcement plays a major role in both operant conditioning and social cognitive theory. Identify two ways in which the role of reinforcement is different in the two perspectives.

•• 32. In each of the situations below, a student's behavior is affected by one of the following phenomena: positive reinforcement, negative reinforcement, punishment, vicarious reinforcement, or vicarious punishment. For each situation: (1) identify which one of the phenomena just listed is affecting the student's behavior, and (2) explain why you made the choice you did.

   a. Because John was caught cheating on an exam, he was removed from the basketball team. John has stopped cheating on exams.
   b. Mary sees her friend Judy get special privileges when she talks very sweetly to the teacher. As a result, Mary begins to sweet-talk the teacher as well.
   c. Ralph brings his science project in a week late. The only reason he did his project at all is because he wanted his mother to stop nagging him about it.

•• 33. Andy uses foul language in your classroom on a regular basis. Explain how you might use each of the following techniques to decrease the problem behavior:

   a. Cueing
   b. Self-monitoring
   c. Reinforcement of an incompatible behavior
   d. Punishment

   For each technique, be specific and concrete as to what you might do.

•• 34. Sarah has a habit of talking to herself as she takes tests and completes independent in-class assignments. She talks loudly enough that other students can often hear her answers. Explain how you might use each of the following techniques to reduce this problem behavior:

   a. Cueing
   b. Self-monitoring
   c. Self-reinforcement
   d. Shaping

   For each technique, be specific and concrete as to what you might do.

•• 35. Jason has difficulty paying attention and staying on task during class. He is not a "discipline" problem in the sense that he distracts other students. Instead he simply spends his time drawing pictures in his notebook. Nevertheless, it is clear that he is not achieving important classroom objectives. Explain how you might use each of the following techniques to improve his classroom behavior:

   a. Cueing
   b. Self-monitoring
   c. Contingency contract
   d. Shaping

   For each technique, be specific and concrete as to what you might do.

•• 36. Margot is a second grader who seems to have little or no motivation to learn in the classroom; as her teacher, you have noticed that she doesn't put much effort into her assignments. Instead, she talks incessantly to the students around her during independent seatwork time. Using at least five of the concepts listed below, describe five different strategies you might use to help Margot improve her academic performance. For each strategy, be specific and concrete about what you would do.

- Intrinsic motivation
- Shaping
- Secondary reinforcement
- Vicarious reinforcement
- Premack principle
- Self-monitoring
- Self-imposed contingency
- Time-out

•• 37. Explain how concepts and principles of <u>operant conditioning</u> play a role in the three instructional methods listed below. For each method, identify at least <u>two</u> concepts and/or principles of operant conditioning.

a. Programmed instruction
b. Mastery learning
c. Cooperative learning

•• 38. This question consists of seven interrelated parts. You should answer Parts a and b first, and you should probably answer Part g last. Be sure that you address each part of each question clearly and concretely. Also be sure that you communicate clearly how theory relates to practice.

a. Identify a particular grade level at which you might eventually be teaching. Then identify a specific topic or skill that you might teach students at this grade level. Describe the nature and scope of this topic in a short paragraph.

b. Identify the specific instructional objectives that you intend to accomplish as you teach that topic or skill. Specify at least two, but no more than five, objectives. Keep the textbook's guidelines in mind as you write these objectives.

c. Using a Piagetian and/or information-processing perspective of cognitive development, identify two age-related characteristics (specific logical thinking abilities, learning strategies, etc., typical of the age group) your students are likely to have. Describe how you would adapt your instruction to match each of the characteristics you identify.

d. Describe how you might teach your topic using at least four of the following concepts and/or principles from the learning theories we have studied:
- Positive reinforcement
- Modeling
- Working memory
- Meaningful learning
- Elaboration
- Effects of prior knowledge

As you describe your instructional approach, identify the specific concepts and/or principles on which your approach is based.

e. Describe at least three things you can do within your instructional unit that should facilitate students' overall development. Your strategies should address at least three of the following areas:
- Self-concept and/or self-efficacy
- Social development
- Moral development
- Appropriate attributions for success and failure

In each case, explain how the things you are doing will facilitate students' development; in other words, provide a theoretical rationale for each strategy you describe.

f. Describe at least one thing you can do to promote students' metacognitive development and/or more effective study strategies. Be realistic about what you can accomplish, given the age range of your students.

g. Describe an appropriate method you might use to assess the extent to which students have mastered the topic or skill you are teaching. Include an explanation of whether your assessment instrument is paper-pencil or performance in nature. Explain why you think your method can adequately assess your objectives—in other words, why you believe your method has content validity.

Note to instructor: Item 38 is a possible question for a comprehensive final exam; give students at least an hour to respond. Despite its length and level of detail, the item provides insufficient structure for you to score students' responses in a totally consistent and reliable fashion (i.e., it is a real "bear" to grade and should probably be graded somewhat leniently). Nevertheless, the item reflects my belief that tests should be learning experiences for students, in that it requires students to pull together many of the things they have studied. I have used variations of this item on several occasions and have found that it is a challenging one indeed. My students have greater success with it when they have previously had in-class experiences (e.g., focused discussion groups) that require them to pull some of the information together ahead of time.

## ANSWER KEY

### Multiple-Choice Questions

1. d
2. d
3. b
4. a
5. b
6. d
7. c
8. c
9. d
10. c
11. a
12. b
13. d
14. c
15. a
16. a
17. b

### Essay Questions

18. The response should identify a specific grade level; some responses may also identify a specific discipline. Then, age-related characteristics (those associated with some ages but not with others) for the grade level should be described with respect to each of the following aspects of development, and a concrete example of each characteristic "in action" should be provided:
    a. Cognitive development (two characteristics from a Piagetian perspective and two from an information processing perspective): see Chapter 2 for possible answers.
    b. Language development (one characteristic): see Chapter 2 for possible answers.
    c. Personal or social development (one characteristic): see Chapter 3 for possible answers.
    d. Moral development (one characteristic): see Chapter 3 for possible answers.

19. Responses to various parts of the question are as follows:
    a. Children develop cognitively only when they encounter events that they cannot interpret in terms of existing schemas (i.e., when they experience disequilibrium).
    b. Children progress in terms of cognitive development only when they encounter tasks within their zone of proximal development (i.e., tasks that they can successfully perform only with the assistance of a more competent individual).
    c. Students' self-efficacy is enhanced when they set and achieve challenging goals.
    d. A challenge is a situation in which students believe there is some probability of success with effort. Students who are intrinsically motivated (e.g., those with a mastery orientation) are more likely to seek challenging tasks. (Either of these is an acceptable response.)

20. Responses to various parts of the question are as follows:
    a. Social interaction provides a feedback mechanism through which students' illogical thinking is challenged (e.g., social interaction is essential for helping children understand that others have perspectives different from their own; it also provides adolescents with feedback regarding their logical but unrealistic idealism about the world).
    b. Children accomplish tasks within their zone of proximal development only by working on these tasks in cooperation with a more competent individual.
    c. Children progress in terms of moral development only when they encounter moral dilemmas and people's reasoning one stage above their own.
    d. An important mechanism through which students learn is modeling—observing and imitating the actions of others. (Other functions of social interaction may also be acceptable here if reasonably justified within the context of social cognitive theory.)
    e. In reciprocal teaching, students learn more effective reading comprehension strategies by questioning one another about the things they read.

21. There are at least four possible reasons for Hope's diminished self-esteem (the response should identify two of these, or it may identify other reasons that can legitimately be justified on the basis of the information provided about Hope):
    - Many students experience a significant drop in self-esteem when they first enter junior high school; this may be due to a dramatically changing school environment or to the onset of puberty.
    - Although girls and boys perform equally well in mathematics and science in elementary school, by the time they reach high school, girls have less self-confidence in their ability to succeed in these disciplines.
    - Especially in traditionally "male" areas such as mathematics and science, girls have a tendency to attribute their successes to effort and their failures to a lack of ability; thus, Hope may be becoming discouraged each time she has a small failure in these disciplines.
    - The mathematics teacher's low expectations for Hope may be communicating the message that Hope has low ability.

22. Responses to this question are likely to vary considerably. At least one strategy from each of the following perspectives should be identified:
    a. Principles of social development: See Chapter 3 for possibilities.
    b. Principles of moral development: See Chapter 3 for possibilities.
    c. Operant conditioning: See Chapter 9 for possibilities.
    d. Social cognitive theory: See Chapter 10 for possibilities.
    e. Intrinsic motivation: See Chapter 12 for possibilities.

23. Responses are likely to go in a variety of different directions here; however, all strategies should be consistent with principles and strategies presented in Chapter 13. A response should include at least four strategies, with a rationale accompanying each one. Some possibilities include these:
    - Relate topics in expository instruction to students' unique background knowledge.
    - Use mastery learning, direct instruction, peer tutoring, or CBI to facilitate mastery of basic skills and/or allow students to learn at their own pace.
    - Allow several seconds of wait time after asking questions to encourage a more diverse group of students to respond.
    - Assign authentic activities that relate school subject matter with tasks that are relevant to students' own lives.
    - Conduct class discussions as a way of soliciting diverse perspectives.
    - Assign cooperative learning activities to accommodate students' desire for cooperation rather than competition and/or to promote cross-group friendships.
    - Use reciprocal teaching to help students with poor reading comprehension skills.

24. Elaboration is adding to, modifying, or interpreting new information using what you already know. The response should illustrate the process with a concrete example in which a learner is clearly going beyond the information given.
    a. Elaboration usually promotes more effective memory of the information over the long run (e.g., better students elaborate more often). Also, multiple elaborations promote multiple connections in LTM, thereby facilitating retrieval at a later time. (The response needs to include only one of these explanations.)
    b. Each person brings a unique knowledge base to new information and therefore makes unique connections.
    c. People may reinterpret new information in light of misconceptions they have.

25. Rote learning is learning new information primarily through repetition, without understanding it. Meaningful learning is learning new information by relating it to what one already knows.
    a. Meaningful learning leads to faster storage because it involves making connections with the existing knowledge base—connections that help the learner interpret, understand, and assimilate the information.
    b. Meaningful learning leads to faster retrieval because the multiple connections with other things in long-term memory provide multiple routes to retrieval.
    c. Meaningful learning promotes better transfer and problem solving because, due to the multiple connections in long-term memory, the information is more likely to be retrieved in situations when it is useful. Also, meaningful learning of problem solving strategies (e.g., algorithms) increases the likelihood that those strategies will be applied in appropriate contexts. (The response need only give one of these reasons.)

26. The response should identify a particular grade level and a particular topic or skill that might be taught at this grade level. Then, it should explain how the topic or skill might be taught using at least <u>three</u> of the bulleted concepts/principles below, identifying each relevant concept/principle as it is being applied:
    - Positive reinforcement: A desirable stimulus is presented contingent on an appropriate response.
    - Modeling: A behavior or skill is demonstrated by someone else.
    - Meaningful learning: Connections are promoted between new information and the things students already know.
    - Elaboration: Students are in some way encouraged to go beyond the information itself, to expand on it in some way.
    - Transfer: Students are in some way encouraged to apply the information or skill to a new situation.

27. Examples of effective study strategies are listed below. The response should describe four of these and/or other strategies that can be justified from either cognitive psychology or social cognitive theory; it should also provide a theoretical justification for why each strategy is likely to be effective.
    - Identifying important information.
    - Taking notes
    - Underlining or highlighting
    - Retrieving relevant prior knowledge and making meaningful connections
    - Organizing (e.g., outlining, concept mapping)
    - Elaborating
    - Summarizing
    - Monitoring comprehension (e.g., self-questioning)
    - Reinforcing oneself for studying
    - Using mnemonics
    - Overlearning and/or learning information to a level of automaticity
    - Reviewing periodically

28. Responses to various parts of the question are as follows:
    a. Both cognitive psychologists and social cognitive psychologists define learning as an internal mental phenomenon that may or may not be reflected in behavior. Behaviorists define learning as a change in behavior.
    b. Appropriate answers to this part of the question are summarized in the "focus of investigation" and "principles of learning" rows of Table 10.4 in the textbook. Correct answers may reflect the cells in either one of these rows, or they may comprise a blend of the two.
    c. Students' responses to this part of the question are likely to vary considerably. Examples of appropriate strategies are:
    Cognitive perspective:
    • Finding out how students are thinking about classroom information
    • Helping students process information effectively
    • Helping students construct an accurate understanding of classroom topics
    • Monitor students' understanding of classroom topics to make sure that it's accurate
    • Encouraging students to relate new information to the things they already know
    • Encouraging students to organize information
    Behaviorist perspective:
    • Helping students acquire more productive behaviors
    • Developing objective measures of student learning
    • Changing the classroom environment to promote learning
    • Having students practice desired responses
    • Rewarding desired responses
    Social cognitive perspective:
    • Helping students learn by observing others
    • Modeling appropriate behavior
    • Taking steps to enhance students' self-efficacy
    • Promoting self-regulation

29. Responses to various parts of the question are as follows:
    a. To store information in working memory, students need to pay attention. Any appropriate strategy for capturing and/or maintaining students' attention is acceptable.
    b. Students have a limited working memory capacity—they can only think about a few pieces of information at a time. Possible strategies for accommodating this limited capacity are (the response need include only one):
       - Pacing the rate at which new ideas are presented.
       - Building redundancy into a lesson.
       - Giving students a few minutes of "processing time" during a lesson.
    c. Meaningful learning involves making connections between new material and things already known. Any appropriate strategy for promoting such connections is acceptable.
    d. Possible strategies for helping students organize material are these (the response need include only one):
       - Giving an advance organizer.
       - Presenting the material in a logical, organized fashion.
       - Providing a visual aid that organizes the information.
       - Having students develop concept maps.
       - Having students summarize the material.
    e. Elaboration involves imposing what one already knows on new information (e.g., interpreting it, identifying new examples, generating applications, etc.). Any appropriate strategy for promoting elaboration (e.g., asking higher-level questions) is acceptable.

30. Responses to various parts of the question are as follows:
    a. Effective long-term memory storage occurs as a result of the following processes (the response should explain at least two):
       - Meaningful learning: Relating new information to one's existing knowledge base
       - Organization: Finding connections among the various pieces of information to be learned
       - Elaboration: Expanding on new information based on what one already knows
       - Visual imagery: Forming a mental image of how something looks
    b. Possible strategies include these (the response should describe four of the strategies listed below or other strategies that are equally likely to facilitate long-term memory storage):
       - Remind students about what they already know about a topic.
       - Make explicit connections between new material and students' existing knowledge base (e.g., by using analogies).
       - Address students' misconceptions about the topic.
       - Provide an advance organizer.
       - Present information in an organized fashion.
       - Use visual aids.
       - Give students time to process information.
       - Ask questions, including higher-level questions.
       - Allow sufficient wait time for students to formulate their answers to questions.
       - Summarize the material.

31. Possible distinctions between the operant conditioning and social cognitive theory perspectives of reinforcement are these (the response should identify two of them):
    - Operant conditioning theorists propose that reinforcement has a direct effect on learning, in that it increases the frequency of the behavior it follows. Social cognitive theorists propose that reinforcement has an indirect effect on learning, in that it affects expectations about future consequences, makes the learner more likely to pay attention, and so on.
    - Awareness of the response-reinforcement contingency is unnecessary in operant conditioning but essential in social cognitive theory.
    - In operant conditioning, the learner must experience reinforcement directly. In social cognitive theory, the learner can also experience it vicariously (i.e., by watching someone else be reinforced).
    - In operant conditioning, the lack of reinforcement simply leads to extinction. In social cognitive theory, a lack of reinforcement that was expected is a form of punishment.

32. Responses to various parts of the question are as follows:
    a. This is punishment (more specifically, removal punishment). When a desirable state of affairs (being on the basketball team) is removed, John's cheating behavior diminishes.
    b. This is vicarious reinforcement. Mary observes Judy being reinforced for sweet-talking, and her sweet-talking behavior increases as a result.
    c. This is negative reinforcement. Ralph's behavior (doing his science project) is reinforced by the removal of something unpleasant (his mother's nagging).

33. Responses to various parts of the question are as follows:
    a. Cueing involves providing a signal that a particular behavior should stop. The response should describe giving a particular signal to Andy that his language is unacceptable.
    b. Self-monitoring involves having students observe and record their own behavior. The response should describe a method whereby Andy keeps track of how many times he uses inappropriate language.
    c. Reinforcement of an incompatible behavior involves reinforcing a behavior that precludes behaving in the manner considered undesirable. The response should describe reinforcing Andy on occasions when he uses appropriate language.
    d. Punishment involves either presenting an unpleasant consequence or removing a desired stimulus when the behavior occurs. The response should describe a punishment for Andy's foul language that is consistent with the guidelines presented in Chapter 9.

34. Responses to various parts of the question are as follows:
    a. Cueing involves providing a signal that a particular behavior should stop. The response should describe giving a particular signal to Sarah that talking at certain times is unacceptable.
    b. Self-monitoring involves having students observe and record their own behavior. The response should describe a method whereby Sarah keeps track of how many times she talks at inappropriate times.
    c. Self-reinforcement involves having students reinforce themselves for behaving in an appropriate fashion. The response should describe teaching Sarah to reinforce herself in some manner for completing seatwork and taking tests quietly.
    d. Shaping involves reinforcing successive approximations to a desired terminal behavior. The response should describe a series of steps through which Sarah is reinforced for increasingly less talkative behavior.

35. Responses to various parts of the question are as follows:
    a. Cueing involves providing a signal that a particular behavior should stop. The response should describe giving a particular signal to Jason that he is not attending to classroom activities or his schoolwork.
    b. Self-monitoring involves having students observe and record their own behavior. The response should describe a method whereby Jason keeps track of how many times he does and does not keep his attention focused on classroom activities.
    c. A contingency contract involves having a teacher and student sign a written contract whereby the student agrees to behave in a certain way and the teacher agrees to follow such behavior with a specified reinforcer. The response should describe Jason and his teacher developing and signing such a contract.
    d. Shaping involves reinforcing successive approximations to a desired terminal behavior. The response should describe a series of steps through which Jason is reinforced for increasingly more attentive behavior.

36. Responses to this question will vary considerably. A response should identify five concrete and plausible strategies for motivating an unmotivated second grader using at least five of the concepts/principles below:
    - Intrinsic motivation: Promoting a sense of self-determination and/or higher self-efficacy.
    - Shaping: Reinforcing increasingly better classroom performance.
    - Secondary reinforcement: Reinforcing desirable classroom performance using a reinforcer that does not satisfy a physiological need (e.g., praise).
    - Premack principle: Reinforcing desirable classroom performance by allowing Margot to engage in an activity she finds enjoyable (e.g., interacting with her classmates).
    - Vicarious reinforcement: Reinforcing Margot's classmates for appropriate classroom behavior.
    - Self-monitoring: Having Margot observe and record her own behavior.
    - Self-imposed contingency: Having Margot reinforce herself for engaging in desired classroom activities.
    - Time-out: Putting Margot in a boring place, away from classmates, when she doesn't complete assignments.

37. Responses to various parts of the question are as follows:
    a. Programmed instruction involves active responding (students answer questions as they go along), shaping (instruction proceeds gradually through increasingly more difficult material), and immediate reinforcement (immediate feedback is given for correct responses). The response should identify two of these ideas or other concepts/principles of operant conditioning that have justified relevance to programmed instruction.
    b. Mastery learning is similar to shaping, in that students proceed through a series of progressively more difficult behaviors, learning each one thoroughly before proceeding to the next. It also involves terminal behavior, because criteria for mastery of each unit are clearly spelled out. And it involves reinforcement, especially in the form of positive feedback when a unit has been mastered. The response should identify two of these ideas or other concepts/principles of operant conditioning that have justified relevance to mastery learning approaches.
    c. Cooperative learning involves terminal behavior in the form of clear goals. It also involves reinforcement for group success (a group contingency). The response should identify two of these ideas or other concepts/principles of operant conditioning that have justifiable relevance to cooperative learning.

38. Parts b through g below should provide clear, concrete explanations of what the teacher should do. Furthermore, each strategy should be connected with at least one concept, principle, or theory described in the textbook.
    a. The response should identify a particular grade level and a specific topic or skill that might be taught at this grade level.
    b. The response should present at least two instructional objectives related to the topic or skill. These objectives should describe specific and observable student outcomes (see Chapter 13 for a more detailed discussion).
    c. The response should present at least two characteristics typical of the age group being taught, using a Piagetian and/or information processing perspective (see Chapter 2 for possible answers).
    d. The response should identify four specific strategies derived from at least four of these concepts/principles:
        - Positive reinforcement: Following a desired student behavior with a pleasant consequence (praise, feedback, etc.).
        - Modeling: Demonstrating the desired behavior.
        - Working memory: Capturing students' attention; limiting the amount of information that students must process at any one time.
        - Meaningful learning: Helping students relate new material to things they already know.
        - Elaboration: Encouraging students to go beyond the material itself, to expand on it in some way.
        - Effects of prior knowledge: Taking what students already know into account.
    e. The response should describe <u>three</u> strategies that address three of the following aspects of students' development:
        - Self-concept and/or self-efficacy: See relevant portions of Chapters 3, 10, and 12 for possible strategies.
        - Social development: See Chapter 3 for possible strategies.
        - Moral development: See Chapter 3 for possible strategies.
        - Appropriate attributions for success and failure: See Chapter 12 for possible strategies.
    f. The response should describe at least one strategy for promoting metacognitive development. See Chapter 8 for possible strategies.
    g. The response should describe a specific way of assessing students' achievement of the instructional objectives identified in Part <u>b</u>. Justifications for using paper-pencil vs. performance assessment should be included. A reasonable defense of the method's content validity (i.e., why it provides a representative sample of what students should have learned) should also be presented.

Appendix A

# DESCRIBING RELATIONSHIPS WITH CORRELATION COEFFICIENTS

## Multiple-Choice Questions

•• 1. You read in a professional magazine that the correlation between test anxiety and classroom test performance is -.30. You should conclude that:

a. Students who have high test anxiety perform at higher levels on classroom tests, almost without exception.

b. Students who have low test anxiety perform at higher levels on classroom tests, almost without exception.

c. Students who have high test anxiety perform at higher levels on classroom tests, but with many students being exceptions to the rule.

d. Students who have low test anxiety perform at higher levels on classroom tests, but with many students being exceptions to the rule.

•• 2. You read a research study about abstract thinking and academic achievement in a professional journal. The researchers report a correlation of +.65 between the amount of abstract thought that students demonstrate and the grade-point-averages that they earn. You should conclude that:

a. Students who think more abstractly are likely to have higher grade-point-averages than their classmates.

b. Students who think more abstractly are likely to have lower grade-point-averages than their classmates.

c. You can promote students' abstract thinking by helping them to earn high GPAs.

d. You can promote students' academic achievement by helping them to think more abstractly.

•• 3. You read in a professional magazine that, in one research study, researchers obtained a correlation of -.50 between the amount of time that college students study and the course grades that they earn. You should conclude that:

a. Studying helps students earn higher grades.

b. Studying interferes with students' class performance.

c. Students who study more get higher grades.

d. Students who study more get lower grades.

•• 4. When analyzing the data she has collected for a research project, a researcher computes a correlation coefficient of +32.9 between self-esteem and classroom performance. The researcher should definitely conclude that:

a. There is a high positive correlation between self-esteem and classroom performance.
b. There is a low positive correlation between self-esteem and classroom performance.
c. One variable causes the other (although she doesn't know in which direction the cause-effect relationship goes).
d. She has made an error in her calculations.

## ANSWER KEY

### Multiple-Choice Questions

1. d
2. b
3. d
4. d

Study Guide and Reader

## READINGS #1–#7

| SUPPLEMENTARY READING | RELEVANT TEST BANK ITEMS |
|---|---|
| Reading #1: Common Themes Throughout the Book | Multiple-Choice 1–2<br>Essay 14 |
| Reading #2: Physical Development Across Childhood and Adolescence | Multiple-Choice 3–4 |
| Reading #3: Parenting Styles and Children's Behavior | Multiple-Choice 5–7 |
| Reading #4: Maslow's Hierarchy of Needs | Multiple-Choice 8–9<br>Essay 15 |
| Reading #5: Example of a Lesson Plan | Multiple-Choice 10 |
| Reading #6: A Shocking Lesson | Multiple-Choice 11—12 |
| Reading #7: Calculating Standard Deviations | Multiple-Choice 13 |

**Multiple-Choice Questions**

• 1. From the perspective of both Piaget's theory of cognitive development and contemporary cognitive psychology, students can only learn something meaningfully and effectively when they know:

a. That they will be evaluated on the basis of how much they know and how well they know it.

b. That their teachers consider the information important enough to spend classroom time on.

c. How the information relates to what they already know.

d. How different the information is from things they have learned previously.

• 2. The theme of <u>relevance</u> has appeared in numerous places throughout the textbook. In which one of the following areas has it <u>not</u> played a significant role?
   a. Social cognitive theorists' discussion of when students are likely to model the behaviors they see.
   b. Vygotsky's discussion of how a child's zone of proximal development changes over time.
   c. Learning theorists' discussion of when transfer is most likely to occur.
   d. Motivation theorists' discussion of how to enhance students' intrinsic motivation for learning in the classroom.

• 3. Three of the following accurately describe the typical physical development of students in the elementary grades. Which one is <u>not</u> accurate?
   a. Students become increasingly sensitive about their physical appearance.
   b. Girls mature earlier than boys.
   c. Students become increasingly fluent in fine-motor skills.
   d. Students show increasing clumsiness in gross-motor skills.

• 4. Three of the following accurately describe the typical physical development of students in the high school years. Which one is <u>not</u> accurate?
   a. Early-maturing girls are more self-confident than later-maturing girls.
   b. Girls mature earlier than boys.
   c. Students' growth rates can be affected by stress factors at home.
   d. Puberty is accompanied by a rapid growth spurt in both boys and girls.

•• 5. An <u>authoritarian</u> parenting style is seen in which one of the following examples involving junior high school students?
   a. Molly's parents are very strict, letting her know their high expectations and imposing strong penalties for failing or breaking their rules.
   b. Fern's parents allow her generous leeway in terms of bedtimes, curfews, and choice of friends.
   c. Henry's parents have high expectations for him, but often ask him for his opinion when they set guidelines for acceptable behavior.
   d. Kelly's parents are very involved in their own lives and problems and do not provide Kelly with much warmth or emotional support.

•• 6. A <u>permissive</u> parenting style is best illustrated by which one of these examples involving high school students?
   a. Jack's parents allow him to take part in major family decisions and are proud that he meets their high expectations.
   b. Mark's parents don't care if Mark brings friends over for a few beers when they are out, as long as they don't make too big a mess.
   c. Bill's parents love their son and want him to be happy, so they let him decide when he wants to go to school and how late he wants to stay out with friends.
   d. Ernie's parents explain why some behaviors are acceptable and some are not because they want him to grow up to be a responsible citizen.

•• 7. Parenting styles are different with respect to the degree of control that parents exert over their children. Which parenting style reflects the most control?
   a. Authoritative
   b. Authoritarian
   c. Uninvolved
   d. Permissive

•• 8. According to Maslow, the need for self-actualization is never completely fulfilled. Which one of the following examples best reflects the need for self-actualization?
   a. Ellen hasn't been feeling well lately, so she is very good about taking her medication.
   b. Foria spends as much of her school time as she can talking to her many friends.
   c. Gail loves art and spends all of her free time drawing on whatever is handy. She takes an art class every chance she gets.
   d. Helen strives for perfection in the speech she will give to her English class because she wants her classmates to think she is smart.

•• 9. From Maslow's perspective, which one of the following best reflects a deficiency need?
   a. Lorne writes and plays folk songs as a way of expressing himself.
   b. Geri finds ancient civilizations absolutely fascinating.
   c. Rachel is curious about why her science experiment didn't turn out the way she expected it would.
   d. Bill is worried that Mark might beat him up on the way home from school.

• 10. A lesson plan is least likely to include:
   a. A description of what students already know
   b. Questions to ask students
   c. Homework assignments to give
   d. Plans for assessing what students learn

• 11. Three of the behaviorist ideas below provide a basis for programmed instruction. Which concept is least relevant to programmed instruction?
   a. shaping
   b. reinforcement
   c. importance of making a response
   d. extinction

• 12. In programmed instruction, a branching program is different from a linear program in that a branching program:
   a. Allows students to make choices about the topics they study.
   b. Provides remedial work for students who need it.
   c. Takes smaller steps in teaching new material.
   d. Provides many more opportunities for review.

• 13. A standard deviation can best be described as reflecting:
   a. How high or low a set of scores is overall
   b. How strongly two sets of scores are interrelated
   c. How lopsided a distribution of scores is in one direction or the other
   d. How far scores tend to be from the average score

## **Essay Questions**

- 14. In four short paragraphs, describe the role of challenge with respect to:
  a. Piaget's theory of cognitive development
  b. Vygotsky's theory of cognitive development
  c. Self-efficacy
  d. Motivation

- 15. Describe the five needs in Maslow's hierarchy. Illustrate each one with a concrete example of how a student might behave.

## ANSWER KEY

### Multiple-Choice Questions

1. c
2. b
3. d
4. a
5. a
6. c
7. b
8. c
9. d
10. a
11. d
12. b
13. d

### Essay Questions

14. Responses to various parts of the question are as follows:
    a. Children develop cognitively only when they encounter events that they cannot interpret in terms of existing schemas (i.e., when they experience disequilibrium).
    b. Children progress in terms of cognitive development only when they encounter tasks within their zone of proximal development (i.e., tasks that they can successfully perform only with the assistance of a more competent individual).
    c. Students' self-efficacy is enhanced when they set and achieve challenging goals.
    d. A challenge is a situation in which students believe there is some probability of success with effort. Students who are intrinsically motivated (e.g., those with a mastery orientation) are more likely to seek challenging tasks. (Either of these is an acceptable response.)

15. The five needs in Maslow's hierarchy (in correct order and underlined below) and examples of behaviors that illustrate each one (in bulleted lists below) are these (the response should illustrate each need with one of the bulleted items or an equivalent example):

Physiological needs = needs related to physical survival
- Asking to use the restroom or drinking fountain
- Being excessively restless
- Acting lethargic due to lack of sleep
- Feeling ill and asking to go see the nurse
- Shivering

Safety needs = the need to feel safe and secure
- Wanting to know what will happen in class
- Staying away from the school bully
- Being truant if the route to school is dangerous
- Being truant if classmates bring weapons to class

Love and belonging needs = needs to have affectionate relationships with others and to feel that one is part of a group
- Dressing in accordance with current fashions
- Conforming to a group
- Preferring group activities to independent seatwork
- Participating in extracurricular activities (e.g., sports, clubs)

Esteem needs = needs to feel good about oneself and to believe that others also feel positively about oneself
- Trying to achieve mastery of a skill
- Seeking recognition for one's accomplishments
- Seeking out prestigious positions at school

Need for self-actualization = the need to grow and become all one is capable of becoming
- Enhancing one's physical well-being
- Developing an outlet for self-expression
- Learning for the sake of learning

## READING #8: LEARNING IN THE CONTENT AREAS

| OUTLINE | RELEVANT TEST BANK ITEMS |
|---|---|
| APPLYING GENERAL PRINCIPLES TO TEACHING CLASSROOM SUBJECT MATTER | Essay 51, 52 |
| READING<br>Emergent Literacy<br>The Nature of Skilled Reading<br>Developmental Changes in Reading<br>General Strategies for Teaching Reading | Multiple-Choice 1-12<br>Essay 49 |
| WRITING<br>The Nature of Skilled Writing<br>Writing as a Facilitator of Learning<br>Developmental Changes in Writing<br>General Strategies for Teaching Writing | Multiple-Choice 13-23<br>Essay 50 |
| MATHEMATICS<br>The Nature of Mathematical Reasoning<br>Developmental Changes in Mathematical Understanding<br>General Strategies for Teaching Mathematics | Multiple-Choice 24-34 |
| SCIENCE<br>The Nature of Scientific Reasoning<br>Developmental Changes in Scientific Reasoning<br>General Strategies for Teaching Science | Multiple-Choice 35-41 |
| SOCIAL STUDIES<br>The Nature of Historical Knowledge and Thinking<br>The Nature of Geographic Knowledge and Thinking<br>Developmental Changes in Thinking About History and Geography<br>General Strategies for Teaching Social Studies | Multiple-Choice 42-46 |
| TAKING STUDENT DIVERSITY INTO ACCOUNT<br>Accommodating Students with Special Needs | Multiple-Choice 47-48 |

| THE BIG PICTURE<br>Reading<br>Writing<br>Mathematics<br>Science<br>Social Studies<br>Revisiting the Five General Principles | Essay 51, 52 |
|---|---|

## Multiple-Choice Questions

•• 1. Which one of the following children is the best example of emergent literacy?
   a. Donna is only five years old, and already she can read many storybooks independently.
   b. When four-year-old Jack plays school with his older sisters, he fills the page with lines of random letters.
   c. When three-year-old Torina pretends to "read," she sometimes holds the book upside-down.
   d. Six-year-old Yasser understands basic rules of phonics but does not yet know how to spell many words that are exceptions to the rules.

• 2. Research indicates that a major advantage of giving children multiple experiences with books during the preschool years is that they:
   a. Develop greater awareness of syllables than they would otherwise
   b. Usually learn to read on their own before they reach school age
   c. Develop more advanced visual perception skills
   d. Learn to read more easily once they begin school

• 3. Phonological awareness can best be described as:
   a. A student's ability to hear the individual sounds within a spoken word
   b. A student's ability to distinguish between words that sound similar but have different meanings
   c. A student's knowledge that people who speak different dialects may pronounce the same word differently
   d. A student's ability to describe what letters typically represent different sounds in words and to apply them in sounding out written words

•• 4. Three of the following teachers are employing strategies to promote phonological awareness in their students. Which teacher is using a strategy that, though potentially beneficial for other reasons, will not necessarily promote phonological awareness?
   a. Ms. Noble has the words "to," "too," and "two" posted on her wall. When students use those words in their speech, she asks them to point to the one they are using.
   b. Mr. Schofield plays a game with his students called "Making the Word." A sample question is "What letter do we add to 'it' to make 'sit?'"
   c. Mr. Gray has his students collect items that begin with the featured letter of the week.
   d. Ms. Leech asks her class, "Who can think of a word that rhymes with 'boat'?"

•• 5. Three of the following teachers are using strategies that should promote word decoding skills. Which teacher is using a strategy that, though potentially beneficial for other reasons, will not necessarily promote word decoding skills?

a. Mr. Scott teaches his students the ing family (e.g., ring, sing, string).

b. Mr. Wing teaches his students the rule, "When there is an e at the end of a word, it remains silent, but the vowel before it says its own name."

c. Ms. Fernald encourages her students to use the pictures in a book to help them get a better sense of what they are reading.

d. Ms. Deutsch asks her students to read nonsense words such as "hent," "dutter," and "rable."

•• 6. Which one of the following students is definitely demonstrating automaticity in word recognition?

a. When Samantha reads aloud, her voice lacks expression.

b. When Werner listens to someone say a new word, he closes his eyes and tries to imagine how it might be spelled.

c. When Kristen reads, she recognizes words by sight and recalls their meanings immediately.

d. When Roland reads, he has to sound out most of the words.

• 7. Ms. Trinh is about to start a unit on sharks. Some of her students have a strong interest in sharks and know a lot about them. Others know very little about sharks. When Ms. Trinh gives a reading assignment about sharks, she should expect that:

a. Students with more background knowledge will understand the reading material more readily than their classmates.

b. Students' reading comprehension will depend almost entirely on their word decoding skills; their prior knowledge won't make much of a difference.

c. Students with more background knowledge are less likely to engage in comprehension monitoring and so will make more comprehension errors.

d. Students with less background knowledge may be reluctant to read about an unfamiliar topic, so motivating them to learn during the unit will be a challenge.

•• 8. Chelsea has excellent word decoding skills, but she often struggles to derive meaning from what she reads. Three of the following strategies are consistent with recommendations for helping students construct meaning from their reading. Which one is not recommended?

a. Asking Chelsea to stop occasionally and imagine what is happening in a story, almost as if she were watching a movie in her head.

b. Drawing comparisons between events in a story and Chelsea's personal experiences.

c. Asking Chelsea to summarize what she has read after she reads each paragraph.

d. Asking Chelsea to read at a slower pace than she usually does—ideally, no more than two words per second.

•• 9. Three of the following students are using metacognitive strategies while reading. Which one is not?
  a. Donavon always thinks about what he wants to learn from his reading before he begins.
  b. Josie likes to make predictions before she starts reading and then revise them as she goes along.
  c. Pablo prefers to read out loud so he can hear what the words sound like.
  d. Keiko ignores parts of the text that don't relate to her purpose for reading.

• 10. A faculty committee is revising the goals for the school district's reading curriculum. Three of the following goals are developmentally appropriate. Which one is not?
  a. By the end of second grade, students should be able to count the number of syllables in words.
  b. By the end of twelfth grade, students should be able to critically examine an author's point of view.
  c. By the end of sixth grade, students should be able to identify symbolism in a novel.
  d. By the end of tenth grade, students should be able to identify the main ideas in a passage.

• 11. Which one of the following conclusions is consistent with current research findings about reading instruction?
  a. Whole-language instruction is clearly superior to a basic-skills approach due to its use of authentic reading materials.
  b. A basic-skills approach is clearly superior to whole language instruction because it fosters phonological awareness.
  c. Each of the two approaches has benefits, so teachers should use both to some degree.
  d. Research tells us that whole-language instruction and basic-skills approaches work equally well as long as one approach is used exclusively.

• 12. Three of the following strategies are consistent with recommendations for teaching reading skills. Which one is generally not recommended?
  a. Give students in early elementary school lots of practice with isolated reading skills before asking them to apply the skills in an actual reading assignment.
  b. Give students frequent opportunities to choose what they read. Students use better reading strategies when they are interested in the material.
  c. Encourage students to meet in small groups to discuss a novel they are all reading.
  d. Use games such as "Twenty Questions" to teach basic reading skills (e.g., phonological awareness, word decoding).

•• 13. Having students set goals for a writing project often helps them write more effectively. Which one of the following goals is most likely to promote good writing?
  a. "When you write today, try to use capital letters and punctuation in all the right places."
  b. "Before you begin writing, ask yourself what it is you want to say to your audience."
  c. "Try to write at least five pages on your topic before you begin to revise your work."
  d. "Before you begin writing, remember what it takes to get an A and make that your goal."

• 14. Students often write more effectively about some topics than others. Three of the following teachers are using strategies consistent with recommendations for helping students write effectively about a topic. Which teacher is probably <u>not</u> using a recommended strategy?

a. Miss Feinstein encourages students to write about something they know a lot about.

b. Mr. Perez encourages students to discuss their topics with one another before they begin to write.

c. Ms. Miner encourages students to choose a topic they know nothing about and then "let your imagination run wild."

d. Mr. Davidson encourages his students to research a topic well before writing about it.

•• 15. Three of the following students are using organizational strategies that should facilitate their writing. Which one is <u>least</u> likely to be effective?

a. Candy writes a first draft off the top of her head. Then she organizes her thoughts as she revises what she has written.

b. Moses starts writing after making a basic list of the points he wants to cover.

c. Before she composes a story, Tatum uses a checklist of elements in fiction to make notes on characters, setting, and plot.

d. Kevin develops a topic sentence and then thinks about how to support it.

• 16. With regard to writing, which one of the following statements most accurately <u>summarizes</u> why knowledge transforming is preferable to knowledge telling?

a. Knowledge transforming reveals a student's ability to form opinions based on factual information, rather than just to repeat the facts.

b. Knowledge transforming helps the reader understand what the author is trying to communicate.

c. Knowledge transforming specifically develops the art of using metaphors, symbolism and allegories in writing.

d. Knowledge transforming is a term used to describe writing that has vivid details and appeals to the imagination.

•• 17. Three of the following teachers are using recommended strategies for teaching writing mechanics. Which teacher is <u>not</u> using a recommended strategy?

a. Rather than explicitly teach grammar and writing mechanics, Mr. Maloof just makes sure that his seventh graders read a great many fiction and nonfiction books.

b. Mrs. Boek encourages her first graders to use invented spellings when they write and to not worry about punctuation and capitalization; she knows that they will begin receiving instruction in spelling and mechanics once they reach second grade.

c. Mr. Durphy teaches his third graders spelling strategies such as thinking about sound-letter correspondences and drawing analogies among similarly spelled words.

d. Ms. Paone tells her high school students that if they want to be taken seriously as writers, they need to know the conventions of spelling and grammar.

•• 18. Which one of the following writing assignments for young writers is most likely to promote an awareness of one's audience?
   a. Write a description of snow for someone who has never seen it.
   b. Write about your favorite animal and its habitat.
   c. Write about a time you were really surprised.
   d. Write a story that takes place in an imaginary land.

• 19. According to the supplementary reading about learning in the content areas, which one of the following is a common problem with the feedback that teachers typically give students about their writing?
   a. Teachers tend to focus too much on writing mechanics and not enough on clarity or style.
   b. Teachers tend to focus too much on style and not enough on factual content.
   c. Teachers tend to provide good feedback on content and organization but to overlook grammatical mistakes.
   d. Teachers tend to overwhelm students with the amount of feedback they provide.

•• 20. Mr. Chu is concerned that Josephine makes only minor changes when she revises her writing. Three of the following strategies are likely to help Josephine learn to make better revisions. Which one is <u>least</u> likely to help?
   a. Give Josephine a list of questions to ask herself as she revises.
   b. Have Josephine work on revisions with one or two of her classmates.
   c. Have Josephine make a list of five things that might improve her writing.
   d. Suggest that Josephine let a word processing program find her errors for her.

• 21. Writing about a topic often helps students learn the topic more thoroughly. Three of the following are reasons why writing facilitates learning. Which one is <u>not</u> a reason?
   a. The writer must retrieve the things he or she knows about the topic.
   b. The writer must organize his or her thoughts about the topic.
   c. The writer must encode his or her thoughts as both visual and auditory images.
   d. While engaging in knowledge transforming, the writer must elaborate on his or her knowledge.

•• 22. Claudette is in fourth grade. When she writes, she does a good job of getting her thoughts down on paper and editing for basic spelling and punctuation errors. But she seldom plans a writing project ahead of time, and she doesn't necessarily write for a particular audience. Based on the description of typical writing development presented in the supplementary reading "Learning in the Content Areas," which one of the following is <u>most</u> likely to be true?
   a. Claudette is probably behind her peers in writing ability; by fourth grade, students are usually fluent in knowledge-transforming techniques.
   b. Claudette is probably ahead of her peers. In fourth grade, most students are concentrating on basic writing mechanics and have trouble expressing their thoughts clearly.
   c. Claudette's writing is fairly typical for a student in the upper elementary grades.
   d. Claudette's lack of planning skills are unusual for her age and may be indicative of a learning disability.

•• 23. Three of the following teachers are using recommended strategies for teaching writing. Which teacher is not using a recommended strategy?

a. Mr. MacAfee doesn't worry about how well students write in his science class; students shouldn't have to worry about both science and writing at the same time.

b. Mrs. Pratt gives her students numerous opportunities to write for real audiences other than herself.

c. Mr. Hendrix occasionally has students work together in pairs on writing assignments; each pair hands in a single paper for which both students get credit.

d. Miss Tharp gives her students instruction on how to use a word processing program and encourages them to use a computer whenever they write.

• 24. Which one of the following statements is most accurate about a typical five-year-old child's understanding of numbers and/or counting?

a. Most five-year-olds do not develop specific methods for adding and subtracting until they are taught such methods in school.

b. Most five-year-olds have already had enough experience adding and subtracting concrete objects that further work with concrete objects isn't necessary.

c. Most five-year-olds do not yet know that a group of objects has the same number of objects regardless of the order in which the objects are counted.

d. Most five-year-olds know that when you count a group of objects, you should count each object in the group once and only once.

• 25. Three of the following statements are accurate with regard to mathematical reasoning. Which statement is not accurate?

a. Using a number line is sometimes recommended as a way of helping children learn how numbers relate to one another.

b. Students solve relational problems more easily than they solve multiplication and division problems.

c. Most people would probably not acquire such concepts as negative number and right angle without formal mathematics instruction.

d. Many high school students have difficulty encoding algebra problems correctly.

•• 26. Three of the following strategies are likely to promote students' problem encoding skills in mathematics. Which one is least likely to have this effect?

a. Mrs. LaMonte and her students play a game in which they categorize problems without solving them.

b. Mr. Jenkins accompanies word problems with real objects or pictures to help students think about them in concrete terms.

c. Ms. Wilkins asks students to draw pictures or diagrams to illustrate the problems they solve.

d. Mr. Gregg introduces only one type of problem at a time and has his students master strategies for solving it.

• 27. Three of the following strategies are recommended for helping students learn mathematical procedures. Which one is not recommended?

a. Provide worked-out examples that illustrate a particular procedure.

b. Encourage students to do problems entirely in their heads whenever possible.

c. Encourage students to use their fingers if they find that their fingers help them.

d. Illustrate abstract procedures with concrete objects.

•• 28. Which one of the following is probably <u>most</u> important in teaching children to solve mathematical problems effectively?
   a. Teaching tricks such as "When you see 'altogether' in a problem, you should add."
   b. Making sure that students know why procedures work as well as how to use them.
   c. Having students practice procedures in isolation before applying them to real-life situations.
   d. Making sure that students demonstrate most of the characteristics of Piaget's formal operations stage before they begin to solve problems.

• 29. Students are most likely to engage in meaningful problem solving in mathematics when they:
   a. Use heuristics rather than algorithms
   b. Have large working memory capacities
   c. Understand the logic behind the procedures they use
   d. Focus on only one small part of a problem at a time

• 30. Three of the following are reasons why real-life mathematical problems are often better than mathematical word problems for promoting mathematical reasoning skills. Which one is <u>not</u> a likely reason why real-life problems are preferable to word problems?
   a. In real life, information needed to solve a problem is not provided in as straightforward a manner as in a word problem.
   b. Real situations give students more opportunities to identify what problem they need to solve to achieve a particular goal.
   c. Students are more likely to identify appropriate mathematical procedures if they actually know the people involved in the problem.
   d. Students are more likely to realize whether or not their answers make sense in real-life situations.

• 31. Three of the following strategies are recommended for teaching mathematics. Which one is <u>not</u> recommended?
   a. Teachers should be aware of students' beliefs about mathematics and should challenge any beliefs that are inaccurate.
   b. Teachers should wean students away from use of concrete problem-solving aids by the eighth or ninth grade.
   c. Teachers should encourage metacognitive processes in mathematics by teaching students how to monitor their problem-solving efforts.
   d. Teachers should encourage young children to use any problem solving techniques they have developed on their own, provided that those techniques yield correct answers.

• 32. Which one of the following conclusions is most warranted from research on peer tutoring in mathematics?
   a. Only the most competent students can effectively tutor their classmates in mathematics.
   b. Low-achieving students can improve their mathematical skills when they tutor students at lower grade levels.
   c. Although peer tutoring fosters a sense of cooperation among students, it has little impact on progress in math.
   d. Peer tutoring sometimes encourages cheating among students, making accurate assessment of students' progress more difficult.

• 33. When students discuss mathematical procedures in a small-group or whole-class context, they are most likely to:
   a. Discover techniques they have never specifically been taught
   b. Develop many misconceptions about math
   c. Develop a greater ability to encode problems correctly, but at the expense of developing automaticity for basic facts
   d. Develop some counterproductive epistemological beliefs about math

• 34. Mr. Blackwell allows his high school students to use calculators frequently on their math tests. A potential benefit of using such tools is that:
   a. They increase students' automaticity for basic number facts.
   b. They enhance students' ability to encode problems correctly.
   c. Students are more likely to transfer what they learn in mathematics to their science classes.
   d. Students are more likely to experiment with mathematics.

• 35. In science, confirmation bias refers to:
   a. Students' tendency to ignore or discount evidence that contradicts their hypotheses
   b. Students' belief that scientific phenomena can be explained without experimentation
   c. Students' tendency during experimentation to try to get the same results that their classmates have obtained
   d. Students' reluctance to put forth hypotheses they think their teacher would not agree with

•• 36. Three of the following teachers are providing scaffolding for students who are conducting science experiments. Which one is not necessarily providing scaffolding?
   a. Mr. Kron makes sure that his students have identified all their variables and know how they will control each one before they begin.
   b. Ms. Archer helps her students distinguish between unexpected results and unreliable results.
   c. Ms. Hyde encourages students to think of more than one hypothesis before beginning an experiment.
   d. Mr. Carlisle requires his students to write their lab reports within 24 hours of conducting their experiments.

• 37. Ms. Allen draws diagrams of the scientific systems she describes. Mr. Black uses analogies to help his students relate scientific principles to things that they already know. Ms. Cheng asks her students to write summaries of particular units in their science class. All three of these strategies are likely to:
   a. Promote students' reading and writing skills in science
   b. Encourage students to integrate what they learn in science
   c. Serve as benchmark lessons in science
   d. Encourage students to undergo conceptual change in science

•• 38. Sometimes students come to school with misconceptions about scientific principles. Three of the following strategies are recommended for promoting conceptual change in such situations. Which one, although possibly beneficial for other reasons, is <u>least</u> likely to promote conceptual change?

a. Mr. Salerno often reminds his students that scientists regularly revise their theories based on new information.

b. Mrs. Dunn uses familiar concrete examples to illustrate abstract ideas.

c. Mr. Yurick describes the life stories of famous scientists to make these people "come alive" for his students.

d. Ms. Irving gives students opportunities to debate the validity of the various theories and models they are studying.

• 39. Three of the following epistemological beliefs about science are likely to lead to development of good study habits in science. Which one is <u>least</u> likely to have this effect?

a. Learning science involves learning to apply scientific principles to real world problems.

b. Learning science involves remembering specific facts that are important to each of the major scientific disciplines.

c. Learning science involves learning how different scientific ideas relate to one another.

d. Learning science involves remembering that scientific theories and models are likely to change over time.

•• 40. Which one of the following teachers is engaging students in a developmentally appropriate science activity?

a. Mrs. Hannigan's third-grade class is studying water molecules as part of a unit on the water cycle.

b. In his high school astronomy class, Mr. Brulet's limits his unit on the solar system to characteristics of each of the nine planets.

c. Ms. Polumbo's tenth-grade biology class is engaged in cataloguing the different kinds of grass that grow in the softball field.

d. Mr. Kirk's kindergartners are hypothesizing about why the sun appears to rise and set in the sky.

• 41. All but one of the following is recommended for teaching science. Which one is <u>not</u> recommended?

a. Always assign experiments that have predetermined answers so you will know by the results whether students have performed them correctly.

b. Give students opportunities to discuss scientific ideas, and encourage them to justify their reasoning.

c. Provide opportunities for students to use computer simulations or other software to investigate scientific phenomena.

d. Encourage students to use the Internet to communicate with outside experts.

• 42. When do most students begin to understand historical time and attach meaning to historical dates?
   a. Usually by kindergarten or first grade
   b. About second grade
   c. About fifth grade
   d. About ninth grade

•• 43. Three of the following high school classes are using recommended strategies for studying history. Which strategy below is least likely to be beneficial?
   a. Ms. Walsh's class is reading journals and letters written by soldiers during the American Civil War and comparing them to newspaper accounts of the time.
   b. Mr. Douglas's class is brainstorming reasons why the United States became involved in Vietnam and doing research to validate their hypotheses.
   c. Mrs. Bigley is having her students read biographies of historical figures and use what they learn to explain why these individuals acted as they did in particular situations.
   d. Mr. Rice is having his students memorize famous speeches and recite them with as much expression as possible.

• 44. According to the text, which one of the following is most likely to give children in the lower elementary grades difficulty when they try to interpret maps?
   a. They don't completely understand that a map is a symbolic representation.
   b. They haven't traveled enough to be able to imagine different topographies and climates.
   c. They confuse the symbols for roads and rivers.
   d. They have insufficient awareness of diverse cultures.

• 45. Given that a social studies curriculum cannot possibly cover every aspect of social studies, the supplementary reading on learning in the content areas urges teachers to focus on:
   a. Important principles that can be broadly applied
   b. Events that have had the greatest impact on students' local community or region
   c. Events that have directly influenced the political and geographic problems currently in the news
   d. Events that have played a crucial role in shaping the nation

• 46. What is the major advantage of having students conduct social studies research using primary resources?
   a. Secondary sources tend to contain more factual errors than primary ones.
   b. Secondary sources invariably present the same perspective on history. Only primary sources present different points of view.
   c. Primary sources give students the opportunity to conduct their own research and contribute to a field of knowledge.
   d. Primary sources are typically easier for students to comprehend.

• 47. Three of the following statements are true regarding student diversity in the content areas. Which one is <u>false</u>?
   a. Students from different ethnic backgrounds may perceive historical events differently.
   b. Boys have a definite advantage over girls in mathematical ability.
   c. Students from different ethnic backgrounds may have had different kinds of early experiences with literacy.
   d. Students who have traveled more may have a better appreciation of distance in geography.

• 48. Tom, a seventh grader who has been identified as having a learning disability, reads and writes at a significantly lower level than his classmates. Three of the following teaching strategies are recommended as being beneficial for a boy like Tom. Which strategy is <u>not</u> recommended?
   a. Give him a specific structure to follow as he writes.
   b. Allow him to use a word processor for his writing, and encourage him to take advantage of the grammar and spelling checkers.
   c. Give him the same reading assignment as his classmates, but urge him to read it several times rather than just once.
   d. Provide simpler reading materials than those that his classmates are given.

## <u>Essay Questions</u>

•• 49. In four paragraphs, describe four processes important in skilled reading, and describe at least one strategy that you would use to promote each process. Your discussion should be based on the knowledge and abilities that the supplementary reading "Learning in the Content Areas" identifies as being essential to good reading.

•• 50. In five paragraphs, describe five processes important in skilled writing, and describe at least one strategy that you would use to promote each process. Your discussion should be based on the knowledge and abilities that the supplementary reading "Learning in the Content Areas" identifies as being essential to good writing.

• 51. In five paragraphs, explain how <u>constructive processes</u> play a role in:
   • Reading
   • Writing
   • Learning mathematics
   • Learning science
   • Learning social studies

• 52. In four paragraphs, explain how <u>metacognition</u> plays a role in <u>four</u> of the following content areas:
   • Reading
   • Writing
   • Learning mathematics
   • Learning science
   • Learning social studies

## ANSWER KEY

### Multiple-Choice Questions

| | | | | |
|---|---|---|---|---|
| 1. b | 11. c | 21. c | 31. b | 41. a |
| 2. d | 12. a | 22. c | 32. b | 42. c |
| 3. a | 13. b | 23. a | 33. a | 43. d |
| 4. a | 14. c | 24. d | 34. d | 44. a |
| 5. c | 15. a | 25. b | 35. a | 45. a |
| 6. c | 16. b | 26. d | 36. d | 46. c |
| 7. a | 17. a | 27. b | 37. b | 47. b |
| 8. d | 18. a | 28. b | 38. c | 48. c |
| 9. c | 19. a | 29. c | 39. b | |
| 10. c | 20. d | 30. c | 40. c | |

### Essay Questions

49. The response should identify at least four of the following processes:
- Recognizing individual sounds and letters
- Using word decoding skills
- Recognizing most words quickly and automatically
- Using context clues to facilitate word recognition
- Constructing an understanding of the writer's intended meaning
- Metacognitively regulating the reading process

The response should include at least one teaching strategy for promoting each of the four processes identified; possible strategies are described in the supplementary reading "Learning in the Content Areas" in the *Study Guide and Reader*.

50. The response should identify at least five of the following processes:
    Planning:
    - Setting one or more goals for a writing project
    - Identifying relevant knowledge
    - Organizing ideas

    Drafting:
    - Writing a first draft
    - Addressing mechanical issues

    Metacognition:
    - Metacognitively regulating the writing process

    Revision:
    - Editing (identifying weaknesses)
    - Rewriting

    The response should include at least one teaching strategy for promoting each of the five processes identified; possible strategies are described in the supplementary reading "Learning in the Content Areas" in the *Study Guide and Reader*.

51. The response should describe constructive processes in each of the five content domains; the following are examples of what a student might say for each domain:
    - Reading: Students construct an understanding of an author's intended meaning using clues in the text; they may also go beyond the specific things that they read (e.g., drawing inferences, making predictions, finding symbolism, etc.)
    - Writing: Effective writing involves knowledge transforming rather than knowledge telling.
    - Math: Over time, students build an increasingly complex and integrated understanding of mathematical concepts and principles.
    - Science: Learning science effectively involves constructing an integrated understanding of concepts and principles related to a particular topic.
    - Social studies: Learning history and geography involves constructing integrated understandings of cause-effect relationships.

52. The response should describe the role of metacognition in four of the content areas and mention at least one aspect of metacognition in each area:
    - Reading: Good readers engage in processes that are likely to increase their comprehension (setting goals, asking questions that they try to answer, monitoring comprehension, etc.).
    - Writing: Good writers set goals for their writing, consider what their audience is likely to know about their topic, and think consciously about how to help the audience understand the message they are trying to communicate.
    - Math: Effective problem solvers monitor their progress toward problem solutions. They also have epistemological beliefs conducive to problem-solving success (e.g., they recognize that mathematical procedures make logical sense and know that they may need to try several different approaches before they are successful).
    - Science: Students' beliefs about what science is influence how they study and learn science (e.g., students who believe that science consists of isolated facts are likely to focus on meaningless memorization). Furthermore, students' ability to conduct meaningful experiments is influenced by the extent to which they reflect on what they are doing and thinking (e.g., by asking themselves questions such as "Have I confirmed my prediction?").
    - Social studies: A true understanding of history involves the recognition that a great deal of historical "knowledge" is interpretive rather than factual.